Charles Adolphe Wurtz (1817–1884), French chemist who first prepared ethylene gly-col, propylene glycol, and many of their derivatives.

GLYCOLS

GEORGE O. CURME, JR., EDITOR
FRANKLIN JOHNSTON, ASSOCIATE EDITOR

Carbide and Carbon Chemicals Company
A Division of Union Carbide and Carbon Corporation

Contributing Authors

A. B. Boese, Jr.

C. K. Fink

H. G. Goodman, Jr.

E. F. Hillenbrand, Jr.

R. F. Holden

W. S. Jones

S. M. Livengood

P. R. Rector

H. C. Schultze

H. F. Smyth, Jr.

W. S. Tamplin

W. J. Toussaint

American Chemical Society
Monograph Series

REINHOLD PUBLISHING CORPORATION
330 West Forty-Second Street   New York, U.S.A.
1952

Printed in the United States of America by
WAVERLY PRESS, INC.

DEDICATED

TO

TWO ARDENT ADVOCATES OF THE

DEVELOPMENT OF TECHNOLOGY

BY SCIENTIFIC RESEARCH

JAMES A. RAFFERTY and JOSEPH G. DAVIDSON

GENERAL INTRODUCTION

American Chemical Society's Series of Chemical Monographs

By arrangement with the Interallied Conference of Pure and Applied Chemistry, which met in London and Brussels in July, 1919, the American Chemical Society was to undertake the production and publication of Scientific and Technologic Monographs on chemical subjects. At the same time it was agreed that the National Research Council, in cooperation with the American Chemical Society and the American Physical Society, should undertake the production and publication of Critical Tables of Chemical and Physical Constants. The American Chemical Society and the National Research Council mutually agreed to care for these two fields of chemical progress. The American Chemical Society named as Trustees, to make the necessary arrangements of the publication of the Monographs, Charles L. Parsons, secretary of the Society, Washington, D. C.; the late John E. Teeple, then treasurer of the Society, New York; and the late Professor Gellert Alleman of Swarthmore College. The Trustees arranged for the publication of the ACS Series of (a) Scientific and (b) Technological Monographs by the Chemical Catalog Company, Inc. (Reinhold Publishing Corporation, successor) of New York.

The Council of the American Chemical Society, acting through its Committee on National Policy, appointed editors (the present list of whom appears at the close of this sketch) to select authors of competent authority in their respective fields and to consider critically the manuscripts submitted.

The first Monograph of the Series appeared in 1921. After twenty-three years of experience certain modifications of general policy were indicated. In the beginning there still remained from the preceding five decades a distinct though arbitrary differentiation between so-called "pure science" publications and technologic or applied science literature. By 1944 this differentiation was fast becoming nebulous. Research in private enterprise had grown apace and not a little of it was pursued on the frontiers of knowledge. Furthermore, most workers in the sciences were coming to see the artificiality of the separation. The methods of both groups of workers are the same. They employ the same instrumentalities, and frankly recognize that their objectives are common, namely, the search for new knowledge for the service of man. The officers of the Society therefore combined the two editorial Boards in a single Board of twelve representative members.

Also in the beginning of the Series, it seemed expedient to construe rather broadly the definition of a Monograph. Needs of workers had to be recognized. Consequently among the first hundred Monographs appeared works in the form of treatises covering in some instances rather broad areas. Because such necessary works do not now want for publishers, it is considered advisable to hew more strictly to the line of the Monograph character, which means more complete and critical treatment of relatively restricted areas, and, where a broader field needs coverage, to subdivide it into logical subareas. The prodigious expansion of new knowledge makes such a change desirable.

These Monographs are intended to serve two principal purposes: first, to make available to chemists a thorough treatment of a selected area in form usable by persons working in more or less unrelated fields to the end that they may correlate their own work with a larger area of physical science discipline; second, to stimulate further research in the specific field treated. To implement this purpose the authors of Monographs are expected to give extended references to the literature. Where the literature is of such volume that a complete bibliography is impracticable, the authors are expected to append a list of references critically selected on the basis of their relative importance and significance.

AMERICAN CHEMICAL SOCIETY

BOARD OF EDITORS

WILLIAM A. HAMOR, *Editor of Monographs*

Associates

L. W. Bass	S. C. Lind
T. H. Chilton	C. H. Mathewson
Barnett Cohen	Laurence L. Quill
Farrington Daniels	W. T. Read
J. Bennett Hill	Walter A. Schmidt
E. H. Huntress	E. R. Weidlein

PREFACE

Glycols have been known for nearly a hundred years, but until 1925 they had little commercial importance. Since then, ethylene glycol has grown to heavy chemical size with production over half a billion pounds per year, the major portion of which is consumed in the automotive, aviation, and explosives industries. In addition to ethylene glycol there are now many other glycols and glycol derivatives useful in such widely diverse fields as textiles, surface coatings, foods, cosmetics, pharmaceuticals, tobacco, petroleum, and many others. In the past, the chemistry and technology of the glycols have been reviewed only in very cursory fashion in textbooks on organic chemistry or in monographs on various subjects such as solvents, detergents, and glycerol. By the end of World War II, glycol technology had advanced so far that all previous discussions of the subject were totally inadequate. Since abundant information on glycols had been accumulated, particularly in industrial circles, but was not in readily available form, the need for a comprehensive review became apparent.

This Monograph is a review of the field of glycols from the technical aspect, treating only those now in commercial production or those whose manufacture has been or could be conducted on a commercial scale. Ethylene glycol and propylene glycol are much more important, of course, than any other glycols and are given major emphasis. As they are derived from the comparably important ethylene oxide and propylene oxide, the latter are also discussed in some detail; however, the subject of oxides is not treated exhaustively and it is hoped that before many years this field will be surveyed in a monograph devoted to olefin oxides. Other subjects that would require separate treatment for adequate coverage are the ethanolamines, thioglycols, solvents based on glycol derivatives, and surface-active agents derived from glycols or olefin oxides.

The reader will find unacknowledged data, particularly in the physical properties and toxicological sections. Such data were previously unpublished and are derived from the laboratories of Carbide and Carbon Chemicals Company, a Division of Union Carbide and Carbon Corporation, at South Charleston, West Virginia, and the Organic Synthesis and Chemical Hygiene Fellowships of Mellon Institute, University of Pittsburgh, Pittsburgh, Pennsylvania. Other major sources of information have been The Dow Chemical Company and E. I. du Pont de Nemours & Company, Inc. For the sake of brevity these sources are often acknowledged in the text as Carbide, Dow, and Du Pont, all well-known names in the chemical industry of America. References from the middle of the nineteenth century are included for historical interest, but most of the intervening work has been recorded in the last twenty-five years. Much of this has been condensed by tabulation for the reader's convenience, since the authors realize the great difficulty of keeping abreast of the present-day flood of scientific literature. This Monograph thus represents a brief but comprehensive account of the glycol industry as it exists at the mid-point of the twentieth century.

Modern industrial research departments are organized into closely knit teams of specialists. These various teams throughout the Carbide organization are represented by the authors of this Monograph, and where possible the chapters carry the names of their respective authors. The material in Chapters 1, 4, 7, and 10 was assembled by Miss Anita P. Schuster from a great number of sources both within and outside the Company. It is not possible, therefore, for all credit to be acknowledged without a cumbersome listing of practically the entire laboratory force of this Company; however, the editors do wish to acknowledge the contributions of all those unnamed individuals whose efforts made this book possible. The editors are indebted to the following persons whose assistance was particularly helpful: Dr. G. A. Perkins and Dr. H. B. McClure who advised and encouraged both editors and authors; Mr. R. K. Kennedy and Mr. C. P. McClelland who helped organize the Monograph in its early stages and who maintained an active interest from the very beginning; Mr. D. C. Lewis who assisted with friendly criticism and suggestions; Dr. G. W. Fowler and Dr. J. T. Fitzpatrick who carefully reviewed the manuscript in its final form; and especially Miss Anita P. Schuster who very capably assumed practically all the technical and routine details of editing.

GEORGE O. CURME, JR.

FRANKLIN JOHNSTON

New York, N. Y.
January 1, 1952

CONTENTS

CHAPTER 1

GLYCOLS—AN INTRODUCTION

Glycols can be defined as those compounds having two hydroxyl (—OH) groups attached to separate carbon atoms in an aliphatic carbon chain. The saturated glycols may be represented by the general chemical formula $C_nH_{2n}(OH)_2$, and as such, they are a class of alcohols. When a second hydroxyl group is introduced into ethyl alcohol (CH_3CH_2OH), the result is ethylene glycol (CH_2OHCH_2OH). A similar alteration of propanol ($CH_3CH_2CH_2OH$) gives either propylene glycol ($CH_3CHOHCH_2OH$) or trimethylene glycol ($CH_2OHCH_2CH_2OH$).

The glycols are discussed here principally in terms of ethylene glycol and propylene glycol. Although numerous glycols are known, only ethylene glycol and propylene glycol are of great commercial importance; a few special glycols such as 2-methyl-2,4-pentanediol, 2-ethyl-1,3-hexanediol, and the butylene glycols are produced on a smaller industrial scale. Diethylene glycol ($HOCH_2CH_2OCH_2CH_2OH$) and triethylene glycol ($HOCH_2CH_2OCH_2CH_2OCH_2CH_2OH$) are actually next in industrial importance to the two simplest glycols, but because of their chemical nature they are treated here as polymeric derivatives of ethylene glycol. The glycols included are those made up solely of carbon, hydrogen, and oxygen including the polymeric derivatives having the carbon chain interrupted only by oxygen. Since Walker[1] has discussed the chemistry of methylene glycol, a very specialized member of the glycol family, this particular compound will not be considered.

Nomenclature

Glycols are also known as diols. Commercial use of the term "glycol" has been so widespread that "ethylene glycol" is generally preferred to "ethanediol" and "propylene glycol" to "1,2-propanediol." In reference to long-chain glycols, the alternative name is more exact, and use of the "diol" or Geneva designation becomes more desirable. Thus five-carbon dihydroxy compounds are generally known as "pentanediols," preceded by the appropriate numbers to specify the positions of the hydroxyl groups. However, commercial practice in naming higher glycols varies also. For example, 2-methyl-2,4-pentanediol is sometimes referred to as "hexylene glycol" and 2-ethyl-1,3-hexanediol as "octylene glycol."

The systematic nomenclature of the polyethylene and polypropylene glycols has been a problem for some years. The *Chemical Abstracts* "oxa-aza" system for hetero- compounds is sometimes applicable, but ordinarily

1

the common tri-, tetra-, penta-, etc., prefixes are used for the lower members and the molecular weight suffixes for the higher members. An example of the former is tetraethylene glycol, and of the latter is polypropylene glycol 2025.

Production

Ethylene glycol and its condensation polymers are prepared commercially through the intermediate ethylene oxide. Although ethylene glycol is also produced by a high-pressure method from formaldehyde and (in Germany) by alkaline hydrolysis of ethylene dichloride, it is manufactured in greatest quantities by hydration of the oxide. The latter is obtained either by dehydrochlorination of ethylene chlorohydrin (see Chapter 2) or by direct oxidation of ethylene (see Chapter 5). Diethylene glycol and triethylene glycol are produced as by-products in this hydration process. Increasing the ratio of ethylene oxide to water in the same reaction results in the formation of higher polyethylene glycols. Propylene glycol and polypropylene glycols are prepared through propylene oxide by methods that are completely analogous.

The higher glycols are prepared by more specialized procedures (see Chapter 14). The two most important of these, 2-methyl-2,4-pentanediol and 2-ethyl-1,3-hexanediol, are obtained by the hydrogenation of diacetone alcohol and butyraldol, respectively.

Physical Properties

The simple glycols are stable, odorless, water-white liquids when pure. They have higher boiling points than water, and most freeze below 0°C. Ethylene glycol and propylene glycol are completely water-soluble, but as the molecular weight of the glycol increases, water solubility decreases until, for example, the eight-carbon 2-ethyl-1,3-hexanediol is soluble in water to the extent of only 4.2 per cent. The lower glycols are extremely hygroscopic and have a selective solvent action for dyes, synthetic resins, essential oils, and certain natural gums and resins. The important physical properties of the simple glycols are listed in Table 1.1.

The high molecular weight polyglycols are stable, nonvolatile, odorless materials. The polyethylene glycols range from water-white liquids to waxlike solids. As the molecular weight increases, the freezing or melting range, specific gravity, flash point, and viscosity increase, while water solubility, vapor pressure, hygroscopicity and solubility in organic compounds decrease. Pure polypropylene glycols are colorless, viscous liquids. The lower molecular weight compounds are completely soluble in water, the higher molecular weight compounds only slightly. Physical properties of the polyglycols are listed in Chapter 7, "Ethylene Glycol Condensation Polymers," and in Chapter 13, "Propylene Glycol Condensation Polymers."

Chemical Properties

In glycols, the chemistry of the individual hydroxyl groups parallels that of those in monohydric alcohols. The deviation from activity typical of alcohols occurs when both hydroxyl groups of the glycol are involved in one reaction.

Although most glycol derivatives are more conveniently prepared on a commercial scale through the oxides, the glycols lend themselves readily to the preparation of esters, ethers, acetals, and similar reaction products. They are easily esterified with organic and inorganic acids under the usual reaction conditions. Ethers can be formed by treating the glycols with alkyl sulfates in the presence of alkali. 1,2-Glycols react with ketones and aldehydes to form dioxolanes. The glycols can be dehydrogenated catalytically in the vapor phase to miscellaneous compounds—ethylene glycol going to 2-hydroxymethyl-1,3-dioxolane, propylene glycol to acetol, and diethylene glycol to 1,4-dioxan-2-one. The catalytic, vapor-phase oxidation of the simple glycols produces the corresponding dicarbonyl compounds in good yields, *e.g.*, glyoxal from ethylene glycol and pyruvic aldehyde from propylene glycol.

The simple glycols can be dehydrated, but not in straightforward reactions. Acetaldehyde is obtained in poor yields from ethylene glycol, allyl alcohol and propionaldehyde from propylene glycol. The higher glycols are much more tractable. For example, butadiene can be obtained from 2,3-, 1,3-, or 1,4-butanediol.

Physiological Properties

The glycols and their polymeric derivatives have, in general, a relatively low order of toxicological effect. For this reason certain of these compounds are considered safe for use in pharmaceuticals, cosmetics, and, in the case of propylene glycol, foodstuffs.

Applications

The glycols and their derivatives are useful compounds finding widespread application in the automotive, textile, cosmetic, pharmaceutical, petroleum, metal, agricultural, and many other industries. The simple glycols are used in anti-freeze solutions for automotive cooling systems and in ice cream plants, breweries, and other commercial refrigeration systems. They are liquid coolants for aircraft engines, machine guns, Army tanks, and the like. Certain of the glycols are humectants for tobacco, cork, gelatin, and glue. Others are valuable components of "steam-set" printing inks, nongrain-raising wood stains, nondrying textile pastes, hydraulic fluids, and electrolytic condenser pastes. They are coupling agents for soluble oils used as agricultural sprays, metal cleaning compounds, and textile

TABLE 1.1 PHYSICAL PROPERTIES OF THE GLYCOLS

Name	Formula	Molecular Weight	Apparent Specific Gravity, 20/20°C.	Boiling Point, °C., at 760 mm.	Freezing Point, °C.	Refractive Index, n_D at 20°C.	Solubility, % by wt., at 20°C. In Water	Water In	Flash Point, °F., Cleveland Open Cup
Ethylene glycol	CH_2OHCH_2OH	62.07	1.1155	197.2	−13	1.4316	Complete	Complete	240
C_3 Glycols									
Propylene glycol	$CH_3CHOHCH_2OH$	76.09	1.0381	188.2	sets to a glass below −50	1.4326	Complete	Complete	225
Trimethylene glycol	$CH_2OHCH_2CH_2OH$	76.09	1.0554	210–211	—	1.4398	Complete	Complete	—
C_4 Glycols									
1,3-Butanediol	$CH_3CHOHCH_2CH_2OH$	90.12	1.0059	207.5	—	1.4401	Complete	Complete	250
1,4-Butanediol	$CH_2OHCH_2CH_2CH_2OH$	90.12	1.020 (20/4)	230	16	—	Complete	Complete	—
2,3-Butanediol	$CH_3CHOHCHOHCH_3$	90.12	1.045	182.5	22.5	1.4364 (25°)	Complete	—	—
2-Butene-1,4-diol (*trans* form)	$CH_2OHCH=CHCH_2OH$	90.12	1.0687 (20/4)	131.5 (12 mm.)	25	1.4772	—	—	—
2-Butyne-1,4-diol	$CH_2OHC\equiv CCH_2OH$	90.12	—	238	64 (m.p.)	Solid	374 g/100 ml. (25°)	—	—
C_5 Glycols									
1,5-Pentanediol	$CH_2OHCH_2CH_2CH_2CH_2OH$	104.15	0.994	239.4	—	1.4499	Complete	Complete	—
2,4-Pentanediol	$CH_3CHOHCH_2CHOHCH_3$	104.15	0.964 (supercooled liquid)	199.0	45	Solid	87.9 (solid)	Complete (supercooled liquid)	210
C_6 Glycols									
1,6-Hexanediol	$CH_2OHCH_2CH_2CH_2CH_2CH_2OH$	118.17	0.958 (45/15.6)	243	42 (m.p.)	—	Very soluble		265
2,5-Hexanediol	$CH_3CHOHCH_2CH_2CHOHCH_3$	118.17	0.9617	220.8	sets to a glass below −50	1.4474	Complete	Complete	220
2-Methyl-1,3-pentanediol	$CH_3CH_2CHOHCH(CH_3)CH_2OH$	118.17	0.9734	215	—	1.4456	10	250 cc. in 100 cc.	230
2-Methyl-2,4-pentanediol	$CH_3CHOHCH_2C(CH_3)OHCH_3$	118.17	0.9234	197.1	sets to a glass below −50	1.4263	Complete	Complete	215

TABLE 1.1. *Continued*

Compound	Formula	Mol. wt.	Density	B.p., °C	Solidification point, °C	n_D	Sol. in water	Sol. of water	Flash point, °F
2,3-Dimethyl-2,3-butanediol (pinacol)	$CH_3C(CH_3)OHC(CH_3)OHCH_3$	118.17	0.967 (d^{15}) (super-cooled liquid)	172.8	41.1	—	—	—	235
C₇ Glycols									
2,4-Heptanediol	$CH_3CH_2CH_2CHOHCH_2CHOHCH_3$	132.20	0.9319	224.9	sets to a glass below −40	1.4414	Complete		—
2,2-Diethyl-1,3-propanediol	$CH_2OHC(C_2H_5)_2CH_2OH$	132.20	1.052 (d^{20})	125 (10 mm.)	61.3	—	25		265
C₈ Glycol									
2-Ethyl-1,3-hexanediol	$CH_3CH_2CH_2CHOHCH(C_2H_5)CH_2OH$	146.22	0.9422	244.2	sets to a glass below −40	1.4511	4.2	11.7	—
C₉ Glycol									
2-Ethyl-2-butyl-1,3-propanediol	$CH_2OHC(C_2H_5)(C_4H_9)CH_2OH$	160.25	0.931 (50/20)	195 (100 mm.)	41.4 (m.p.)	Solid	0.8		—
Polyglycols*									
Diethylene glycol	$O(CH_2CH_2OH)_2$	106.12	1.1184	245.0	−8	1.4472	Complete		290
Triethylene glycol	$HOC_2H_4OC_2H_4OC_2H_4OH$	150.17	1.1254	287.4	−7.2	1.4559	Complete		330
Tetraethylene glycol	$HO(CH_2CH_2O)_3CH_2CH_2OH$	194.22	1.1247	327.3	−6.2	1.4598	Complete		345
Dipropylene glycol	$O(CH_2CHOHCH_2)_2$	134.17	1.0252	231.8	sets to a glass below −50	1.4440	Complete		280

* Physical properties of polyethylene glycols are listed in Chapter 7, "Ethylene Glycol Condensation Polymers," while those of the polypropylene glycols are listed in Chapter 13, "Propylene Glycol Condensation Polymers."

lubricants. Some of them are employed in gas dehydration and in air treatment. The polyethylene glycols, alone or in blends, are lubricants for rubber molds, textile fibers, and metal-forming operations. Certain of them serve as bases for pharmaceutical ointments and cosmetic creams, while propylene glycol acts as a solvent, hygroscopic agent, and preservative in the same formulations. Glycol derivatives are used as resins, plasticizers, lubricants, emulsifying agents, and solvents. The dinitrates find use in low-freezing dynamites. Glyoxal is essential in a process for shrinkproofing rayon. In short, the usefulness of these materials is practically boundless, for almost any object around us has been affected in some manner during its manufacture by either a glycol or a glycol derivative.

More detailed information on the production, properties, and applications of individual glycols and glycol derivatives is presented later in this Monograph. Ethylene glycol is first reviewed from the standpoint of production (Chapter 2), properties (Chapter 3), and applications (Chapter 4). Separate discussions of ethylene oxide (Chapter 5), ethylene glycol derivatives (Chapter 6), and polymeric ethylene glycols (Chapter 7) follow. Propylene glycol is reviewed in a similar manner in Chapters 8 through 13. Other industrially important glycols are described in Chapter 14. Chapter 15 summarizes the physiological properties of all these compounds. The analytical chemistry of the glycols is discussed in Chapter 16. For the location of specific factual material, it is suggested that the reader refer to the index.

Literature Cited

1. Walker, J. F., "Formaldehyde," A. C. S. Monograph No. 98, New York, Reinhold Publishing Corp., 1944.

CHAPTER 2

ETHYLENE GLYCOL PRODUCTION

P. R. RECTOR AND W. J. TOUSSAINT

COMMERCIAL HISTORY

Ethylene glycol was first prepared in 1859 by Wurtz, who saponified ethylene glycol diacetate with potassium hydroxide. In 1860 he also prepared ethylene glycol by the hydration of ethylene oxide, a method which later became the basis for its manufacture on a commercial scale.

Ethylene glycol remained a laboratory curiosity prior to studies in Europe on the effectiveness of nitrated glycols for lowering the freezing point of nitroglycerin used in dynamite. The first statements in the literature regarding ethylene glycol dinitrate appeared in German Patent 179,789 (1904), claiming it as an additive for nitroglycerin explosives to prevent freezing. Similar claims appeared in British Patent 12,770 (1912). However, there appears to have been no commercial manufacture of ethylene glycol nor any practical application of it at that time.

The scarcity of glycerol in Germany during World War I turned attention to ethylene glycol dinitrate as a possible substitute for nitroglycerin. All known methods of preparing ethylene glycol were studied and the commercial process of synthesizing it from alcohol via ethylene and ethylene dichloride was developed. During the War, many thousands of pounds of ethylene glycol were produced, mainly by T. Goldschmidt A.-G. in Essen, and furnished to the explosives industry. It was nitrated to ethylene glycol dinitrate, used partly as such and partly in mixtures with nitroglycerin as a completely equivalent substitute for the latter in mining explosives

In this country, McElroy obtained a series of patents on ethylene glycol manufacture, beginning in 1915. He appears to be the first to have suggested the use of ethylene chlorohydrin for the industrial production of ethylene glycol. Starting with his methods, The Commercial Research Company developed the process to a semi-commercial scale in 1917 and continued in operation at Flushing, Long Island, until 1920. They prepared ethylene and propylene largely by the Pintsch gas process. Although the use of ethylene glycol as an anti-freeze in automobiles was foreseen at that time, the chief interest was in the manufacture of explosives.

Meanwhile, a more adequate source of ethylene resulted from an attempt to find a cheaper method than the calcium carbide process for producing acetylene. Working at Mellon Institute, Pittsburgh, Pennsylvania, for The

Courtesy of Mellon Institute

FIGURE 2.1. The building at Mellon Institute, Pittsburgh, Pennsylvania, where Dr. G. O. Curme, Jr., and his associates had developed by 1920 commercial methods for synthesizing ethylene oxide, ethylene glycol, ethylene dichloride, and a long list of other ethylene derivatives.

Prest-O-Lite Company, Inc.,* Curme discovered that acetylene could be produced from gas oil by cracking under certain conditions. In this work, he produced as by-products mixtures of ethylene, propylene, and butylene, which were split into pure fractions at the Buffalo laboratories of The Linde Air Products Company to give him working materials. This led to attempts to utilize ethylene. When it was found useful as a starting material in the manufacture of ethylene glycol, efforts were concentrated upon optimum conditions for cracking gas oil to ethylene. By 1920, Curme and his fellow workers had developed methods for the synthesis of ethylene oxide, ethylene glycol, ethylene dichloride, and other derivatives[1, 2].

Shortly thereafter, Carbide and Carbon Chemicals Corporation** began manufacturing ethylene glycol in a semi-works plant at Clendenin, West Virginia, and in August, 1922, announced its availability in commercial quantities. In 1925, or more than sixty years after ethylene glycol was first described in the literature, this company erected at South Charleston, West Virginia, the first plant for its large-scale commercial manufacture.

In 1927 ethylene glycol was being substituted in part for glycerol by a number of explosives manufacturers inasmuch as the Bureau of Mines had approved 25 ethylene glycol-derived explosives as being permissible

---

* Now a part of Linde Air Products Company, a Division of Union Carbide and Carbon Corporation.

** Now Carbide and Carbon Chemicals Company, a Division of Union Carbide and Carbon Corporation.

for use in coal mines. By 1929, practically every manufacturer of dynamite in the United States was using ethylene glycol.

The second commercial use for ethylene glycol was as an anti-freeze material for automobile cooling systems. This large outlet for ethylene glycol received its start in 1917 when Hibbert obtained United States Patent 1,213,368 relating to the use of ethylene glycol for lowering the freezing point of water in automobile cooling systems. Following its first manufacture of glycol on a large commercial scale in 1925, Carbide sold small amounts of uninhibited ethylene glycol for anti-freeze use. Three years later, Linde research laboratories established that untreated ethylene glycol solutions could become corrosive to the cooling system metals. By 1930, however, National Carbon Company, Inc.,* had developed, in conjunction with Linde's laboratories, a chemical and protective oil inhibitor formulation to prevent this corrosive action. National Carbon took over the marketing of ethylene glycol in the anti-freeze field. At that time, "Prestone" brand anti-freeze (inhibited ethylene glycol) and glycerol were the sole commercial, nonvolatile type anti-freeze materials in competition with the older methanol and alcohol brands then on the market.

Carbide continued to be substantially the sole volume producer until

---

* Now National Carbon Company, a Division of Union Carbide and Carbon Corporation.

Courtesy of Carbide and Carbon Chemicals Company

FIGURE 2.2. The semi-works plant at Clendenin, West Virginia, where Carbide and Carbon Chemicals first produced ethylene glycol.

shortly before the outbreak of World War II when the demand for ethylene glycol as an anti-freeze, as an aircraft engine coolant, and for other purposes related to the war effort increased. In order to decrease its dependence on chlorine purchased from outside sources, Carbide, in 1937, had supplemented its chlorohydrin process at South Charleston by a new method based on Lefort's discovery of the direct catalytic oxidation of ethylene. Additional glycol plants based on the oxidation method were put into operation in 1941 at Texas City, Texas, and in 1950 at Whiting, Indiana, and Institute, West Virginia.

Courtesy of Carbide and Carbon Chemicals Company

FIGURE 2.3. Looking up towards the glycol evaporators in an early ethylene glycol unit at South Charleston, West Virginia.

FIGURE 2.4. A modern ethylene glycol installation. Converters and scrubbers are on the left, glycol stills in the center, and storage tanks on the right.

During World War I The Dow Chemical Company had produced ethylene for the wartime-production of mustard gas, and in 1920 attempted to find markets for ethylene chorohydrin and ethylene glycol[3]. It was not til the late thirties, however, that Dow went to large-scale production of ethylene glycol at Midland, Michigan. It increased its capacity early in the forties with a second plant at Freeport, Texas, for the production of ethylene glycol and the related intermediates—chlorine, caustic soda, and ethylene. To meet the shortage of ethylene glycol which developed in Canada during and following World War II, The Dow Chemical Company of Canada, Ltd., an affiliate of the American Company, constructed a glycol plant based on the chlorohydrin process which began production at Sarnia in Ontario in January, 1948. Ethylene purified from the cracking oil gas of the nearby refinery of Imperial Oil, Ltd., is used.

In September, 1940, E. I. du Pont de Nemours & Company, Inc., after four years of research and development, put into operation at Belle, West Virginia, the only existing commercial glycol manufacturing plant based on the hydrogenation of methyl glycolate, the raw materials for which included its own high pressure synthesis products, formaldehyde and methanol. By 1951, production of the Belle plant had increased 180 per cent. During the same period, U. S. Industrial Chemicals, Inc., operated a small commercial plant for ethylene glycol production at Baltimore, Maryland. Operation of this plant, which produced ethylene oxide by direct oxidation of ethylene, was apparently discontinued about 1943.

A substantial increase in ethylene glycol output occurred sometime toward the end of the first quarter of 1948 when Jefferson Chemical Company, Inc., jointly owned by The Texas Company and American Cyanamid Company, put into full commercial operation its large plant near Port Neches, Texas. This plant, utilizing ethylene chlorohydrin as the intermediate, was made up of three process units: an ethylene unit, a combined ethylene oxide and ethylene glycol unit, and a unit to purify ethylene dichloride obtained as a by-product during the manufacture of ethylene chlorohydrin.

By the middle of 1948, another large glycol plant, operated by Wyandotte Chemicals Corporation at Wyandotte, Michigan, began full-scale operation. The raw materials used at this plant were petroleum, chlorine, and caustic soda. The Wyandotte glycol plant differed from any of its predecessors in that the manufacturing processes involved the joint hypochlorination and alkaline saponification of a mixture of ethylene and propylene to produce the oxides from which a 4:1 ethylene glycol-propylene glycol mixture may be produced. This process has the advantage that the cost of completely separating these olefins, as in conventional processes, is eliminated; this is somewhat counteracted by the difficulties entailed in separating the resulting glycols.

In the fall of 1951, five companies in the United States (Carbide, Dow, Du Pont, Jefferson, and Wyandotte) were producing ethylene glycol in nine plants located in the states of West Virginia, Texas, Indiana, and

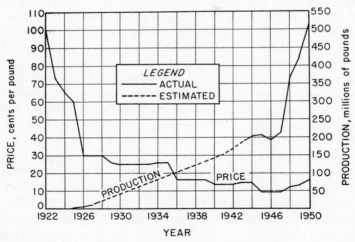

FIGURE 2.5. Ethylene glycol production and price statistics (source: U. S. Tariff Commission and *Oil, Paint and Drug Reporter*).

Michigan. In November a new producer, Mathieson Chemical Corporation, completed initial operations of its chlorohydrin-based glycol plant at Doe Run, Kentucky. United States production had grown from slightly over two million pounds in 1925 to 599,000,000 pounds in 1951. Concurrent with expanded production, the selling price of ethylene glycol dropped from about $0.60 per pound in 1925 to a level of $0.17 per pound in tank car quantities as of November, 1951. This increase in production and drop in price are shown graphically in Figure 2.5.

During the period between World Wars I and II, Germany became a large-scale producer of ethylene glycol via ethylene chlorohydrin, although ethylene dichloride saponification was also utilized to a lesser degree. Published estimates give the productive capacity of the various plants at the end of 1940 to the beginning of 1942 as follows:

	Metric Tons per Year	Ref.
I. G. Farbenindustrie A.-G. (Ludwigshafen)	12,000 [a]	4
I. G. Farbenindustrie A.-G. (Huels)	10,000 [a]	4
I. G. Farbenindustrie A.-G. (Schkopau)	7,200 [a]	4
Anorgana G.m.b.H. (Gendorf)	12,000 [b]	5

[a] includes higher glycols   [b] capacity as of May, 1945.

A partial list of foreign companies currently reported as producers of ethylene glycol in other countries includes the following:

Great Britain*	Imperial Chemical Industries, Ltd. (London)
	Petrochemicals, Ltd. (Manchester)
Canada	The Dow Chemical Company (Sarnia)
France	Société Marles-Kuhlman (Chaques, Pas-de-Calais)
Germany	Anorgana G.m.b.H. (Gendorf)
Italy	Societa Generale Montecatini (Milan)
	Vetro Coke, S.P.A. (Turin)
Belgium**	Union Chimique Belge (Brussels)
Sweden	Mo och Domsjo (Ornskoldsvik)

Ethylene glycol has also been produced by several companies in Japan since as far back as 1937.

---

* In 1951, Imperial Chemical Industries, Ltd., was planning to expand ethylene glycol capacity using ethylene oxide made by the chlorohydrin process from ethylene produced at the naphtha cracking plant under construction at Wilton: Lowe, A. J., and Chapman, E., *Mfg. Chemist,* **22,** 103 (1951).

** Ethylene glycol has been produced in Belgium since 1936 through ethylene chlorohydrin using ethylene obtained from coke-oven gas: *Chem. Age London,* **61,** 8 (1949).

METHODS OF PRODUCTION

Early reviews on glycol manufacture may be found in Lawrie's "Glycerol and the Glycols"[6] and Ellis' "Chemistry of the Petroleum Derivatives"[7]. A review of German practice in glycol manufacture as it existed prior to 1928 appears in Symmes' translation of Naoum's "Nitroglycerine and Nitroglycerine Explosives"[8]. More recently Sherwood[9] critically evaluated the relative merits of competitive manufacturing processes.

LABORATORY METHODS

Hydrolysis of readily available ethylene dihalides, such as ethylene dichloride and ethylene dibromide, or of ethylene glycol diacetate (obtained from ethylene dibromide) has been the most commonly employed method for the preparation of ethylene glycol on a laboratory scale. Ethylene dibromide is hydrolyzed by heating with water at 140 to 150°C.[10] or by heating with aqueous potassium carbonate [11, 12, 13]. Ethylene glycol diacetate has been hydrolyzed using such alkaline agents as potassium hydroxide[14]; powered lime (with a 93 per cent yield)[15]; sodium ethylate in alcohol[16]; and barium oxide[17]. Methanol containing 2.5 per cent by weight of hydrogen chloride has also been used[18]. Ethylene glycol has also been prepared from ethylene glycol monoacetate by heating with barium oxide or water in a sealed tube[19]. The preparation of glycol from ethylene dichloride is described in a separate section (page 15).

Ethylene glycol has also been obtained, along with other products, in several other ways: by heating neurine, $CH_2\!\!=\!\!CHN(CH_3)_3OH$[20]; from glycolaldehyde by reduction with aluminum amalgam[21] or with fermenting yeast[22]; by the dry distillation of choline[23]; and by irradiation of a 1:2 mixture of acetone and methanol[24].

DIRECT HYDROXYLATION OF ETHYLENE

Direct hydroxylation of ethylene can be accomplished by the use of such agents as potassium permanganate[25], ozone, or hydrogen peroxide, or by employing osmium tetroxide to catalyze a mild oxidation by potassium chlorate[26, 27]. Glycol yields as high as 97 per cent have been obtained by treating ethylene with hydrogen peroxide in anhydrous tertiary butyl alcohol in the presence of an osmium tetroxide catalyst[28].

Although several processes have been proposed for the direct hydroxylation of ethylene to glycol by molecular oxygen[29, 30, 31, 32], it seems likely that the first step is the formation of ethylene oxide, as described in Chapter 5, "Ethylene Oxide." Studies[33] of the slow combustion of a 2:1 mixture of ethylene in air show that at a temperature of 276°C. and an initial pressure of 30 atmospheres, about 21 per cent of the oxygen in the condensable oxidation products appears as ethylene glycol. The glycol contains only traces of ethylene oxide, which hydrolyzes rapidly under these conditions. Other products of the oxidation include acetic acid, formic acid, formaldehyde, acetaldehyde, carbon monoxide, carbon dioxide, and water. Increasing the initial pressure to 100 atmospheres doubles the yield of glycol.

HYDROGENATION OF SUGARS AND POLYHYDROXY COMPOUNDS

Sugars containing two to four carbon atoms such as glyceraldehyde, dihydroxyacetone, ketotetrose, and various aldotetroses in aldehyde or lactol forms, have also received attention in the past as starting materials for ethylene glycol[34, 35, 36, 37]. These sugars are usually obtained by the condensation of formaldehyde. Hydrogenation results in a mixture of ethylene glycol (about 25 per cent by weight), glycerol, erythritol, xylitol, and sorbitol.

HYDROLYSIS OF ETHYLENE DICHLORIDE

Ethylene dichloride can be hydrolyzed to ethylene glycol in 82 per cent yields by heating it with aqueous sodium carbonate in an autoclave at a temperature of 150°C. for four hours [11, 38, 39, 40, 41]. Stronger alkalies result in the formation of vinyl chloride and acetylene[42]. Among the different hydrolyzing agents reported in the literature are lead oxide[43], moist silver oxide[44], and sodium formate in methanol[45].

Although numerous patents[46, 47, 48, 49, 50, 51, 52, 53, 54, 55, 56, 57, 58, 59] have been issued, ethylene dichloride hydrolysis never attained commercial importance in the United States. In Germany, however, T. Goldschmidt A.-G. produced considerable amounts of glycol by this method during World War I. During World War II, this process continued to be used in Germany, although on a minor scale[60].

DIRECT HYDROLYSIS OF ETHYLENE CHLOROHYDRIN

Numerous patents[61, 62, 63, 64, 65, 66, 67, 68, 69, 70, 71, 72, 73] have been granted for hydrolyzing ethylene chlorohydrin to the corresponding glycol without isolating ethylene oxide as an intermediate. The chlorohydrin is generally treated with sodium hydroxide or a sodium hydroxide-sodium carbonate mixture in such processes.

CURRENT METHODS OF MANUFACTURE

Practically all the ethylene glycol made in the United States is obtained by the hydration of ethylene oxide or by a high-pressure process from formaldehyde. The ethylene oxide is produced by the oxidation of ethylene or by the dehydrochlorination of the intermediate, ethylene chlorohydrin. These methods employ the readily available raw materials ethylene and air on the one hand, and ethylene, chlorine, and alkalies on the other. The formaldehyde process is based on the high-pressure, high-temperature reaction between formaldehyde, carbon monoxide, and hydrogen. Raw materials for this method are likewise available in ample supply.

ETHYLENE OXIDE METHOD

Production of Ethylene Oxide

Via Ethylene Chlorohydrin. The industrially important chlorohydrins have their principal use in the manufacture of the corresponding glycols. The commercial production of the chlorohydrins is accomplished by the reaction of ethylene or propylene with aqueous hypochlorous acid. Ethylene chlorohydrin was first prepared in this manner by Carius[74] in 1863*, but the first large-scale manufacture was undertaken by the Badische Anilin und Soda Fabrik[75] during World War I in the production of mustard gas. In this country patents issued to McElroy[76] and to Curme and Young[77] were attended by full scale manufacture of both ethylene chlorohydrin and propylene chlorohydrin as intermediates in the production of ethylene glycol and propylene glycol.

Pure ethylene chlorohydrin boils at 128.7°C. under atmospheric pressure. It forms a homogeneous constant boiling mixture with water which distills at 97.8°C. and contains 42.3 per cent by weight ethylene chlorohydrin.

Reaction of Ethylene and Hypochlorous Acid. The basic facts of the process for producing ethylene chlorohydrin were reported in 1919 by Gomberg[78], who proposed the following scheme for the reaction of chlorine, water, and ethylene:

$$HOH \quad + \quad Cl_2 \quad \rightleftharpoons \quad HOCl \quad + \quad HCl$$

$$C_2H_4 \big\downarrow \qquad\qquad \big\downarrow C_2H_4$$

$$C_2H_4Cl_2 \qquad\qquad C_2H_4(OH)Cl$$

He recognized that although hypochlorous acid can exist only at low concentration in water, the relative amounts of ethylene dichloride and ethylene chlorohydrin would be determined by the relative rates of reaction of ethylene with chlorine and hypochlorous acid, respectively. He found that ethylene dichloride formation remained low up to a concentration of 6 to 8 per cent ethylene chlorohydrin. Beyond that point, increase in yield and in concentration of the chlorohydrin became slow, although he attained final concentrations of 14 to 15 per cent. In the narrow temperature range

---

* It is interesting to note that the closely related bis(2-chloroethyl) ether was first prepared by D'Arcet [*Ann. chim. et phys.*, (2) **66,** 108 (1837)] in 1837 and assigned the correct structure by Lieben [*Ann.*, **146,** 186–8 (1868)] in 1868.

of 0 to 12°C., little effect of temperature was observed. Neutralization of the hydrochloric acid, instead of being beneficial, was harmful to the yield of chlorohydrin. The factors adversely affecting the yield in order of increasing influence were ethylene chlorohydrin, hydrochloric acid, magnesium chloride, calcium chloride, and sodium chloride. Adequate stirring to dissolve the ethylene was of the utmost importance.

Tropsch and Kassler[79] found that introduction of ethylene dichloride increased the loss to this by-product through reaction of ethylene with chlorine in the oil phase. They also noted that the yield of ethylene dichloride increased with temperature in the range of 40 to 60°C.

Murray[80] extended and generally confirmed Gomberg's findings. He used a continuous type of apparatus, following essentially the suggestions in issued patents[81, 82]. Since the operation was continuous, an approximately 5 per cent concentration of ethylene chlorohydrin rather than the 8 per cent stated by Gomberg (for the batch process) was necessary to avoid undue losses to the by-products, ethylene dichloride and bis(2-chloroethyl) ether. Under the best conditions, Murray obtained a yield of 87 to 90 per cent ethylene chlorohydrin and of 6 to 9 per cent ethylene dichloride. No significant effect on yields was noted over the temperature range of 12 to 50°C. At 15 to 20 per cent ethylene chlorohydrin concentration, the yield of ethylene dichloride was approximately 20 per cent and of bis(2-chloroethyl) ether, approximately 7.5 per cent.

Mechanism of the Reaction. The earlier view on the course of the reaction as occurring between ethylene and hypochlorous acid does not explain the results satisfactorily. It now seems probable that a chlorine cation first reacts with ethylene[83, 84, 85, 86, 87] and that the formation of the chlorohydrin occurs through subsequent reaction with the hydroxyl ion:

$$Cl_2 \rightarrow Cl^+ + Cl^-$$

$$CH_2{=}CH_2 + Cl^+ \rightarrow CH_2\!\!\overset{\diagdown\;\diagup}{\underset{Cl^+}{}}\!\!CH_2$$

$$CH_2\!\!\overset{\diagdown\;\diagup}{\underset{Cl^+}{}}\!\!CH_2 + OH^- \rightarrow CH_2(OH)CH_2Cl$$

The formation of ethylene dichloride occurs through reaction with a chloride ion:

$$CH_2\!\!\overset{\diagdown\;\diagup}{\underset{Cl^+}{}}\!\!CH_2 + Cl^- \rightarrow CH_2Cl{-}CH_2Cl$$

Evidence for the existence of the postulated intermediate ethylene chloronium ion is found in the formation of the by-product bis(2-chloroethyl) ether, which is best explained by the reaction of the ethylene chloronium ion with ethylene chlorohydrin as indicated in the following equation[88]:

$$C_2H_4Cl^+ + HOCH_2CH_2Cl \rightarrow CH_2ClCH_2OCH_2CH_2Cl + H^+$$

Further evidence for this intermediate is supplied by the reaction of ethylene and chlorine with dioxane. In this instance, triglycol dichloride and bis(2-chloroethyl) ether are obtained. This is explained by reaction of the chloronium ion[89] in the following sequence:

$$C_2H_4Cl^+ + O(CH_2CH_2)_2O \rightarrow ClCH_2CH_2\overset{+}{O}(CH_2CH_2)_2O$$

$$ClCH_2CH_2\overset{+}{O}(CH_2CH_2)_2O + Cl^- \rightarrow ClCH_2CH_2OCH_2CH_2OCH_2CH_2Cl$$

$$C_2H_4Cl^+ + ClCH_2CH_2OCH_2CH_2OCH_2CH_2Cl \rightarrow (ClCH_2CH_2)_2\overset{+}{O}CH_2CH_2OCH_2CH_2Cl$$

$$(ClCH_2CH_2)_2\overset{+}{O}CH_2CH_2OCH_2CH_2Cl + Cl^- \rightarrow 2ClCH_2CH_2OCH_2CH_2Cl$$

A similar intermediate is likely in the reaction of ethylene and chlorine with polyglycol chlorohydrins where it causes fragmentation of the ether chain with the eventual production of low molecular weight glycol dichlorides and chlorohydrins.

Commercial Production of Ethylene Chlorohydrin. The patent literature[90] contains descriptions of numerous methods of industrializing the ethylene chlorohydrin process, many of which, in view of the above scientific reports, seem undesirable.* The evidence favors the use of a simple aqueous solution of chlorine[78, 80, 82, 91] prepared by adding chlorine to water while the solution is reacted simultaneously with ethylene. In continuous operation, a concentration of about 5 per cent ethylene chlorohydrin is maintained in the reaction liquid.

A sketch of German apparatus (Figure 2.6) illustrates the main features of the equipment[92, 93]. The introduction of the ethylene should be conducted in such a manner that good dispersion of the gas is obtained. The chlorine should be added so that no significant amount escapes into the gas cycle; otherwise recovery of ethylene from the purge gas would be difficult. The German operating personnel believed that it was preferable to react all of the chlorine with water before contacting the mixture with ethylene. Circulation of the reaction liquid through cooling coils is necessary for control of temperature.

The acidic chlorohydrin solution is highly corrosive toward the usual materials of construction[91, 94]. The tower is, therefore, constructed of acid-resisting brick with rubber backing, and the lines are made of glass, ceramic, high silica iron, or tantalum metal.

Conversion to Ethylene Oxide. Ethylene chlorohydrin was first converted to

---

* A comprehensive review of the literature has been made by Ellis[8].

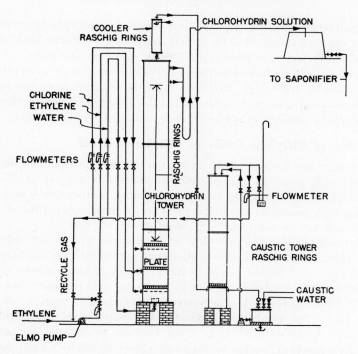

FIGURE 2.6. Flow sheet for the manufacture of ethylene chlorohydrin at Ludwigshafen, Germany[93].

ethylene oxide by Wurtz[95], who reacted it with potassium hydroxide. Hydrogen chloride is split off, and dioxane is formed as a by-product. Other ethylene halohydrins can be employed in place of the chlorohydrin, and either dilute or concentrated solutions of many alkalies may be used[96, 97, 98].

The reaction proceeds under relatively mild conditions[99]. In practice, the crude ethylene chlorohydrin solution is freed of ethylene dichloride and bis(2-chloroethyl) ether by layering and a topping distillation. It is then reacted with caustic soda[100] or hydrated lime[91, 93, 101]. Maximum yields (about 95 per cent) are obtained when the ethylene oxide is removed by distillation from the reaction medium as fast as it is formed.

By Direct Oxidation of Ethylene. The catalytic oxidation of ethylene to ethylene oxide is thoroughly reviewed in Chapter 5, "Ethylene Oxide." The oxidation reaction is carried out at 150 to 500°C. at atmospheric or subatmospheric pressures, using generally nonexplosive mixtures of ethylene, oxygen, and diluent. Silver is the preferred catalyst. The reaction proceeds with the liberation of much heat, most of which arises from the formation of carbon dioxide as a by-product. The reaction equipment used is designed, therefore, for excellent heat removal and temperature control. Tubular reactors surrounded by a shell containing a suitable heat transfer medium are preferred in fixed-bed ethylene oxidation processes.

The effluent gas contains a mixture of ethylene oxide, unreacted ethylene, carbon dioxide, and water. Ethylene oxide is removed from the mixture by adsorption on activated carbon or by absorption in water, methanol, or other solvents. Refined ethylene oxide is obtained by distillation.

Hydration of Ethylene Oxide to Ethylene Glycol

The theory and history of the hydration of ethylene oxide are discussed in Chapter 5, page 95. Large-scale conversion is accomplished in the aqueous phase by operating either at elevated temperatures and corresponding high pressures or in the presence of small quantities of strong acids, which act as catalysts[102, 103, 104, 105, 106, 107, 108, 109, 110].

In Germany at Gendorf[5], ethylene oxide is mixed with sweet water from the glycol evaporators in a ratio of about one part of ethylene oxide to seven parts of water and heated to 190 to 200°C. under 22 atmospheres pressure. The contact time is about one-half to one hour, and complete reaction of ethylene oxide is secured. The conversion equipment used is shown in Figure 2.7[111]. The product is separated by evaporation and purified by distillation. Representative data from German operations are given in Table 2.1[5]; however, yields to ethylene glycol of 92 to 95 per cent are obtainable, the remainder of the ethylene oxide going principally to higher glycols[92].

In the U. S. Industrial Chemicals, Inc., process[112], ethylene oxide is dissolved in water containing an acid hydration catalyst, preferably sulfuric

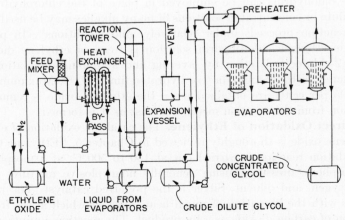

FIGURE 2.7. Ethylene oxide conversion equipment used at Gendorf, Germany[111].

TABLE 2.1. OVERALL YIELDS IN GENDORF PROCESS
(Based on 100 pounds of ethylene oxide)

	Molecular Weight	Theoretical Yield, lbs.	Practical Yield, lbs.	Efficiency, %
Ethylene glycol..............	62	140.8	114.1	81
Diethylene glycol.............	106	120.5	10.2	8.5
Triethylene glycol............	150	113.6	1.6	1.4

acid, in the proportion of about one-half per cent of the weight of the solution. The solution is subjected to heating for a period of about 30 minutes at a temperature of 50 to 70°C. to convert the ethylene oxide to ethylene glycol.

The continuous production of ethylene glycol by the above procedure produces an aqueous solution of glycol containing the acid used as the catalyst. The solution is continuously withdrawn from the conversion chamber. The recovery of the glycol from the solution presents considerable difficulty because some of the acid catalyst is present as such in the solution and the remainder is combined with the glycol. The latter cannot be titrated as free acid and is not precipitated by the addition of barium chloride. Due to the presence of this combined acid, an extra step is necessary to remove the acid from the glycol solution[113].

FORMALDEHYDE METHOD

The unique process operated by Du Pont at Belle, West Virginia, although never fully described in the literature, appears to be based on the reaction at high pressure and temperature of formaldehyde and a mixture of carbon monoxide and water[114, 115] or methanol[116] to produce glycolic acid or methyl glycolate, respectively. The acid is esterified with methanol or *n*-propanol to form the corresponding alkyl glycolates. These are then hydrogenated to ethylene glycol by contact with a catalyst containing copper and magnesium oxides at a temperature of 125 to 325°C. and pressures above 400 atmospheres[117, 118, 119, 120, 121].

The steps in the synthesis from formaldehyde are illustrated by the following equations:

$$CH_3OH \rightarrow CH_2O + H_2 \tag{1}$$
$$CH_2O + CO + H_2O \rightarrow HOCH_2COOH \tag{2}$$
$$CH_2O + CO + CH_3OH \rightarrow HOCH_2COOCH_3 \tag{3}$$
$$HOCH_2COOH + CH_3OH \rightarrow HOCH_2COOCH_3 + H_2O \tag{4}$$
$$HOCH_2COOCH_3 + 2H_2 \rightarrow HOCH_2CH_2OH + CH_3OH \tag{5}$$

The reaction is not quantitative, and consequently the reaction product must be separated from unreacted ester, as well as methanol formed in the hydrogenation. The boiling point differences are such that recovery by fractional distillation would appear to be simple and effective. The recovery of the constituents of such a mixture by normal distillation, however, has been found to be low. Recovery can be carried out by distillation and without uneconomical loss of the ethylene glycol produced or of unreacted methyl glycolate only if the glycol and ester are not permitted to remain in liquid phase contact with each other for any appreciable period of time under the reaction conditions, which are favorable to an ester interchange or condensation reaction. This may be accomplished by circulating small amounts of the liquid mixture, at approximately atmospheric pressure, to a surface having a temperature 5 to 10°C. above the initial boiling point of the mixture. The resulting vapors are richer in the lower boiling constituent than the liquid mixture before vaporization. By repeating this operation, effective separation is accomplished without appreciable losses. Losses are eliminated in the distillation of the hydrogenation mixture when the maximum temperature of the mixture in the vapor phase is kept below 125°C. by reducing the pressure, and if the time of contact is not more than one hour; above 150°C. considerable losses occur. Under these conditions, the temperature of distillation and the rates of the reaction are so low that substantially no esterification or condensation occurs. Methanol required in the process to form the methyl ester is regenerated in the hydrogenation step, recovered, and returned to the process.

Literature Cited

1. Curme, G. O., Jr., *Chem. & Met. Eng.*, **25**, 907–9 (1921); *Ind. Eng. Chem.*, **25**, 582 (1933); **27**, 223 (1935).
2. Curme, G. O., Jr., and Young, C. O., *Chem. & Met. Eng.*, **25**, 1091–2 (1921).
3. Campbell, M., and Hatton, H., "Herbert H. Dow: Pioneer in Creative Chemistry," New York, Appleton-Century-Crofts, Inc., 1951.
4. Hasche, R. L., *Chem. & Met. Eng.*, **52** (10), 116 (1945).
5. Gartshore, J. F. C., BIOS Final Report No. 360, Item 22, 1945.
6. Lawrie, J. W., "Glycerol and the Glycols—Production, Properties, and Analyses," pp. 361–7, Am. Chem. Soc. Monograph No. 44, New York, Chemical Catalog Co., Inc. (Reinhold Publishing Corp.), 1928.
7. Ellis, C., "Chemistry of the Petroleum Derivatives," Vol. **1**, pp. 506–11, New York, Chemical Catalog Co., Inc. (Reinhold Publishing Corp.), 1934; Vol. **2**, pp. 532–5, 1937.
8. Naoum, P., translated by Symmes, E. M., "Nitroglycerine and Nitroglycerine Explosives," pp. 211–6, Baltimore, The Williams & Wilkins Co., 1928.
9. Sherwood, P. W., *Petroleum Refiner*, **28** (3, 7), 129, 120 (1949).
10. Niederist, G., *Ann.*, **186**, 393 (1877); **196**, 354 (1879).
11. Bernouilli, A. L., and Kambli, W., *Helv. Chim. Acta*, **16**, 1187 (1933).
12. Haworth, E., and Perkin, W. H., Jr., *J. Chem. Soc.*, **69**, 175 (1896).
13. Zeller, A., and Hüfner, G., *J. prakt. Chem.*, (2) **11**, 229 (1875).
14. Wurtz, A., *Ann. chim. et phys.*, (3) **55**, 406 (1859).
15. Henry, L., *Rec. trav. chim.*, **18**, 221 (1899).

16. Bainbridge, E. G., *J. Chem. Soc.*, 105, 2298 (1914).
17. Erlenmeyer, E., *Ann.*, 192, 244 (1878).
18. Henry, L., *Chem. Zentr.*, 1907, I, 1314.
19. Debus, H., *Ann.*, 110, 316 (1859).
20. Wurtz, A., *Ann., Suppl.*, 6, 200 (1868).
21. Pribam, R., and Franke, A., *Monatsh. Chem.*, 33, 426 (1912).
22. Neuberg, C., and Schwenk, E., *Biochem. Z.*, 71, 114 (1915).
23. Meyer, K. H., and Hopff, H., *Ber.*, 54, 2279 (1921).
24. Ciamician, G., and Silber, P., *Ber.*, 44, 1281 (1911).
25. Wagner, G., *Ber.*, 21, 1234 (1888).
26. Hofmann, K. A., Ehrhart, O., and Schneider, O., *Ber.*, 46, 1657 (1913).
27. Hofmann, K. A., and Schneider, O., *Ber.*, 48, 1585 (1915).
28. Milas, N. A., and Sussman, S., *J. Am. Chem. Soc.*, 59, 2345 (1937).
29. Chemische Fabrik Griesheim-Elektron, German Patent 300,122 (Oct. 20, 1919).
30. Youtz, M. A. (to Standard Oil Co.), U. S. Patent 1,875,310 (Aug. 30, 1932).
31. Skärbloom, K. E., U. S. Patent 1,982,545 (Nov. 27, 1934); Swedish Patent 83,413
     (Sept. 25, 1936); British Patent 369,141 (Aug. 26, 1931); French Patent 722,000
     (Aug. 27, 1931); German Patents 561,049 (Nov. 7, 1930) and 619,195 (Sept.
     25, 1935).
32. Smith, F. J. (to Standard Oil Co.), U. S. Patent 2,249,986 (July 22, 1941).
33. Newitt, D. M., and Mene, P. S., *J. Chem. Soc.*, 1946, 97–100.
34. Wohl, A., and Bräunig, K., German Patent 373,975 (March 19, 1923).
35. Lazier, W. A. (to E. I. du Pont de Nemours & Co.), U. S. Patent 2,060,880 (Nov.
     17, 1936).
36. Lorand, E. J. (to Hercules Powder Co.), U. S. Patents 2,271,083 (Jan. 27, 1942)
     and 2,325,783 (Aug. 3, 1943).
37. Bottoms, R. R., U. S. Patent 2,335,731 (Nov. 30, 1943).
38. Bahr, H., and Zieler, H., *Z. angew. Chem.*, 43, 286 (1930).
39. Klebanskii, A. L., and Dolgopol'skii, I. M., *J. Applied Chem. (U. S. S. R.)*,
     7, 790 (1934).
40. Takahashi, S., and Makishima, G., *J. Soc. Chem. Ind. Japan*, 38, Suppl. binding
     425 (1935).
41. Wada, N., and Sato, M., *J. Soc. Chem. Ind. Japan*, 38, Suppl. binding 497 (1935).
42. Eltekow, A., *Ber.*, 11, 989 (1878).
43. Eltekow, A., *Ber.*, 6, 558 (1873).
44. Simpson, M., *Ann., Suppl.*, 6, 253 (1868).
45. Brooks, B. T., and Humphrey, I., *J. Ind. Eng. Chem.*, 9, 750 (1917).
46. Hough, A., U. S. Patent 1,206,222 (Nov. 28, 1916).
47. Brooks, B. T., and Humphrey, I. (to Gulf Refining Co.), U. S. Patent 1,215,903
     (Feb. 13, 1917).
48. Matter, O., U. S. Patent 1,237,076 (Aug. 14, 1917); German Patents 299,074
     (Feb. 24, 1920), 369,502 (Feb. 20, 1923), and 373,187 (April 3, 1923).
49. Englehardt, A. (to Farbenfabriken vorm Friedr. Bayer & Co.), German Patent
     410,857 (March 18, 1925).
50. Hibbert, H., U. S. Patent 1,270,759 (June 25, 1918).
51. McElroy, K. P. (to Chemical Development Co.), U. S. Patents 1,259,757–8
     (March 19, 1918).
52. Rodebush, W. H., U. S. Patent 1,402,317 (Jan. 3, 1922).
53. Schlegal, K., Arnold, M., Arnold, H., and Arnold, R., German Patent 487,103
     (May 9, 1925).
54. Rohm & Haas A.-G., French Patent 629,204 (Nov. 7, 1927).

55. Maier, A., German Patent 537,448 (July 2, 1927) and French Patents 656,651 (July 29, 1928) and 697,171 (June 10, 1930).

56. Britton, E. C. (to The Dow Chemical Co.), U. S. Patent 1,709,605 (April 16, 1929).

57. Askenasy, P., and Heller, A., U. S. Patent 1,928,240 (Sept. 26, 1933).

58. Taveau, R. de M. (to The Texas Co.), U. S. Patent 2,041,272 (May 19, 1936).

59. Société Carbochimique, British Patent 424,159 (Feb. 15, 1935) and French Patent 774,186 (Dec. 3, 1934).

60. Morley, R. J., BIOS Final Report No. 776, Item 22, 1946.

61. Société anon. d'explosifs et de produits chimiques, French Patent 458,733 (Aug. 13, 1912) and British Patent 251,652 (May 1, 1925).

62. Curme, G. O., Jr., and Young, C. O. (to Union Carbide Corp.), U. S. Patent 1,442,386 (Jan. 16, 1923).

63. Oehme, H. (to Chemische Fabrik Kalk G.m.b.H), French Patent 612,825 (Nov. 2, 1926).

64. Essex, H., and Ward, A. L. (to E. I. du Pont de Nemours & Co.), U. S. Patent 1,626,398 (April 26, 1927).

65. Curme, G. O., Jr. (to Carbide and Carbon Chemicals Corp.), U. S. Patent 1,695,250 (Dec. 11, 1928); British Patent 264,124 (Jan. 7, 1926); German Patent 540,513 (July 14, 1926); and Canadian Patent 268,570 (Feb. 22, 1927).

66. Saunders, K. H., and Wignall, H. (to British Dyestuffs Corp., Ltd.), U. S. Patent 1,737,545 (Nov. 26, 1929) and British Patent 286,850 (Feb: 8, 1927).

67. Lewis, H. A. (to E. I. du Pont de Nemours & Co.), U. S. Patent 1,895,517 (Jan. 31, 1933); (to Canadian Industries, Ltd.), Canadian Patent 359,058 (July 14, 1936).

68. Dunstan, A. E., and Birch, S. F. (to Anglo-Persian Oil Co., Ltd.), U. S. Patent 1,996,193 (April 2, 1935); French Patent 725,150 (Sept. 18, 1930); British Patent 365,589 (Sept. 18, 1930); and German Patent 590,578 (Jan. 5, 1933).

69. Weihe, F. A., Jr. (to McAleer Manufacturing Co.), U. S. Patent 2,047,811 (July 14, 1936).

70. Mnookin, N. M. (to Synthetic Products, Inc.), U. S. Patent 2,130,891 (Sept. 20, 1938).

71. Ruys, J. D., and McCombie, H. R. (to Shell Development Co.), U. S. Patent 2,148,304 (Feb. 21, 1939).

72. Reed, C. F. (to C. L. Horn), U. S. Patent 2,378,104 (June 12, 1945).

73. Ramage, A. S. (to A. A. F. Maxwell), U. S. Patent 2,398,157 (April 9, 1946).

74. Carius, L., *Ann.*, **126**, 197 (1863).

75. Norris, J. F., *J. Ind. Eng. Chem.*, **11**, 817 (1919).

76. McElroy, K. P. (to Chemical Development Co.), U. S. Patents 1,253,615–6 (Jan. 15, 1918).

77. Curme, G. O., Jr., and Young, C. O. (to Carbide and Carbon Chemicals Corp.), U. S. Patent 1,456,916 (May 29, 1923).

78. Gomberg, M., *J. Am. Chem. Soc.*, **41**, 1416 (1919).

79. Tropsch, H., and Kassler, R., *Mitt. Kohlenforsch. Inst. Prag.*, **1**, 16–42 (1931); *Chem. Abstracts*, **26**, 1242 (1932).

80. Murray, K. E., *J. Council Sci. Ind. Research*, **17**, 213 (1944).

81. Britton, E. C., Nutting, H. S., and Huscher, M. E. (to The Dow Chemical Co.), U. S. Patent 2,130,226 (Sept. 13, 1948).

82. Ferreo, P., and Valendries, C. (to Société Carbochimique), U. S. Patent 2,103,813 (Dec. 28, 1937).

83. Taft, R. W., Jr., *J. Am. Chem. Soc.*, **70**, 3364 (1948).

84. Remick, A. E., "Electronic Interpretations of Organic Chemistry," 2nd Ed., pp. 43–5, 332–8, New York, John Wiley & Sons, Inc., 1949.
85. Wheland, G. W., "Advanced Organic Chemistry," 2nd Ed., pp. 290–9, New York, John Wiley & Sons, Inc., 1949.
86. Price, C. C., "Mechanisms of Reactions at Carbon-Carbon Double Bonds," pp. 35–40, New York, Interscience Publishers, Inc., 1946.
87. Williams, G., *Trans. Faraday Soc.*, **37,** 749 (1941).
88. Perkins, G. A. (to Union Carbide and Carbon Corp.), U. S. Patent 2,042,862 (June 2, 1936).
89. Toussaint, W. J., and MacDowell, L. G., Jr. (to Carbide and Carbon Chemicals Corp.), U. S. Patents 2,352,745 (July 4, 1944) and 2,383,091 (Aug. 21, 1945).
90. McElroy, K. P. (to Chemical Development Co.), U. S. Patents 1,253,615–6 (Jan. 15, 1918); 1,295,339 (Feb. 25, 1919); 1,308,796 (July 8, 1919); and 1,315,229 (Sept. 9, 1919); (to Carbide and Carbon Chemicals Corp.), U. S. Patent 1,510,790 (Oct. 7, 1924).
91. Kern, J. G., Murray, R. L., and Subhoff, R. W., P.B. Report No. 485, 1945.
92. Sherwood, P. W., *Petroleum Refiner*, **28** (7), 120 (1949).
93. Goepp, R. M., Jr., FIAT Final Report No. 874, 1947.
94. Iskra, E. V., *J. Chem. Ind. (U. S. S. R.)*, **12,** 947–53 (1935); *Chem. Abstracts,* **30,** 711 (1936).
95. Wurtz, A., *Ann.*, **110,** 125 (1859).
96. Brooks, B. T. (to Chadeloid Chemical Co.), U. S. Patent 1,446,872 (Feb. 27, 1923).
97. Schoeller, W., Schwenk, E., Borgwardt, E., and Aichner, F. (to Schering-Kahlbaum A.-G.), U. S. Patent 1,967,433 (July 24, 1934).
98. Britton, E. C., Nutting, H. S., and Petrie, P. S. (to The Dow Chemical Co.), U. S. Patent 1,996,638 (April 2, 1945).
99. Curme, G. O., Jr. (to Carbide and Carbon Chemicals Corp.), U. S. Patent 1,695,250 (Dec. 11, 1928).
100. Burdick, J. N. (to Carbide and Carbon Chemicals Corp.), U. S. Patent 1,589,358 (June 22, 1926).
101. Bidlack, V. C., Curtis, F. J., and Harris, J. M., P.B. Report No. 163, 1945.
102. Oehme, H. (to Chemische Fabrik Kalk G.m.b.H), German Patent 416,604 (July 24, 1925).
103. Untiedt, F. H., U. S. Patent 1,641,710 (Sept. 6, 1927).
104. Youtz, M. A. (to Standard Oil Co.), U. S. Patent 1,875,312 (Aug. 30, 1932).
105. Reynhart, A. F. A. (to Shell Development Co.), U. S. Patent 2,236,919 (April 1, 1941).
106. N. V. Bataafsche Petroleum Maatschappij, French Patent 847,406 (Oct. 10, 1939).
107. Archibald, F. M., and Cohen, C. A. (to Standard Alcohol Co.), U. S. Patent 2,228,431 (Jan. 14, 1941).
108. Cohen, C. A., Beamer, E., and Beamer, C. M. (to Standard Alcohol Co.), U. S. Patent 2,255,411 (Sept. 9, 1941).
109. Solvay & Cie, Belgian Patent 448,518 (Jan. 1943).
110. Balcar, F. R. (to U. S. Industrial Alcohol Co.), U. S. Patent 2,325,576 (July 27, 1943).
111. Dennis, N., BIOS Final Report No. 1059, Item 22, 1947.
112. Balcar, F. R. (to U. S. Industrial Alcohol Co.), U. S. Patent 2,135,271 (Nov. 1, 1938).
113. Metzger, F. J. (to U. S. Industrial Chemicals, Inc.), U. S. Patent 2,409,441 (Oct. 15, 1946).

114. Loder, D. J. (to E. I. du Pont de Nemours & Co.), U. S. Patent 2,152,852 (April 4, 1939).
115. Larson, A. T. (to E. I. du Pont de Nemours & Co.), U. S. Patent 2,153,064 (April 4, 1939).
116. Loder, D. J. (to E. I. du Pont de Nemours & Co.), U. S. Patent 2,211,625 (Aug. 13, 1945).
117. Loder, D. J. (to E. I. du Pont de Nemours & Co.), U. S. Patent 2,285,448 (June 9, 1942).
118. Cockerill, R. F. (to E. I. du Pont de Nemours & Co.), U. S. Patent 2,258,444 (Oct. 7, 1941).
119. Pardee, F. W., Jr. (to E. I. du Pont de Nemours & Co.), U. S. Patent 2,305,104 (Dec. 15, 1942) and British Patent 555,240 (Aug. 12, 1943).
120. Larson, A. T. (to E. I. du Pont de Nemours & Co.), British Patent 575,380 (Feb. 15, 1946).
121. Gresham, W. F., and Brooks, R. E. (to E. I. du Pont de Nemours & Co.), U. S. Patent 2,451,333 (Oct. 12, 1948).

CHAPTER 3

PHYSICAL PROPERTIES OF ETHYLENE GLYCOL

W. S. Jones and W. S. Tamplin

Ethylene glycol is a colorless, practically odorless liquid with a sweetish taste. It is relatively viscous and nonvolatile, and is completely miscible with water and many organic liquids.

This chapter contains physical data determined on the substantially pure compound, summarized in Table 3.1, and on its more important aqueous and nonaqueous solutions. In the following discussion, the physical properties follow in alphabetical order, except for those so closely related that they are best treated together.

Much of the aqueous solution data is given in both °C. and °F. Use of the Fahrenheit temperature scale in connection with ethylene glycol anti-freeze solutions is standard industrial practice.

Absorption Spectra

The infrared absorption spectrum of ethylene glycol was published by Weniger[1] in 1910. Although the work was performed over 40 years ago, the curves compare closely to those obtained by present-day apparatus and techniques. However, from a study of the absorption, especially in the region of 6 microns, it is apparent that the sample was contaminated with moisture, probably during the process of introducing it into the cell.

A later absorption curve submitted by The Dow Chemical Company[2] is shown in Figure 3.1. The curve was obtained on the pure liquid using a 0.010-mm. cell.

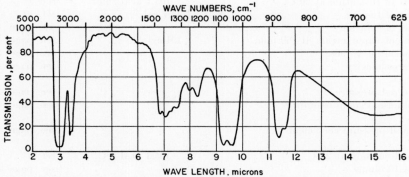

FIGURE 3.1. Infrared absorption spectrum of ethylene glycol at 26°C. (cell length, 0.010 mm.).

TABLE 3.1. Physical Properties of Ethylene Glycol

$$CH_2OH$$
$$|$$
$$CH_2OH$$

Absorption spectra		see page 27
Acid dissociation constant at 19°C.	$K_a = 5.7 \times 10^{-15}$	ref. 5
Azeotropes		see page 29
Boiling point at 760 mm.	197.6°C.	see page 52
at 50 mm.	123°C.	
at 10 mm.	89°C.	
Δb.p./Δp, 740 to 760 mm.	0.043°C./mm.	
Boiling point diagrams		see page 55
Coefficient of expansion at 20°C.	0.00062/°C.	
Density (true) at 20°C.	1.11336 g./ml.	see page 31
Dew points		see page 44
Dielectric constant at 20°C. and 150 meters	38.66 esu	see page 37
Dipole moment at 30°C.	$2.20 \pm 0.02 \times 10^{18}$ esu	ref. 6
Electrical conductivity at 25°C.	1.07×10^{-6} reciprocal ohms (mhos)	ref. 7
Entropy of formation at 25°C.	39.9 kcal./mol/°C.	ref. 8
Fire point	250°F.	see page 38
Flash point	240°F.	see page 38
Free energy of formation at 25°C.	−80.2 kcal./mol	ref. 8
Freezing point	−13°C.	see page 38
Heat of combustion at constant pressure and 20°C.	−283.3 kcal./mol	see page 42
Heat of formation at 20°C.	−108.1 kcal./mol	ref. 9
Heat of fusion	44.7 cal./g.	ref. 10
Heat of solution		see page 42
Heat of vaporization at 760 mm.	191 cal./g.	see page 43
Humectant values		see page 44
Hygroscopicity		see page 44
Internal pressure		see page 46
Isothermal compressibility		see page 46
Liquid pressure coefficient		see page 46
Molal entropy at 25°C.	−105.4 kcal./°C.	ref. 8
Molal volume		see page 46
Molecular refraction at 20°C.	14.49	ref. 11
Molecular refractivity at 20°C.	24.03	ref. 11
Molecular weight, 1951	62.07	

Parachor	148.9 (152.2 calculated)	ref. 12
Ramsay and Shields constant	1.06	ref. 12
Refractive index, n_D at 20°C.	1.4316	see page 47
$\Delta n_D/\Delta t$, 20 to 40°C.	0.00026/°C.	
Solubility		see page 47
Specific gravity (apparent) at 20/20°C.	1.1155	see page 31
ΔSp.gr./Δt, 0 to 40°C.	0.00070/°C.	
Specific heat at 20°C.	0.561 cal./g./°C.	see page 49
Spontaneous ignition temperature		see page 39
Surface energy at the boiling point (total)	74.52 ergs	ref. 12
Surface tension at 20°C.	48.4 dynes/cm.	see page 50
Thermal conductivity at 20°C.	0.000690 cal.-cm./sec./cm.^{2}/°C.	see page 51
Vapor pressure at 20°C.	0.06 mm.	see page 52
Verdet constant at 25°C. and 5461 Å	0.01456 min./gauss cm.	ref. 13
5893 Å	0.01232 min./gauss cm.	ref. 13
Viscosity (absolute) at 20°C.	20.93 cp.	see page 57

Using a 10-foot glass absorption tube, Badger and Bauer[3] studied by photographic methods the absorption of ethylene glycol vapor in the region of the O—H harmonic band at 9500 Å. Although absorption maxima were found at approximately 9547 Å and 9610 Å, ethylene glycol absorbed very weakly in this range in comparison with monohydroxy aliphatic alcohols. The authors attributed this to chelation or association of the glycol molecule.

There is relatively little information on the Raman spectra of the polybasic alcohols. The information on ethylene glycol is summarized by Hibben[4] as follows: "The strongest observed shifts with ethylene glycol are $\Delta\bar{\nu}$ 865, 1035, 1465, and 2873. In addition to less intense low frequencies, three other shifts of some significance appear. These are the doublet frequencies $\Delta\bar{\nu}$ 1070 and 1090 and $\Delta\bar{\nu}$ 3400. These shifts, which occur in most of the alcohols, are probably connected with the R—OH oscillation and the H $\leftrightarrow$ O vibrations, respectively. In glycol this last shift, $\Delta\bar{\nu}$ 3400, is much sharper than in water or methyl alcohol, apparently due to the more specific quantization of the vibrational energy."

Azeotropes

Table 3.2 for the most part is taken from a compilation of data by Horsley[14]. It includes typical compounds that have been investigated for possible azeotrope formation with ethylene glycol. The systems are arranged according to empirical formula. Water is listed first and then organic sys-

TABLE 3.2. AZEOTROPES OF ETHYLENE GLYCOL

Second Component		Boiling Point of Azeotrope, °C. at 760 mm.	Ethylene Glycol, % by Wt.
Formula	Name		
H_2O	Water	no azeotrope	
CH_3NO_2	Nitromethane	no azeotrope	
C_2Cl_4	Tetrachloroethylene	199.1	6
C_2H_5NO	Acetamide	no azeotrope	
$C_4H_8Cl_2O$	Bis(2-chloroethyl) ether	164	17.8
$C_4H_8O_3$	Glycol monoacetate	184.75	25
$C_4H_{10}O$	1-Butanol	no azeotrope	
$C_5H_{12}O_3$	2-(2-Methoxyethoxy)ethanol	192	30
C_6H_5Br	Bromobenzene	150.2	12.5
C_6H_5Cl	Chlorobenzene	130.05	5.6
$C_6H_5NO_2$	Nitrobenzene	185.9	59
C_6H_6	Benzene	no azeotrope	
C_6H_7N	Aniline	180.55	24
C_6H_{12}	Cyclohexane	no azeotrope	
$C_6H_{12}O$	Cyclohexanol	no azeotrope	
$C_6H_{14}O$	1-Hexanol	no azeotrope	
$C_6H_{14}O_3$	2-(2-Ethoxyethoxy)ethanol	195.0	29.5
$C_7H_7NO_2$	o-Nitrotoluene	188.55	48.5
C_7H_8	Toluene	110.20	6.5
C_7H_8O	Benzyl alcohol	193.1	56
C_7H_8O	p-Cresol	195.2	53.5
C_7H_{14}	Methylcyclohexane	100.8	4
C_7H_{16}	n-Heptane	98.3	3
$C_7H_{16}O$	n-Heptyl alcohol	174.1	17
C_8H_8O	Acetophenone	185.65	52
C_8H_{10}	Ethylbenzene	133.0	13.5
C_8H_{10}	o-Xylene	139.6	16
$C_8H_{12}O_4$	Diethyl maleate	193.1	55
$C_8H_{18}O$	Dibutyl ether	140.0	10
$C_8H_{18}O_3$	2-(2-Butoxyethoxy)ethanol	196.2	72.5
$C_8H_{18}O_3$	Bis(2-ethoxyethyl) ether	178.0	26.1
$C_9H_{10}O_2$	Ethyl benzoate	186.1	46
$C_9H_{12}O$	3-Phenylpropanol	195.5	75
$C_9H_{14}O$	Phorone	184.5	42
$C_{10}H_8$	Naphthalene	183.9	51
$C_{10}H_{20}O$	Menthol	188.55	51.5
$C_{10}H_{22}O$	Decyl alcohol	193.0	67
$C_{11}H_{22}O_3$	Diisoamyl carbonate	188.45	46
$C_{12}H_{10}$	Biphenyl	192.25	66.5
$C_{12}H_{10}O$	Diphenyl ether	192.3	64.5
$C_{12}H_{26}O$	Dihexyl ether	112.8 [a]	35.6

[a] At 50 mm.

tems according to ascending number of atoms in the order C, H, Br, Cl, I, N, and O. All compounds with the same number of carbon atoms are placed together.

Density

Density is the most conveniently determined property of ethylene glycol which can be used as an index of purity. Consequently, many investigators[9, 11, 15, 16, 17, 18, 19, 20, 21, 22, 23, 24, 25, 26, 27, 28, 29, 30, 31, 32, 33, 34, 35, 36, 37, 38, 39] of this compound have reported the density at least at one temperature, although relatively few series of determinations have been made over an extended temperature range. From a large-scale graphical comparison of these data and a consideration of the experimental techniques employed, the results of Gibson and Loeffler[40] were found to be the most reliable of those reported in the literature. It was noted that most of the other literature values were low. This very probably was due to the presence of water which had not been completely removed during purification or which had been absorbed from the atmosphere due to the hygroscopic nature of this compound.

Using the method of least squares, Gibson and Loeffler derived the following equation from their experimental data:

$$V = 0.924848 + 6.2796 \times 10^{-4} \, (t - 65) + 9.2444 \times 10^{-7} \, (t - 65)^2 + 3.057 \times 10^{-9} \, (t - 65)^3$$

where V is specific volume, ml./g., and t is temperature, °C. Values calculated from this equation deviate from the experimental values by less than 0.001 per cent over the range of 25 to 105°C. The density column in Table 3.3, covering the range of 0 to 40°C., gives the values obtained by averaging Carbide experimental data and the corresponding values calculated from the equation of Gibson and Loeffler. The maximum deviation of 0.00005 g./ml. may be considered the extent of uncertainty of the values.

Table 3.3 also contains the commonly used values for the apparent specific gravity of ethylene glycol over the same temperature range. These data were derived from the density values by means of the equations:

$$\text{True sp. gr. } t/t' = \text{Density at } t°\text{C.} \times \frac{\text{Density water at 4°C.}}{\text{Density water at } t'°\text{C.}}$$

$$\text{Apparent sp. gr. } t/t' = (\text{True sp. gr. } t/t' \times 1.0012) - 0.0012$$

where 0.0012 is weight in g. of 1 ml. air (approximately).

The data in Table 3.4, covering the temperature range —13°C. (8.6°F.) to 200°C. (392°F.), also were calculated from the equation of Gibson and Loeffler. These values are plotted in Figure 3.2. The change of density

TABLE 3.3. DENSITY AND SPECIFIC GRAVITY OF ETHYLENE GLYCOL

Temperature, °C.	True Density, g./ml.	Apparent Specific Gravity			
		t/4°C.	t/15°C.	t/20°C.	t/25°C.
0	1.12724	1.1274	1.1284	1.1294	1.1307
1	655	67	77	87	00
2	585	60	70	80	1.1293
3	516	53	63	73	86
4	446	46	56	66	79
5	1.12377	1.1239	1.1249	1.1259	1.1272
6	309	32	42	52	65
7	239	25	35	45	58
8	170	18	28	38	51
9	100	11	21	31	44
10	1.12031	1.1204	1.1214	1.1224	1.1237
11	1.11961	1.1197	07	17	30
12	892	90	00	10	23
13	822	83	1.1193	03	16
14	753	76	86	1.1196	09
15	1.11684	1.1169	1.1179	1.1189	1.1202
16	614	65	75	85	1.1198
17	545	62	72	82	95
18	475	55	65	75	88
19	406	48	58	68	81
20	1.11336	1.1135	1.1145	1.1155	1.1168
21	265	28	38	48	61
22	195	21	31	41	54
23	126	14	24	34	47
24	056	07	17	27	40
25	1.10986	1.1100	1.1110	1.1120	1.1133
26	916	1.1093	03	13	26
27	846	86	1.1096	06	19
28	777	79	89	1.1099	12
29	706	72	82	92	05
30	1.10637	1.1065	1.1075	1.1085	1.1098
31	567	58	68	78	91
32	496	51	61	71	84
33	426	44	54	64	77
34	355	37	47	57	70
35	1.10286	1.1030	1.1040	1.1050	1.1063
36	215	23	33	43	56
37	144	17	26	36	49
38	073	10	19	29	42
39	002	04	13	23	36
40	1.09932	1.0997	1.1006	1.1016	1.1029

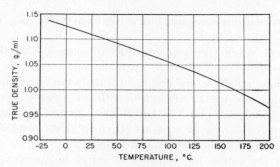

FIGURE 3.2. Density of ethylene glycol, −13 to 200°C.

TABLE 3.4. DENSITY OF ETHYLENE GLYCOL, −13 to 200°C.

Temperature, °C.	True Density, g./ml.	Temperature, °C.	True Density, g./ml.
−13 [a]	1.137	100	1.055
−10	1.134	105	1.051
−5	1.131	110	1.047
		115	1.043
0	1.127	120	1.039
5	1.124		
10	1.120	125	1.035
15	1.117	130	1.031
20	1.113	135	1.027
		140	1.022
25	1.110	145	1.018
30	1.106		
35	1.103	150	1.014
40	1.099	155	1.010
45	1.096	160	1.005
		165	1.000
50	1.093	170	0.995
55	1.089		
60	1.085	175	0.991
65	1.081	180	0.986
70	1.078	185	0.982
		190	0.977
75	1.074	195	0.972
80	1.070		
85	1.066	200	0.967
90	1.063		
95	1.059		

[a] Freezing point.

with temperature is not constant, but varies from 0.0007 per °C. at −13°C. to 0.0010 per °C. at 200°C.

The apparent specific gravity of aqueous solutions of ethylene glycol at 20/20°C. is given in Table 3.5. Such data are useful for determining the compositions and freezing points of anti-freeze solutions. These and other data commonly used in connection with anti-freezes are shown graphically in Figures 3.3, 3.4, and 3.5. Additional information may be found in the comprehensive survey of aqueous ethylene glycol solution data made by Cragoe[41] of the National Bureau of Standards.

Specific gravity values for mixtures of ethylene glycol and diethylene glycol are given in Table 3.6. Mixtures containing 85 to 100 per cent diethylene glycol have, within the limits of experimental error, a constant specific gravity of 1.11836 at 20/20°C.

The only author reporting data for the system ethylene glycol-propylene glycol is Romstatt[37]. If these data are plotted to show the variation of density with composition on a weight basis using temperature as a parameter, it is found that within 0.001 g./ml., the density is a linear function of composition. However, a comparison of Romstatt's densities for the pure components with the best values indicated that some impurities were present in both of his materials. Consequently, in order to obtain density-composition data for this system consistent with the best density values for the pure components, the equation on page 37 was established:

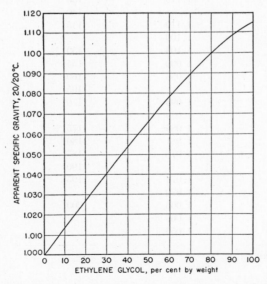

FIGURE 3.3. Specific gravity of aqueous solutions of ethylene glycol.

TABLE 3.5. APPARENT SPECIFIC GRAVITY OF AQUEOUS SOLUTIONS
OF ETHYLENE GLYCOL

Apparent Sp. Gr., 20/20°C.	Ethylene Glycol, % by wt.	Apparent Sp. Gr., 20/20°C.	Ethylene Glycol, % by wt.	Apparent Sp. Gr., 20/20°C.	Ethylene Glycol, % by wt.
1.0000	0.00	1.0400	29.88	1.0800	60.93
1.0010	0.80	1.0410	30.60	1.0810	61.80
1.0020	1.59	1.0420	31.33	1.0820	62.27
1.0030	2.38	1.0430	32.07	1.0830	63.56
1.0040	3.17	1.0440	32.80	1.0840	64.45
1.0050	3.95	1.0450	33.53	1.0850	65.35
1.0060	4.73	1.0460	34.27	1.0860	66.26
1.0070	5.51	1.0470	35.01	1.0870	67.19
1.0080	6.29	1.0480	35.75	1.0880	68.13
1.0090	7.07	1.0490	36.49	1.0890	69.08
1.0100	7.85	1.0500	37.24	1.0900	70.03
1.0110	8.62	1.0510	37.98	1.0910	70.98
1.0120	9.39	1.0520	38.73	1.0920	71.95
1.0130	10.15	1.0530	39.47	1.0930	72.93
1.0140	10.91	1.0540	40.23	1.0940	73.92
1.0150	11.65	1.0550	40.98	1.0950	74.92
1.0160	12.40	1.0560	41.73	1.0960	75.93
1.0170	13.15	1.0570	42.48	1.0970	76.95
1.0180	13.90	1.0580	43.23	1.0980	77.99
1.0190	14.63	1.0590	43.98	1.0980	79.05
1.0200	15.36	1.0600	44.74	1.1000	80.12
1.0210	16.09	1.0610	45.52	1.1010	81.23
1.0220	16.81	1.0620	46.28	1.1020	82.38
1.0230	17.54	1.0630	47.05	1.1030	83.55
1.0240	18.26	1.0640	47.82	1.1040	84.73
1.0250	18.99	1.0650	48.59	1.1050	85.90
1.0260	19.72	1.0660	49.38	1.1060	87.10
1.0270	20.44	1.0670	50.18	1.1070	88.33
1.0280	21.18	1.0680	50.98	1.1080	89.59
1.0290	21.92	1.0690	51.78	1.1090	90.90
1.0300	22.65	1.0700	52.60	1.1100	92.24
1.0310	23.39	1.0710	53.43	1.1110	93.62
1.0320	24.12	1.0720	54.25	1.1120	95.01
1.0330	24.85	1.0730	55.08	1.1130	96.43
1.0340	25.58	1.0740	55.90	1.1140	97.88
1.0350	26.30	1.0750	56.72	1.1150	99.34
1.0360	27.02	1.0760	57.54	1.1155	100.00
1.0370	27.74	1.0770	58.37		
1.0380	28.46	1.0780	59.21		
1.0390	29.17	1.0790	60.07		

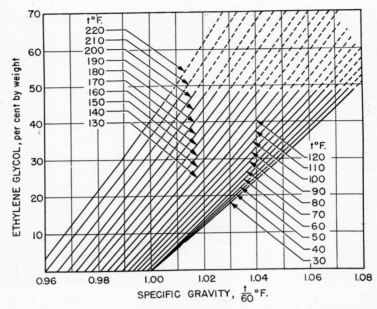

FIGURE 3.4. Specific gravity of aqueous solutions of ethylene glycol at various temperatures.

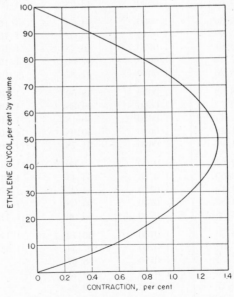

FIGURE 3.5. Contraction of ethylene glycol-water mixtures at 20°C.

TABLE 3.6. APPARENT SPECIFIC GRAVITY OF MIXTURES OF ETHYLENE GLYCOL
AND DIETHYLENE GLYCOL AT 20/20°C.

Apparent Sp. Gr., 20/20°C.	Diethylene Glycol, % by wt.	Apparent Sp. Gr., 20/20°C.	Diethylene Glycol, % by wt.	Apparent Sp. Gr., 20/20°C.	Diethylene Glycol, % by wt.
1.11545	0.00	1.11645	18.6	1.11745	41.0
1.11550	0.96	1.11650	19.5	1.11750	42.4
1.11555	1.9	1.11655	20.5	1.11755	43.8
1.11560	2.8	1.11660	21.5	1.11760	45.2
1.11565	3.8	1.11665	22.5	1.11765	46.7
1.11570	4.7	1.11670	23.5	1.11770	48.2
1.11575	5.6	1.11675	24.6	1.11775	49.8
1.11580	6.5	1.11680	25.6	1.11780	51.5
1.11585	7.4	1.11685	26.7	1.11785	53.2
1.11590	8.3	1.11690	27.8	1.11790	55.0
1.11595	9.2	1.11695	28.9	1.11795	57.0
1.11600	10.1	1.11700	30.0	1.11800	59.1
1.11605	11.0	1.11705	31.1	1.11805	61.5
1.11610	11.9	1.11710	32.3	1.11810	64.1
1.11615	12.9	1.11715	33.4	1.11815	67.0
1.11620	13.8	1.11720	34.6	1.11820	70.2
1.11625	14.7	1.11725	35.8	1.11825	73.7
1.11630	15.7	1.11730	37.1	1.11830	78.3
1.11635	16.6	1.11735	38.4	1.11835	84.5
1.11640	17.6	1.11740	39.7		

$$y = 1.0400 + 0.00078x$$

where y is density, 15°C., and x is ethylene glycol, per cent by weight. The constants of this equation were derived using the values 1.1168 and 1.0400 for the densities at 15°C. of ethylene glycol and propylene glycol, respectively.

Dielectric Constant

Dielectric constant values for pure ethylene glycol and its aqueous solutions are given in Table 3.7. These data were reported by Akerlof[42], who used a resonance method at a wavelength of 150 meters. Other values for the pure compound have been reported[43, 44].

Flammability

Since flammability tests attempt to duplicate the conditions under which materials susceptible to combustion are stored, transported, and handled, such values as flash point and fire point are usually determined on the

TABLE 3.7. DIELECTRIC CONSTANT OF ETHYLENE GLYCOL-WATER MIXTURES

Ethylene Glycol, % by wt.	Dielectric Constant, 150 meters, esu at				
	20°C.	40°C.	60°C.	80°C.	100°C.
0	80.37	73.12	66.62	60.58	55.10
10	77.49	70.29	63.92	58.02	52.64
20	74.60	67.52	61.20	55.36	50.39
30	71.59	64.51	58.37	52.59	47.56
40	68.40	61.56	55.48	49.81	44.78
50	64.92	58.25	52.30	46.75	41.96
60	61.08	54.53	48.75	43.68	39.13
70	56.30	50.17	44.98	40.19	35.94
80	50.64	45.45	40.72	36.36	32.52
90	44.91	40.43	36.35	32.58	29.27
100	38.66	34.94	31.58	28.45	25.61

commercial product rather than on the pure chemical. A survey of the available data indicates that ethylene glycol has a flash point of 240°F. and a fire point of 250°F. The variations in the results of several investigators[41, 45, 46, 47] do not exceed the tolerance of 5°F. customary for these tests. The flash and fire points of aqueous solutions of ethylene glycol are shown in Table 3.8.[41]

Other flammability data for ethylene glycol and its aqueous solutions have been reported. Thompson[48] determined values ranging from 780 to 975°F. for the "apparent ignition temperature in air" of ethylene glycol. The results of experiments performed by the Bureau of Standards[41] and by Sullivan, Wolfe, and Zisman[47] on the spontaneous ignition temperatures of ethylene glycol and its aqueous solutions are summarized in Table 3.8. Results of spray flammability and incendiary bullet tests by these same investigators[47] are also listed in Table 3.8.

Duggan and Green[49] investigated the flammable characteristics of aqueous ethylene glycol solutions. They found that inhibited ethylene glycol anti-freeze solutions containing as low a concentration of water as 40 per cent by volume (freezing point −62°F.) did not burn when sprayed onto wood or gasoline fires. In fact, such solutions acted as control and extinguishing agents. The National Bureau of Standards[50] found that inhibited ethylene glycol-water solutions were nonflammable when sprayed on a hot engine exhaust manifold.

Freezing Point

The accurate determination of the freezing point of ethylene glycol is

TABLE 3.8. FLAMMABILITY VALUES FOR ETHYLENE GLYCOL
AND ITS AQUEOUS SOLUTIONS

Ethylene Glycol, % by wt.	Flash Point, °F.[a]	Fire Point, °F.[b]	Spontaneous Ignition Temperature, °F.		Spray Flammability Limits, % Oxygen[d]	Incendiary Fire Test Flame Height, Feet[e]
			Ref. 41	Ref. 47		
100	245	250	750	1170	856	40	3 to 8
95	260	270				
90	270	280			862	
85	c					3
80			770	1200	871	48
75						1
70					880	
65					885	67	2
60			790	1230	892	no flame
50					903	>80
40			815	1270		
20			840	1350	956	

[a] Approximately the same results were obtained with two open cup instruments (Cleveland, Tag) and two closed cup instruments (Pensky-Martens, Tag).   [b] Determined with a Cleveland open cup instrument.   [c] Solutions containing not more than 85 per cent ethylene glycol by weight boil actively on continued heating and the test flame is extinguished.   [d] Minimum amount of oxygen required in an oxygen-nitrogen stream to cause the ignition of a fine spray of the solution by means of an electric arc.   [e] Height of flame produced by fragments of an incendiary bullet piercing and bursting a 1-gallon container of the liquid.

complicated by the high viscosity of the liquid near the freezing temperature. This condition tends to cause supercooling of the liquid, making equilibrium between liquid and solid phase difficult to attain. The most probable value for the freezing point is − 13°C. (+ 8.6°F.), which is an average of the more reliable values given in the literature[10, 18, 32, 36, 39, 44, 51, 52, 53, 54, 55].

Ethylene glycol and water form a eutectic mixture in the range 58 to 80 per cent glycol by weight, although the exact eutectic composition and temperature have not been accurately defined. Solutions up to 58 per cent by weight form ice crystals on cooling to the freezing point. A nonrigid "slush" formation results. Solutions in the 80 to 100 per cent glycol range form ethylene glycol crystals upon freezing. Such solutions have a pronounced tendency to "supercool" or remain liquid at temperatures below their true freezing point.

Ethylene glycol solutions in the 0 to 58 per cent range in general expand continuously from their freezing points to −54°F. There is some evidence that the more dilute solutions go through a maximum volume and then contract a little on cooling to $-54°F$. Solutions in the 80 to 100 per cent range contract continuously on cooling below their freezing points.

The average of freezing point values reported by Carbide, Dow, Du Pont, and the National Bureau of Standards is given in Table 3.9. Data are not included for the range 58 to 80 per cent ethylene glycol for the reasons stated above. Figures 3.6 and 3.7 show the relationship between these freezing point data and the specific gravity of aqueous ethylene glycol solutions. "Solution temperature" in Figure 3.7 means the temperature at which the specific gravity of the solution is determined. Such data are commonly used to indicate the protection carried in automotive cooling systems when the temperatures of the sample taken may vary from the freezing point to the boiling point of water.

Mixtures of ethylene glycol and diethylene glycol have been used on a limited scale in anti-freeze preparations. Diethylene glycol is, however, a solvent for the nitrocellulose in auto paint finishes. The glycol mixtures,

TABLE 3.9. FREEZING POINTS OF AQUEOUS SOLUTIONS OF ETHYLENE GLYCOL

Ethylene Glycol		Freezing Point		Ethylene Glycol		Freezing Point	
% by wt.	% by vol.	°C.	°F.	% by wt.	% by vol.	°C.	°F.
0	0.0	0.0	32.0	40	37.8	−24	−11
2	1.8	−0.6	30.9	42	39.8	−26	−15
4	3.6	−1.3	29.7	44	41.8	−28	−18
6	5.4	−2.0	28.4	46	43.8	−31	−23
8	7.2	−2.7	27.0	48	45.8	−33	−27
10	9.1	−3.5	25.6	50	47.8	−36	−32
12	10.9	−4.4	24.0	52	49.8	−38	−37
14	12.8	−5.3	22.4	54	51.9	−41	−42
16	14.6	−6.3	20.6	56	53.9	−44	−48
18	16.5	−7.3	18.8	58	56.0	−48	−54
20	18.4	−8	17	80	78.9	−47	−52
22	20.3	−9	15	82	81.0	−43	−46
24	22.2	−11	12	84	83.1	−40	−40
26	24.1	−12	10	86	85.2	−36	−33
28	26.0	−13	8	88	87.3	−33	−27
30	28.0	−15	5	90	89.4	−29	−21
32	29.9	−17	2	92	91.5	−26	−15
34	31.9	−18	−1	94	93.6	−23	−9
36	33.8	−20	−4	96	95.8	−19	−3
38	35.8	−22	−7	98	97.9	−16	+3
				100	100.0	−13	+9

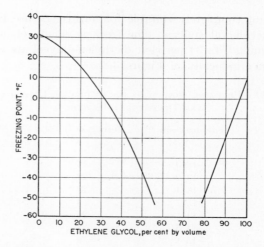

FIGURE 3.6. Freezing point vs. volume per cent for aqueous solutions of ethylene glycol.

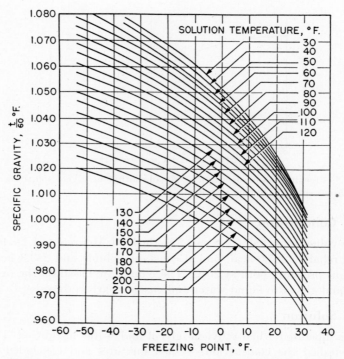

FIGURE 3.7. Freezing points of aqueous ethylene glycol solutions vs. specific gravities at various temperatures.

therefore, are not completely suitable for anti-freeze use because of the possibility of accidental spillage. The freezing points of ethylene glycol solutions containing 0 to 34 per cent diethylene glycol are given in Table 3.10 and shown graphically in Figure 3.8.

TABLE 3.10. FREEZING POINTS OF SOLUTIONS OF ETHYLENE GLYCOL
AND DIETHYLENE GLYCOL

Diethylene Glycol, % by wt.	Freezing Point, °C.	Diethylene Glycol, % by wt.	Freezing Point, °C.
0	−13.0	18	−17.4
2	−13.2	20	−18.3
4	−13.4	22	−19.4
6	−13.7	24	−20.6
8	−14.1	26	−22.0
10	−14.5	28	−23.5
12	−15.1	30	−25.3
14	−15.8	32	−27.2
16	−16.5	34	−29.3

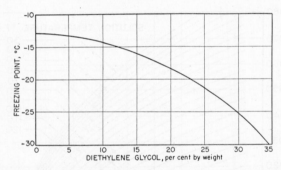

FIGURE 3.8. Freezing points of ethylene glycol-diethylene glycol solutions containing 0 to 35 per cent diethylene glycol.

Heat of Combustion

Of the values reported[8, 10, 56, 57, 58, 59], those of Moureu and Dodé[9] seem the most reliable: 285.0 kcal./mol at constant volume and 283.3 kcal./mol at constant pressure, both at 20°C. These data are based on the oxidation of the liquid glycol to liquid water and gaseous carbon dioxide.

Heat of Solution

Heat is liberated when ethylene glycol and water are mixed. De Forcrand[18] studied the contraction of such mixtures and concluded that a hydrate having the composition $C_2H_4(OH)_2 \cdot 2H_2O$ was formed and a heat of 0.60 calorie liberated. Schwers[22] also studied the effect of mixing various proportions of ethylene glycol and water and found that the maximum effect is obtained by mixing 37 parts of glycol and 63 parts of water by weight (Figure 3.9), indicating the formation of a hydrate of composition $C_2H_4(OH)_2 \cdot 6H_2O$. Taylor and Rinkenbach[25] stated that de Forcrand's conclusion as to the composition of the molecular compound was correct; that Schwers found the point of maximum exothermic effect at another concentration could be ascribed to the fact that the molecular compound has a positive heat of solution.

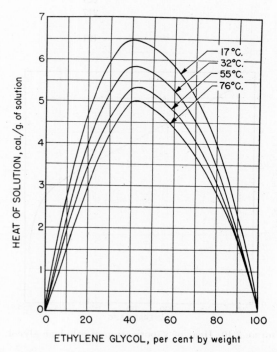

FIGURE 3.9. Heats of solution of ethylene glycol in water at various temperatures.

Heat of Vaporization

Experimental data determined over the temperature range 56 to 140°C. by a modification of the Coolidge condensation method[60] were plotted together with a value obtained by Louguinine[61] at the atmospheric boiling point. The values in Table 3.11, taken from this curve (Figure 3.10), are in fair agreement with those calculated by de Forcrand[18] from vapor pressure data using the Clapeyron equation.

TABLE 3.11 Heat of Vaporization of Ethylene Glycol

Temperature, °C.	Heat of Vaporization, cal./g.
40	258
60	252
80	247
100	241
120	236
140	229
160	224
180	217
198	191

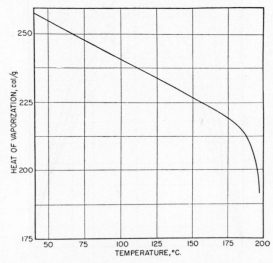

FIGURE 3.10. Heat of vaporization of ethylene glycol.

Hygroscopicity

Although ethylene glycol is known to be very hygroscopic, very few quantitative data are available. The work of Rae[62] indicates that the glycol is about one and one-half times as hygroscopic as glycerol at room temperature and 100 per cent relative humidity.

Equilibrium dew points for gases in contact with aqueous solutions of ethylene glycol have been published by Dow[46]. Their results are presented graphically in Figure 3.11.

Table 3.12 contains relative humectant values for ethylene glycol.[46] This

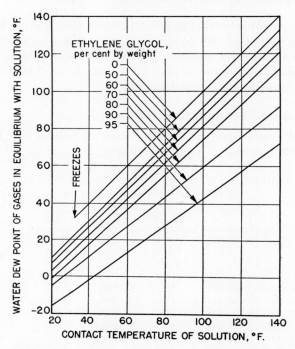

FIGURE 3.11. Approximate water-vapor dew points for gases in equilibrium with aqueous solutions of ethylene glycol.

TABLE 3.12. RELATIVE HUMECTANT VALUES OF ETHYLENE GLYCOL

Air Temperature, °F.	Relative Humidity, %							
	20	30	40	50	60	70	80	90
	Ethylene Glycol, % by wt. in water							
0	85.0	85.0	71.0	60.0	45.0			
10	93.0	85.0	71.0	62.5	47.0		30.0	
20	92.0	85.0	73.0	63.5	48.0	38.0	30.0	20.0
30	92.0	85.0	75.0	64.5	53.0	40.0	32.5	20.0
40	92.0	86.0	77.0	68.5	57.0	45.0	33.0	20.0
50	92.0	87.0	80.0	71.0	61.2	48.0	35.5	20.0
60	92.2	88.0	81.3	72.5	61.5	50.0	37.5	23.5
70	92.5	88.5	81.3	73.0	63.5	52.5	38.5	23.5
80	92.5	88.0	81.5	74.0	65.0	53.0	40.0	26.0
90	92.5	88.0	82.0	75.0	69.5	55.0	42.5	27.0
100	92.5	88.0	82.0	75.5	67.0	56.5	44.0	28.0
110	92.4	88.0	82.5	76.0	67.5	58.0	45.0	30.0
120	92.3	88.0	82.5	76.0	69.0	59.0	46.0	30.0

is a property closely related to hygroscopicity in that it is the limiting concentration of water that will be absorbed in contact with air of a specified temperature and relative humidity. It also may be described as the composition of an aqueous solution that will remain in equilibrium with air of a given temperature and relative humidity.

Pressure-Volume-Temperature Data

Table 3.13 summarizes the excellent work of Gibson and Loeffler[40] on the volumetric behavior of liquid ethylene glycol over an extended range

TABLE 3.13. PRESSURE-VOLUME-TEMPERATURE DATA
FOR LIQUID ETHYLENE GLYCOL

Temperature, t	Pressure, P	Molal Volume, V	Isothermal Liquid Compressibility, $\dfrac{T(\partial v/\partial p)}{V} \times 10^4$	$-\dfrac{\Delta V}{\Delta V_0}$	Thermal Expansion Coefficient, $P(\partial v/\partial T) \times 10^4$	Isochoric Pressure Coefficient, $V(\partial P/\partial T) \times 10^3$	Internal Pressure, $V(\partial P/\partial T) \times T$
25	0.001	55.904	371	0.0000	5.68_7	17.0_0	5.06_9
	0.250	55.411	338	0.0088_2	5.36_3	17.5_9	5.24_4
	0.500	54.958	311	0.0169_2	5.08_9	18.1_9	5.42_3
	0.750	54.541	287	0.0243_8	4.85_3	18.7_7	5.59_6
	1.000	54.155	267	0.0312_9	4.64_7	19.3_4	5.76_6
45	0.001	56.625	400	0.0000	5.94_7	16.3_0	5.18_6
	0.250	56.090	362	0.0094_6	5.57_7	16.9_0	5.37_7
	0.500	55.600	330	0.0181_0	5.26_7	17.4_8	5.56_1
	0.750	55.152	304	0.0260_1	5.00_2	18.0_5	5.74_3
	1.000	54.739	281	0.0333_1	4.77_5	18.6_2	5.92_1
65	0.001	57.383	432	0.0000	6.28_0	15.7_1	5.31_2
	0.250	56.799	388	0.0101_9	5.85_5	16.3_2	5.51_9
	0.500	56.268	352	0.0194_3	5.50_3	16.9_1	5.71_8
	0.750	55.786	322	0.0278_4	5.20_6	17.4_9	5.91_4
	1.000	55.343	297	0.0355_6	4.95_2	18.0_5	6.10_4
85	0.001	58.187	470	0.0000	6.68_6	15.1_8	5.43_7
	0.250	57.545	418	0.0110_3	6.19_0	15.7_9	5.65_5
	0.500	56.968	376	0.0209_4	5.78_9	16.4_0	5.87_4
	0.750	56.446	342	0.0299_1	5.45_2	16.9_9	6.08_5
	1.000	55.970	314	0.0381_0	5.16_7	17.5_5	6.28_6
105	0.001	59.045	513	0.0000	7.16_6	14.6_7	5.54_8
	0.250	58.338	452	0.0119_9	6.58_5	15.3_0	5.78_6
	0.500	57.707	404	0.0226_7	6.11_9	15.9_2	6.02_0
	0.750	57.141	365	0.0322_6	5.73_7	16.5_2	6.24_7
	1.000	56.626	333	0.0409_7	5.41_6	17.1_0	6.46_7

Symbols: P = pressure, kilobars (1 kilobar = 986.92 atmospheres); T = temperature, °K.; t = temperature, °C.; v = specific volume, ml.; V = molal volume, ml.; V_0 = molal volume at 0.001 kilobars, ml.

of pressures and temperatures. Very few comparable data can be found in the literature. Updike, Langdon, and Keyes[63] reported a value of 4400 atmospheres for the internal pressure at 20°C., which is somewhat lower than that derived from Gibson and Loeffler's data. Richards, Stull, Mathews, and Speyers[64], in 1912, reported several values for the isothermal compressibility which are in fair agreement with those given in the table.

Refractive Index

The determination of refractive index affords a rapid and precise method of establishing the purity of ethylene glycol. Over the temperature range 15 to 35°C., the refractive index of the pure material varies linearly at the rate of 0.00026 per °C., the index at 20°C. being 1.4316 for a light of wavelength 5893Å, corresponding to the sodium D line.

Data at various wavelengths other than the sodium D line have been determined by Karvonen[27] and Timmermans and Hennaut-Rowland[32]. Additional refractive properties have been reported by other investigators[9, 11, 24, 30, 34, 36, 39, 54, 65, 66, 67, 68].

The refractive index of aqueous solutions of ethylene glycol varies linearly with composition. This same relationship also holds for the systems ethylene glycol-diethylene glycol and ethylene glycol-propylene glycol.

Solubility

Ethylene glycol is completely miscible with water and the lower aliphatic alcohols, aldehydes, and ketones, but is practically insoluble in hydrocarbons and similar compounds. Trimble and Frazer[69] have reported solubility data on a number of ternary systems containing ethylene glycol, an aromatic hydrocarbon or hydrocarbon derivative, and ethanol or acetone as a mutual solvent (Figure 3.12). They found that of the compounds

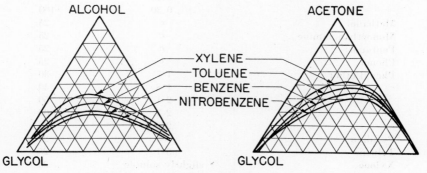

FIGURE 3.12. Solubilities of ternary systems containing ethylene glycol.

investigated nitrobenzene required the least amount of ethanol or acetone to effect complete solution; then, in order, benzene, chlorobenzene, bromo-benzene, toluene, and xylene. Ethanol was found to be a more effective mutual solvent than acetone.

Ethylene glycol is a satisfactory solvent for many substances. Solubilities of a number of common organic and inorganic materials are given in Tables 3.14[46, 53, 69], 3.15[46, 71, 72], and 3.16[73, 74]. Scott[75] has reported that vulcanisates of natural rubber, neoprene and Perbunan are not swelled to

TABLE 3.14. SOLUBILITY OF VARIOUS ORGANIC SOLVENTS IN ETHYLENE GLYCOL

Compound	Solubility, g./100 g. of Ethylene Glycol	Temperature, °C.
Acetic acid	∞	25
Acetone	∞	25
Benzene	6.0	25
Bis(2-chloroethyl) ether	11.8	25
Carbon disulfide	slightly soluble	25
Carbon tetrachloride	6.6	25
Chlorobenzene	6.0	25
Chloroform	slightly soluble	25
Dibutyl phthalate	0.5	25
o-Dichlorobenzene	4.7	25
Diethanolamine	∞	25
Ethanol	∞	25
Ethyl ether	8.9	25
Furfural	∞	25
Glycerol	∞	25
Hexyl ether	0.06	0
	0.09	20
	0.12	40
	0.17	60
	0.23	80
	0.30	100
Methanol	∞	25
Monoethanolamine	∞	25
Pentanol	∞	25
Phenol	∞	25
Phenyl ether	1.7	30
	1.8	40
	2.1	50
	2.3	60
	2.6	70
Pyridine	∞	25
Toluene	3.1	25
Xylene	slightly soluble	25

any appreciable extent by ethylene glycol at 25°C. Perbunan shows the greatest resistance to the swelling action of the glycol at 130°C.

Specific Heat

A tabulation of specific heat data reported by several investigators[10, 16, 18, 22, 61, 76] indicates that this property varies linearly with temperature:

$$x = 0.538 + 0.00113t$$

where x is specific heat, cal./g./°C., and t is temperature, °C.

For pure ethylene glycol the specific heat at 20°C. is 0.561 calories per

TABLE 3.15. SOLUBILITY OF MISCELLANEOUS COMMERCIAL MATERIALS IN ETHYLENE GLYCOL AT ROOM TEMPERATURE

Material	Solubility, g./100 g. of Ethylene Glycol.
Animal glue	very slightly soluble
Castor oil	insoluble
Cellulose acetate	insoluble
Coconut oil	insoluble
Cottonseed oil	insoluble
Dextrin	slightly soluble
Dextrin (10% in water)	∞
Glycol distearate	slightly soluble
Gum damar	slightly soluble
Hydrous wool fat	slightly soluble
Kauri gum	slightly slouble
Lard oil	insoluble
Linseed oil	insoluble
Methyl orange	1.8
Nitrocellulose	insoluble
Olive oil	insoluble
Paraffin oil	insoluble
Pine oil	∞
Rosin	slightly soluble
Rubber	insoluble
Shellac	very slightly soluble
Soya bean oil	very slightly soluble
Sperm oil	very slightly soluble
Sudan III	slightly soluble
Sulfur dioxide	∞ (above −20°C.)
Tall oil	1.1
Tung oil	insoluble
Turkey Red oil	3.3
Urea	44.0
"Vinylite" resin AYAF	insoluble
"Vinylite" resin VYHH	insoluble

TABLE 3.16. SOLUBILITY OF INORGANIC SALTS IN ETHYLENE GLYCOL

Compound	Solubility, g./100 g. of Ethylene Glycol	Temperature, °C.
Barium chloride	36.8	25
Calcium chloride	20.6	25
Copper sulfate ($CuSO_4 \cdot 5H_2O$)	46.88	30
Lithium bromide	39.4	25
Lithium chloride	14.3	25
Mercuric acetate $Hg(C_2H_3O_2)_2$	17.8	25
Potassium bromide	15.5	25
	15.85	30
Potassium chlorate	1.21	25
Potassium chloride	5.18	25
	5.37	30
Potassium iodide	49.9	25
	50.58	30
Potassium perchlorate	1.03	25
Potassium sulfate	0.0	30
Sodium bromide	35.4	25
Sodium chlorate	16.0	25
Sodium chloride	7.15	25
	7.09	30
Sodium iodide	107.4	25
Sodium perchlorate	75.5	25
Strontium chloride	36.4	25

gram per °C. This value is numerically equal to the specific heat at 68°F. expressed as Btu per pound per °F.

Table 3.17 is based largely on the specific heat measurements of Neumann and Kurlyankin[77] as reported by Cragoe[41]. Higher values reported in the literature may be attributed to uncertainties in the water content of the ethylene glycol and to neglect or incorrect evaluation of heat losses from evaporation or other means.

Surface Tension

Reliable surface tension measurements on ethylene glycol were reported by Gallaugher and Hibbert[12]. Their experimental data, which extended over the temperature range of 30 to 160°C., were fitted to the empirical equation

$$x = 50.21 - 0.089t$$

where x is surface tension, dynes/cm., and t is temperature, °C.

No references to the surface tension of aqueous solutions of ethylene glycol have been found in the literature. However, a compilation of Carbide and Du Pont data is shown graphically in Figure 3.13.

TABLE 3.17. SPECIFIC HEAT OF ETHYLENE GLYCOL AND ITS AQUEOUS SOLUTIONS

Ethylene Glycol, % by wt. % by vol.	0 0	20 18.4	40 37.8	60 58.0	80 78.9	100 100
Temperature, °F.	Specific Heat, Btu/lb./°F.					
60	0.9996	0.928	0.835	0.734	0.642	0.556
80	0.9982	0.933	0.847	0.750	0.658	0.569
100	0.9980	0.938	0.858	0.766	0.672	0.581
120	0.9985	0.942	0.868	0.780	0.687	0.594
140	0.9994	0.947	0.877	0.794	0.700	0.606
160	1.0008	0.951	0.886	0.805	0.713	0.619
180	1.0027	0.956	0.894	0.816	0.726	0.631
200	1.0052	0.961	0.902	0.826	0.739	0.644
220	1.008	0.966	0.909	0.836	0.750	0.656
240	1.013	0.972	0.917	0.846	0.762	0.668
260	1.018	0.979	0.926	0.857	0.774	0.681
280	1.024	0.986	0.935	0.867	0.786	0.693
300	1.030	0.994	0.943	0.878	0.798	0.706
320	1.039	1.003	0.953	0.889	0.810	0.718
340	1.050	1.013	0.963	0.900	0.822	0.731
350	1.056	1.018	0.968	0.906	0.828	0.737

Thermal Conductivity

Values for the thermal conductivity of ethylene glycol have been reported by Goldschmidt[78] and Bates and Hazzard[79]. For the pure compound the change in thermal conductivity with temperature is a linear function which may be expressed

$$x = 7.25 \times 10^{-4} - 1.8t \times 10^{-7}$$

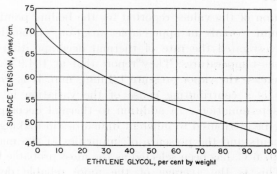

FIGURE 3.13. Surface tension of aqueous solutions of ethylene glycol at 25°C.

where x is thermal conductivity, cal.-cm./sec./cm.^{2}/°C., and t is temperature, °C.

Table 3.18 is taken from the compilation by Cragoe[41]. It is based largely on unpublished data by O. K. Bates of St. Lawrence University, who made thermal conductivity measurements on pure ethylene glycol and its aqueous solutions over the temperature range 20 to 80°C.

TABLE 3.18.   THERMAL CONDUCTIVITY OF ETHYLENE GLYCOL
AND ITS AQUEOUS SOLUTIONS

Ethylene Glycol, % by wt. % by vol.		0 0	20 18.4	40 37.8	60 58.0	80 78.9	100 100
Temperature		Thermal Conductivity, cal.-cm./sec./cm²./°C.					
°F.	°C.						
50	10	0.00137	0.00121	0.00106	0.00093	0.00081	0.00071
75	24	144	124	107	93	79	68
100	38	149	127	108	92	77	66
125	52	154	130	109	91	76	63
150	66	0.00158	0.00132	0.00109	0.00090	0.00074	0.00061
175	79	160	133	109	89	72	58
200	93	162	134	109	88	70	56
225	107	163	134	108	86	68	53
250	121	0.00164	0.00134	0.00107	0.00085	0.00066	0.00051
275	135	164	133	106	83	64	48
300	149	164	132	105	81	62	46
325	163	163	131	103	79	60	43
350	177	162	130	102	77	57	41

Vapor Pressure

An examination of the values reported for the boiling point of ethylene glycol at 760 mm. reveals an appreciable variation. Gallaugher and Hibbert[38] have investigated the rate of thermal decomposition of ethylene glycol at various temperatures. They report that at 164.9°C., the rate is sufficient to increase the vapor pressure 1.3 mm./min. It is evident, therefore, that this is a contributing cause of the variation in atmospheric boiling point determinations. In addition to thermal decomposition, discrepancies may be attributed to inherent difficulties in making vapor pressure measurements and the presence of impurities in the materials used.

A value of 197.6°C. has been selected as the most probable boiling point at 760 mm. This is the average of the more reliable determinations reported in the literature[9, 15, 18, 20, 25, 26, 27, 29, 30, 31, 32, 34, 35, 38, 44, 55, 61, 63, 76, 80, 81, 82, 83, 84, 85, 86].

In order to determine the most probable values for the vapor pressure at various temperatures, all of the data were plotted on large-scale vapor pressure paper (log pressure vs. reciprocal of absolute temperature). After discarding obviously erroneous data, the best smooth curve was drawn through the remaining points so as to include a vapor pressure of 760 mm. at 197.6°C. (Figure 3.14).

It has been shown by work at the Bureau of Standards[87] that an equation of the type

$$\log p = a - \frac{b}{c + t}$$

(where p is vapor pressure, mm., t is temperature, °C., and a, b, c are constants) represents the relationship between vapor pressure and temperature within the limits of experimental error over the range of 100 to 1500

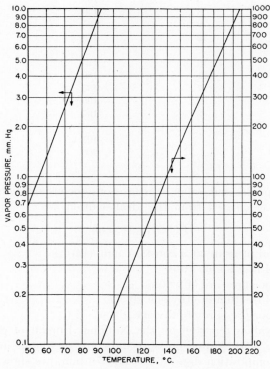

FIGURE 3.14. Vapor pressure of ethylene glycol at various temperatures.

mm. It may be used over a much wider range with small loss of precision. For ethylene glycol this equation may be written:

$$\log p = 7.8808 - \frac{1957}{193.8 + t}$$

The values in Table 3.19 were calculated from this expression.

TABLE 3.19. VAPOR PRESSURE OF ETHYLENE GLYCOL

Temperature, °C.	Vapor Pressure, mm.	Temperature, °C.	Vapor Pressure, mm.
50	0.7	125	54
55	0.9	130	68
60	1.3	135	83
65	1.9	140	103
70	2.6	145	125
75	3.7	150	153
80	5.0	155	183
85	6.7	160	219
90	9.2	165	263
95	12	170	312
100	16	175	373
105	21	180	435
110	27	185	520
115	33	190	605
120	43	195	710
		197.6	760
		200	820

The boiling points and vapor pressures of aqueous solutions of ethylene glycol may be calculated from the ideal-solution law

$$P = x_1 p_1 + x_2 p_2$$

where P = total pressure at a constant temperature
x_1 = mol fraction of water
p_1 = vapor pressure of water
x_2 = mol fraction of ethylene glycol
p_2 = vapor pressure of ethylene glycol

Boiling point values reported by the National Bureau of Standards are given in Table 3.20. Vapor pressure data are presented in Table 3.21. Liquid-vapor composition data at 760 and 76 mm. are shown graphically in Figures 3.15 and 3.16, respectively.

TABLE 3.20. BOILING POINT OF AQUEOUS SOLUTIONS OF ETHYLENE GLYCOL
AT ONE ATMOSPHERE

| Ethylene Glycol | | Boiling Point, °F. | Ethylene Glycol | | Boiling Point, °F. |
% by wt.	% by vol.		% by wt.	% by vol.	
0	0.0	212	80	78.9	252
10	9.1	214	81	79.9	254
20	18.4	216	82	81.0	256
25	23.2	217	83	82.0	258
30	28.0	218	84	83.1	260
35	32.8	219	85	84.1	262
40	37.8	221	86	85.2	265
45	42.8	223	87	86.2	268
50	47.8	225	88	87.3	271
55	52.9	227	89	88.4	275
60	58.0	230	90	89.4	279
62	60.1	232	91	90.5	284
64	62.2	233	92	91.5	289
66	64.2	235	93	92.6	294
68	66.3	236	94	93.6	301
70	68.4	238	95	94.7	309
72	70.5	240	96	95.8	319
74	72.6	243	97	96.8	330
76	74.7	245	98	97.9	345
78	76.8	248	99	98.9	363
			100	100.0	388

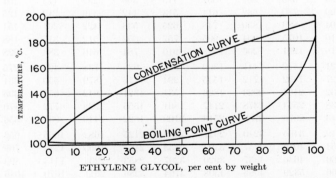

FIGURE 3.15. Boiling point diagram at 760 mm. pressure for the system ethylene glycol-water.

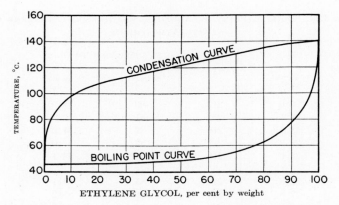

FIGURE 3.16. Boiling point diagram at 76 mm. pressure for the system ethylene glycol-water.

TABLE 3.21. VAPOR PRESSURE OF ETHYLENE GLYCOL AND ITS AQUEOUS SOLUTIONS

Ethylene Glycol, % by wt. % by vol.		0 0	20 18.4	40 37.8	60 58.0	70 68.4	80 78.9	90 89.4	95 94.7	100 100
Temperature		Absolute Pressure, mm. at 0°C.								
°F.	°C.									
140	60	149	139	125	105	—	—	—	—	—
150	66	192	179	161	135	116	90	55	31	2
160	71	245	229	206	172	147	115	70	40	3
170	77	310	289	260	217	187	146	89	51	4
180	82	388	363	326	272	234	183	112	65	6
190	88	483	451	406	339	291	228	140	81	8
200	93	596	557	501	419	360	282	173	101	11
210	99	730	682	614	513	442	346	213	125	15
220	104	889	830	748	625	538	422	261	154	21
230	110	1075	1004	905	757	652	512	317	188	27
240	116	1291	1206	1088	910	784	616	383	228	35
250	121	1542	1441	1300	1088	938	738	460	275	46
260	127	1832	1712	1545	1294	1116	879	550	331	59
270	132	2164	2023	1826	1531	1321	1042	653	395	75
280	138	2544	2378	2147	1801	1555	1228	772	470	94
290	143	2976	2783	2513	2109	1822	1440	909	556	118
300	149	3465	3240	2927	2458	2125	1682	1065	656	146
310	154	4016	3757	3394	2853	2467	1955	1242	769	180
320	160	4636	4337	3920	3297	2853	2264	1443	899	221
330	166	5329	4986	4508	3794	3286	2611	1670	1046	269
340	171	6102	5711	5165	4350	3770	2999	1925	1213	326
350	177	6961	6517	5896	4969	4309	3432	2211	1401	392

Viscosity

The values in Table 3.22 were derived from data published by the National Bureau of Standards[41] giving the viscosity of pure ethylene glycol (Figure 3.17) and its aqueous solutions from −50 to 350°F. The experimental points were not reported. Other measurements have been recorded in the literature[19, 21, 28, 32, 33, 80, 88, 89].

The effects of the addition of ethyl alcohol and isopropyl alcohol on the viscosity of aqueous glycol solutions are shown in Figures 3.18 and 3.19.

Clendenning[90] reported that mixtures of ethylene glycol and other glycols

TABLE 3.22. Absolute Viscosity of Ethylene Glycol
and its Aqueous Solutions

Ethylene Glycol, % by wt. % by vol.		0 0	20 18.4	40 37.8	60 58.0	80 78.9	100 100
Temperature,		Viscosity, centipoises					
°F.	°C.						
−50	−46				286.4	835	
−40	−40				161.9	449	
−30	−34				97.8	259	
−20	−29				62.4	158.2	
−10	−23			19.82	41.7	101.7	
0	−18			14.14	29.04	68.19	
20	−7		4.23	7.93	15.51	34.06	86.9
40	+4	1.55	2.74	4.91	9.19	19.03	45.0
60	16	1.12	1.90	3.28	5.89	11.60	25.66
80	27	0.86	1.39	2.32	4.03	7.58	15.82
100	38	0.68	1.07	1.72	2.89	5.23	10.38
120	49	0.56	0.85	1.33	2.17	3.78	7.17
140	60	0.47	0.69	1.06	1.68	2.83	5.17
160	71	0.40	0.58	0.86	1.34	2.19	3.86
180	82	0.35	0.49	0.72	1.09	1.74	2.97
200	93	0.30	0.43	0.61	0.91	1.41	2.34
220	104	0.27	0.37	0.53	0.77	1.17	1.89
240	116	0.24	0.33	0.46	0.66	0.97	1.56
260	127	0.22	0.30	0.41	0.58	0.84	1.30
280	138	0.20	0.27	0.37	0.51	0.73	1.10
300	149	0.18	0.25	0.33	0.45	0.64	0.95
320	160	0.17	0.23	0.30	0.41	0.57	0.83
340	171	0.16	0.21	0.28	0.37	0.51	0.72
350	177	0.15	0.20	0.26	0.35	0.48	0.68

show higher viscosities at $-10°C$. than pure ethylene glycol and that they
are extremely viscous at low temperatures. Kinematic viscosity values of
500 and 1000 centistokes are attained by the glycol mixtures referred to
in Figure 3.20 at -17.5 to $-27°C$. and at -24 to $-33.5°C$., respectively.
Polyethylene glycol mixtures are less viscous than those prepared with
propylene glycol or dipropylene glycol, and, within the polyethylene glycols,
the expected relation to molecular size is exhibited.

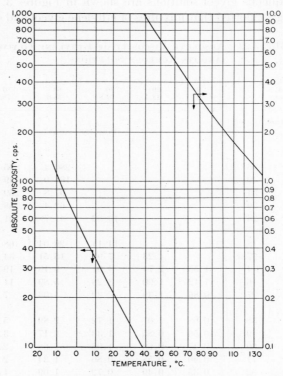

FIGURE 3.17. Absolute viscosity of ethylene glycol, -13 to $140°C$.

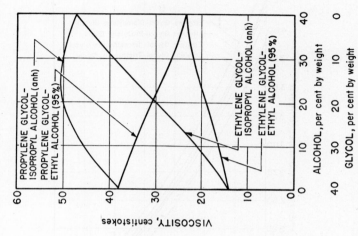

Figure 3.19. Viscosities of glycol-alcohol solutions containing 60 per cent by weight of water at 0°F.

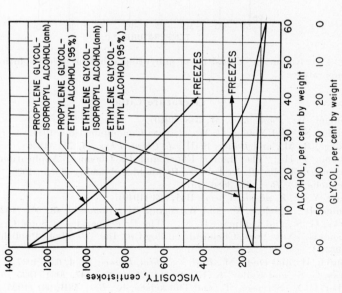

Figure 3.18. Viscosities of glycol-alcohol solutions containing 40 per cent by weight of water at −40°F.

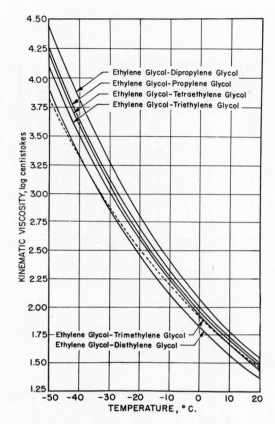

FIGURE 3.20. Kinematic viscosities of anhydrous ethylene glycol solutions (1:1) at low temperatures.

Literature Cited

1. Weniger, W., *Phys. Rev.*, **31,** 388 (1910).
2. Wright, N., and Young, C. W., Private Communication, 1949.
3. Badger, R. M., and Bauer, S. H., *J. Chem. Phys.*, **4,** 711 (1936).
4. Hibben, J. H., "The Raman Effect and Its Chemical Applications," A.C.S. Monograph No. 80, New York, Reinhold Publishing Corp., 1939.
5. Michaelis, L., *Ber.*, **46,** 3686 (1913).
6. Wang, Y. L., *Z. physik. Chem.*, **B45,** 323 (1940).
7. Müller, R., Raschka, V., and Wittmann, M., *Monatsh.*, **48,** 661 (1928).
8. Parks, G. S., and Huffman, H. M., "The Free Energies of Some Organic Compounds," New York, Chemical Catalog Co., Inc. (Reinhold Publishing Corp.), 1932.
9. Moureu, H., and Dodé, M., *Bull. soc. chim. France*, (5) **4,** 637 (1937).
10. Parks, G. S., and Kelley, K. K., *J. Am. Chem. Soc.*, **47,** 2089 (1925).
11. Riiber, C. N., Sörensen, T., and Thorkelsen, K., *Ber.*, **58B,** 964 (1925).

12. Gallaugher, A. F., and Hibbert, H., *J. Am. Chem. Soc.*, **59**, 2521 (1937).
13. Lagemann, R., *J. Polymer Sci.*, **3**, 663 (1948).
14. Horsley, L. H., *Anal. Chem.*, **19**, 508 (1947); **21**, 842 (1949).
15. Wurtz, A., *Ann. chim. et phys.*, (3) **55**, 400–31 (1859).
16. de Heen, P., *Mem. acad. roy. sci. Belg.*, **1884**, 68.
17. Ramsay, W., and Shields, J., *Z. physik. Chem.*, **12**, 433 (1893).
18. de Forcrand, R., *Compt. rend.*, **132**, 569 (1901).
19. Dunstan, A. E., *Z. physik. Chem.*, **51**, 734 (1905).
20. Walden, P., *Z. physik. Chem.*, **65**, 138 (1908).
21. Getman, F. H., *J. Am. Chem. Soc.*, **30**, 1078 (1908).
22. Schwers, M. F., *Rec. trav. chim.*, **28**, 44 (1909).
23. Lowry, T. M., *J. Chem. Soc.*, **105**, 91 (1914).
24. Eykman, J. F., *Rec. trav. chim.*, **14**, 187 (1895).
25. Taylor, C. A., and Rinkenbach, W. H., *Ind. Eng. Chem.*, **18**, 676 (1926).
26. Kailan, A., and Melkus, K., *Monatsh.*, **48**, 9 (1927).
27. Karvonen, A., *Acta Chem. Fennica*, **3**, 101 (1930).
28. Bingham, E. C., and Fornwalt, H. J., *J. Rheol.*, **1**, 372 (1930).
29. Smyth, C. P., and Walls, W. S., *J. Am. Chem. Soc.*, **53**, 2115 (1931).
30. Romstatt, G., *Industrie chimique*, **22**, 648 (1935).
31. Pukirev, A. G., *Trans. Inst. Pure Chem. Reagents (U. S. S. R.)*, **15**, 45 (1937).
32. Timmermans, J., and Mme. Hennaut-Roland, *J. chim. phys.*, **32**, 501 (1935).
33. Noll, A., and Bolz, F., *Papier-Fabr.*, **33**, 193 (1935).
34. Schierholtz, O. J., and Staples, M. L., *J. Am. Chem. Soc.*, **57**, 2709 (1935).
35. Romstatt, G., *Industrie chimique*, **23**, 567 (1936).
36. Ewert, M., *Bull. soc. chim. Belg.*, **46**, 90 (1937).
37. Romstatt, G., *Industrie chimique*, **24**, 227 (1937).
38. Gallaugher, A. F., and Hibbert, H., *J. Am. Chem. Soc.*, **59**, 2514 (1937).
39. Conrad, F. H., Hill, E. F., and Ballman, E. A., *Ind. Eng. Chem.*, **32**, 542 (1940).
40. Gibson, A. F., and Loeffler, O. H., *J. Am. Chem. Soc.*, **63**, 898 (1941).
41. Cragoe, C. S., "Properties of Ethylene Glycol and Its Aqueous Solutions," Washington, D. C., National Bureau of Standards, 1943.
42. Akerlof, G., *J. Am. Chem. Soc.*, **54**, 4125 (1932).
43. Berliner, E., and Rüter, R., *Kolloid-Z.*, **47**, 251 (1929).
44. Walden, P., *Z. physik. Chem.*, **70**, 569 (1910).
45. The Associated Factory Mutual Fire Insurance Companies, *Ind. Eng. Chem.*, **32**, 880 (1940).
46. "Dow Glycols," Midland, Michigan, The Dow Chemical Co., 1947.
47. Sullivan, M. V., Wolfe, J. K., and Zisman, W. A., *Ind. Eng. Chem.*, **39**, 1607 (1947).
48. Thompson, N. J., *Ind. Eng. Chem.*, **21**, 134 (1929).
49. Duggan, J. J., and Green, D. H., "The Non-flammable Characteristics of Water Solutions of Ethylene Glycol Anti-freeze," Paper Presented at the 77th Annual Conference of International Association of Fire Chiefs, San Francisco, California, Sept. 12–15, 1950.
50. Brooks, D. B., and Streets, R. E., "Automotive Anti-freezes," Circular 474, National Bureau of Standards, U. S. Dept. of Commerce, U. S. Government Printing Office, Washington, D. C., Nov. 10, 1948.
51. Bouchardat, G., *Compt. rend.*, **100**, 452 (1885).
52. Ladenburg, A., and Krügel, C., *Ber.*, **32**, 1821 (1899); **33**, 638 (1900).
53. Lawrie, J. W., "Glycerol and the Glycols—Production, Properties and Analyses," A.C.S. Monograph No. 44, New York, Chemical Catalog Co., Inc. (Reinhold Publishing Corp.), 1928.

54. Gallaugher, A. F., and Hibbert, H., *J. Am. Chem. Soc.*, **58,** 813 (1936).
55. Delaplace, R., and Béchard, C., *Compt. rend.*, **208,** 103 (1938).
56. Louguinine, W., *Ann. chim. et phys*, (5) **20,** 561 (1880).
57. Stohmann, and Langbein, *J. prakt. Chem.*, **45,** 305 (1892).
58. Thomsen, S., *Z. physik. Chem.*, **52,** 343 (1905).
59. Kharasch, M. S., *J. Research Natl. Bur. Standards*, **RP 41** (2), 359 (1929).
60. Coolidge, A. S., *J. Am. Chem. Soc.*, **52,** 1874 (1930).
61. Louguinine, W., *Ann. chim. et phys.*, (7) **13,** 289 (1898).
62. Rae, J., *Pharm. J.*, **155,** 151 (1945).
63. Updike, O. L., Jr., Langdon, W. M., and Keyes, D. B., *Trans. Am. Inst. Chem. Engrs.*, **41,** 717 (1945).
64. Richards, T. W., Stull, W. N., Mathews, J. H., and Speyers, C. L., *J. Am. Chem. Soc.*, **34,** 989 (1912).
65. Landolt, M., *Ann. Physik.*, **122,** 545 (1864).
66. Walden, P., *Z. physik. Chem.*, **59,** 395 (1907).
67. Spangler, J. A., and Davies, E. C. H., *Ind. Eng. Chem.*, *Anal. Ed.*, **15,** 96 (1943).
68. Voellmy, H., *Z. physik. Chem.*, **127,** 343 (1927).
69. Trimble, H. M., and Frazer, G. E., *Ind. Eng. Chem.*, **21,** 1063 (1929).
70. Trimble, F., *Ind. Eng. Chem.*, **33,** 660 (1941).
71. "Synthetic Organic Chemicals," New York, Carbide and Carbon Chemicals Corp., 1946.
72. Foote, H. W., and Fleischer, J., *J. Am. Chem. Soc.*, **56,** 870 (1934).
73. Isbin, H. S., and Kobe, K. A., *J. Am. Chem. Soc.*, **67,** 464 (1945).
74. Trimble, H. M., *Ind. Eng. Chem.*, **23,** 165 (1931).
75. Scott, J. R., *J. Rubber Research*, **16,** 216 (1947).
76. Kurbatov, V. J., *J. soc. phys. chim. russe*, **35,** 319 (1903).
77. Neumann, M. B., and Kurlyankin, I. A., *J. Gen. Chem.* (*U. S. S. R.*), **2,** 317 (1932).
78. Goldschmidt, R., *Physik. Z.*, **12,** 417 (1911).
79. Bates, O. K., and Hazzard, G., *Ind. Eng. Chem.*, **37,** 193 (1945).
80. Walden, P., *Z. physik. Chem.*, **55,** 219 (1906).
81. Curme, G. O., Jr., and Young, C. O., *Ind. Eng. Chem.*, **17,** 1117 (1925).
82. Kireev, V. A., and Popov, A. A., *J. Applied Chem.* (*U. S. S. R.*), **7,** 489 (1934).
83. Trimble, H. M., and Potts, W., *Ind. Eng. Chem.*, **27,** 66 (1935).
84. Oguri, S., Hinonishi, S., and Uesugi, K., *Mem. Faculty Sci. & Eng.*, *Waseda Univ.*, Tokyo, 1937.
85. DeMol, A., *Ing. Chim.*, **22,** 262 (1938).
86. Stull, D. R., *Ind. Eng. Chem.*, *Anal. Ed.*, **18,** 234 (1946).
87. Smith, E. R., *J. Research Natl. Bur. Standards*, **24,** 229 (1940).
88. Rinkenbach, W. H., *Ind. Eng. Chem.*, **19,** 4741 (1927).
89. Estel, E., *Physik. Z.*, **41,** 413 (1940).
90. Clendenning, K. A., *Can. J. Research*, **26F,** 213 (1948).

CHAPTER 4

COMMERCIAL APPLICATIONS OF ETHYLENE GLYCOL

Six different glycols and fifty glycol derivatives were made commercially available in the decade after 1925, the year during which ethylene glycol was first produced in large-scale quantities. Their uses multiplied quickly. A count in 1939[1] indicated that there were 143 different applications for all the glycols, without even considering their derivatives. Ethylene glycol, however, remains the most important of the group.

While the biggest outlet for ethylene glycol is in anti-freezes for automobile-engine cooling systems, it has many other applications. Its use as an airplane-engine coolant developed rapidly during World War II. It is consumed as ethylene glycol dinitrate in the manufacture of explosives. Polyethylene glycols, alkyd resins, and other miscellaneous materials are manufactured from it. Consumption is significant in cellophane, hydraulic fluids, adhesives, and radio condenser pastes. Newer applications include its use as an intermediate for the synthetic fiber "Dacron" and for glyoxal (see pages 138 and 125, respectively). An estimated 1949 end-use distribution for ethylene glycol is shown in Table 4.1[2].

TABLE 4.1. ESTIMATED END USE DISTRIBUTION FOR ETHYLENE GLYCOL, 1949

	Millions of Pounds	Per Cent
Automotive anti-freeze..................	330	75.0
Industrial explosives.....................	24	5.4
Cellophane, fibers, paper, and leather.....	19	4.4
Polyethylene glycols, esters, and miscellaneous chemicals.....................	14	3.2
Alkyd resins............................	5	1.1
Industrial coolant and anti-freeze.........	5	1.1
Hydraulic fluids........................	4	0.9
Adhesives..............................	2	.4
Glyoxal................................	1	.2
Export.................................	10	2.4
Miscellaneous..........................	26	5.9
	440	100.0

Anti-Freezes

One of the first uses[3] for ethylene glycol was as a nonvolatile, permanent anti-freeze for automobile cooling systems (see Chapter 2, "Ethylene Glycol Production"). The ethylene glycol-base anti-freeze lowers the freezing point

63

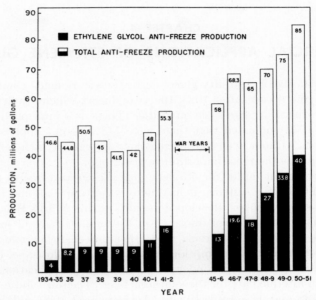

FIGURE 4.1. Estimated percentage of ethylene glycol anti-freeze in total anti-freeze production.

of water sufficiently to protect the engine during the lowest winter temperatures, reduces the corrosive tendencies of water, and does not impart to water any undesirable properties that would interfere with its primary function of cooling the engine efficiently. Its outstanding advantage over the lower alcohols is its high boiling point, but in addition, it is odorless and without effect on automotive finishes[4]. At the present time, ethylene glycol-base anti-freeze is used by millions of motorists, as the data in Figure 4.1 indicate[5]. Brand names for such products include "Prestone," "Permaguard," "Permazone," "Zerex," "Stet," "Peak," "Mopar" permanent type and "Sinclair" permanent type.

To adapt ethylene glycol to anti-freeze use, specially developed inhibitors are added[6]. Two types are in general use—soluble oils and salts[7]. Although nitrogen-containing compounds are favored, satisfactory inhibitors vary greatly as to chemical composition and include the following: ethanolamines[8]; triethanolamine and fatty acid salts[9]; phosphate and borate salts[10]; glycol and glycerol monoricinoleates[11]; guanidine carbonate[12]; washed allyl oil[13]; 1,4-piperazinediethanol[13]; polymethylpyridine[14]; benzopyridines and monomethylbenzopyridines[15]; and borax and mercaptobenzothiazole[16].

The possibility of obtaining improved anti-freeze blends based on ethylene glycol has been studied with such secondary components as methanol[17], ethanol[18], propylene glycol, diethylene glycol[19], 2,3-butanediol[20], 2-methyl-2,4-pentanediol[21], and sorbitol[22]; however, with the exception of propylene glycol, such blends are not important commercially.

Ethylene glycol has other applications that depend on its freezing point depressing properties. It is incorporated into water-containing products such as asphalt-emulsion paints[23]. Its use lowers the freezing point of the water sufficiently to avoid breaking the emulsion by freezing. It is an ingredient of de-icing compositions[24] used on airplane wings and of refill charges for nonfreezing-type fire extinguishers. The anti-freeze grade of ethylene glycol is also used in sprinkler systems for unheated buildings and in place of salt solutions in brine cooling systems where corrosion is a factor.

Low-Freezing Dynamites

Since the original invention of dynamite by Nobel in 1866, one of the important advances in the science of explosives has been the inclusion of freezing inhibitors in nitroglycerin dynamites, the most effective of which

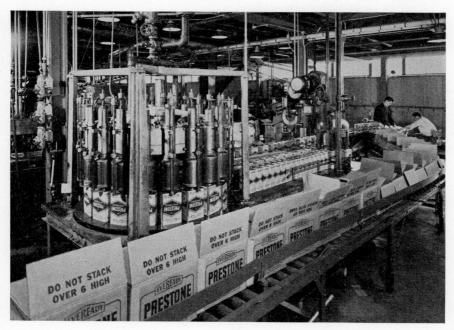

Courtesy of Carbide and Carbon Chemicals Company

FIGURE 4.2. "Prestone" brand anti-freeze being canned for sale to the great American motoring public.

is ethylene glycol dinitrate[25, 26, 27, 28]. Surveys have indicated that prior to the successful solution of the problem of frozen dynamite, 89 per cent of the accidents in handling dynamite occurred during the winter months and were the indirect result of freezing. Frozen dynamite is relatively insensitive and cannot be detonated by a commercial blasting cap. The hazard arises when insufficient precautions are taken in thawing it.

Mixtures of glycerol and ethylene glycol are nitrated with sulfuric and nitric acids to form solutions of nitroglycerin in ethylene glycol dinitrate. These low-freezing dynamites are slightly less sensitive to shock, but they can be detonated just as readily[29]. The solutions remain liquid at −87°F. (see page 130). In practice they are the equivalent of standard nitroglycerin dynamite, and are used in a major portion of mining, road-building, and construction work.

Courtesy of Du Pont Company

FIGURE 4.3. A ditching blast resulting from the use of a low-freezing dynamite containing ethylene glycol dinitrate.

As indicated in Table 4.2, consumption of ethylene glycol in high explosives has probably doubled during the past decade. The average "oil" content (mixture of nitroglycerin and ethylene glycol dinitrate) ranges from 10 per cent by weight in permissible* explosives to as high as 36 per cent in gelatin dynamites, with the ethylene glycol dinitrate content of the "oil" running about 25 to 50 per cent, depending on market conditions.

---

* For use in coal mines

TABLE 4.2. INDUSTRIAL CONSUMPTION OF HIGH EXPLOSIVES CONTAINING ETHYLENE GLYCOL DINITRATE[a]

	Consumption pounds			
	1935–1939 Average	1947	1948	1949
Permissible..............	45,683,634	122,348,571	126,282,153	91,629,597
Other Than Permissible...	253,624,298	476,016,727	550,085,616	505,601,047
Total.................	299,307,932	598,365,298	676,367,769	597,230,644

[a] Bureau of Mines, Mineral Market Reports No. M.M.S. 1656, 1948, and No. M.M.S. 1908, 1950.

Cellophane

Cellophane, prepared in sheet form by regeneration of cellulose from viscose, becomes rather brittle and fragile when it is air-dried. To give it the desired physical properties, 10 to 20 per cent of ethylene glycol, glycerol, or some other glycol is added. These additives act as softening agents which make the brittle cellophane more pliable as well as more resistant to mechanical stress[30]. They act similarly on fibers, paper, and leather.

Resins and Plasticizers

Because of its ready availability at a low price, ethylene glycol has been used as a starting material in the production of a wide variety of synthetic polyesters useful as resins and plasticizers. The types of polyesters produced and some of their more important uses are discussed in Chapter 6, "Derivatives of Ethylene Glycol" (page 134).

Ethylene glycol also acts as a stabilizer against gelation in the production of urea-formaldehyde or melamine-formaldehyde resins. Water dispersions of such resins are generally unstable, and white precipitates or gels form in a few hours. Dispersions prepared by adding 1 to 5 mols of ethylene glycol per 1 mol of urea and 3 mols of aqueous formaldehyde under special conditions are stable and show no increase in viscosity after six months[31, 32, 33].

Ethylene glycol has also been used in the manufacture of various resins of the phenolic type. A flexible, thermosetting phenolic resin (Beckonit 540) involves both ethylene glycol and triethylene glycol in its preparation[34].

Ethylene glycol has another resin application. Copolymers of 95 per cent methyl acrylate and 5 per cent maleic anhydride are converted to an elastic substance similar to vulcanized rubber by heating the resin with the glycol[35].

Engine Coolants

Cooling airplane engines with ethylene glycol[36] permits normal operation at temperatures of 275 to 300°F. Inhibited ethylene glycol in undiluted form is used in engines with unpressurized systems and a 30 per cent aqueous solution in engines with pressurized systems[37]. The chief advantage of high-temperature cooling is reduced frontal area. The small radiator required offers less resistance than an air-cooled reciprocal engine of the same horsepower, resulting in greater speed and better maneuverability.

Various inhibiting agents are added to coolant-grade ethylene glycol. In 1938 the British Air Ministry, followed shortly thereafter by the United States Army Air Corps, issued a specification covering the use of triethanolamine phosphate as a satisfactory inhibitor[38, 39]. Subsequently, the Air Corps inhibitor formulation was modified to include sodium mercaptobenzothiazole[40]. The reaction product of aniline and allyl oil is also recommended as an excellent stabilizer for ethylene glycol at temperatures around 300°C.[41]. The addition of 1 per cent potassium fluoride to ethylene glycol coolant gives good protection against corrosion of magnesium alloys[42].

The use of ethylene glycol as a high temperature coolant has been extended to the cooling systems of x-ray tubes, machine guns, and army tanks.

Hydraulic Fluids

Many hydraulic-brake and shock-absorber fluids on the market are formulated with glycols and their derivatives[43]. The glycols tend to inhibit rubber swelling and act as solvents for the inhibitors. Ethylene glycol itself is a constituent of several formulations having bases of castor oil[44], modified castor oil[45, 46], and miscellaneous materials[47, 48, 49, 50]. One of the earliest fluids contained a eutectic mixture of ethylene glycol and diethylene glycol[51].

Ethylene glycol is also a component of the aqueous-base, nonflammable hydraulic fluids known as "hydrolubes"[52, 53, 54, 55, 56]. They are used in aircraft controls, hydraulically operated die-casting machinery, furnace controls, manipulators, presses, and similar mechanisms.

Electrolytic Condensers

Solutions of boric acid or its salts in ethylene glycol[57] are widely used to form the electrolyte in electrolytic condensers[58, 59, 60, 61, 62]. These condensers consist of sheets of aluminum foil separated by sheets of paper or cloth impregnated with the glycol-boric acid paste. According to one patent[63], the electrolyte is a mixture of 500 g. of ethylene glycol, 500 g. of water, 70 g. of boric acid, and 12 cc. of 1 N ammonium hydroxide. Another patent[64] claims an electrolyte of 2 to 5 per cent ammonium borate, 3 to

Courtesy of Carbide and Carbon Chemicals Company

FIGURE 4.4. "Hydrolube" hydraulic fluids based on polyalkylene glycols and incorporating ethylene glycol reduce fire and explosion hazards of hydraulic equipment.

18 per cent hydrous (ortho) boric acid, and 80 to 95 per cent ethylene glycol. Another electrolyte[65] consists of an ammonium pentaborate-polyhydric alcohol mixture.

Commercially, ethylene glycol free of iron and chlorides is used for this purpose; it gives one of the best nonvolatile liquid conductors of electric current that will not corrode aluminum. The nonconductor of the condenser is the film of aluminum oxide that is anodically deposited on the surface of the aluminum foil. The function of the glycol paste is to give a more intimate contact between the oxide film and the other sheet of aluminum. The condensers are installed extensively in household electric refrigerators to attain a high initial torque when the motor starts under load. They are also widely used in midget radio sets, in frequency modulation receivers, and in radar, television, and similar electronic equipment.

Miscellaneous

Among the miscellaneous commercial applications for ethylene glycol may be mentioned the following: raw material in the manufacture of the brake fluid diluent, methoxymethoxyethanol, by interaction with methylal[66]; starting material in the preparation of anhydrous solutions of BAL (British Anti-Lewisite) eye ointment[67]; liquid dispersion medium in the preparation of suspensions of alkaline earth carbonates and alumina for coating radio tube filaments[68, 69]; ingredient of carbon-remover formulations for treating aluminum aircraft engine pistons[70] and of nongrain-raising wood stains[71, 72]; stabilizer in the soybean liquid-base airfoam widely used in extinguishing oil and chemical plant fires[73]; starting material in the manufacture of terpene-ethylene glycol ether insecticides[74]; selective solvent for the extraction of indene and coumarone from coal tar light oils[75], of butadiene from isobutylene[76], of toluene from methylcyclohexane[77], of barium and calcium chlorides from the reaction products of calcium chloride and barium sulfate[78], of toluene from natural and reformed petroleum stocks[79], and of unsaturated hydrocarbons[80]; reaction medium for the dehydrohalogenation of ethylene dichloride[81]; component of hydrochloric acid baths for electropolishing steel[82] and of phosphoric acid baths for electropolishing aluminum[83]; heat treating fluid to remove cooling strains in polystyrene parts before machining[84]; and heat transfer fluid in the manufacture of phthalocyanine colors[85]. The addition of about 6 per cent ethylene glycol gives optimum hysteresis heat lowering in GR-S and neoprene vulcanizates containing hydrated calcium silicate as the reinforcing pigment[86, 87]. Additional applications include the use of ethylene glycol in mixtures for reducing coal dust[88], in water-base printing inks[89], in dust filter adhesives[90], in oxidizable hair-waving compositions[91], in vat dye baths for nylon fibers[92], and for the preparation of anhydrous ethyl alcohol by azeotropic distillation[93].

Literature Cited

1. McClure, H. B., *Ind. Eng. Chem., News Ed.*, **17,** 149 (1939).
2. Messing, R. F., *Chem. Inds.*, **67,** 41 (1950).
3. Hibbert, H., U. S. Patent 1,213,368 (Jan. 23, 1917).
4. Curme, G. O., Jr., and Young, C. O., *Ind. Eng. Chem.*, **11,** 1117 (1925).
5. Kuhn, W. E., and Hutcheson, J. W., *Chem. Week*, **69** (13), 19 (1951).
6. Wilson, W. H., *Automotive Inds.*, **65,** 84–7 (1931).
7. Green, D. H., Lamprey, H., and Sommer, E. E., *J. Chem. Educ.*, **18,** 488 (1941).
8. Calcott, W. S., and Walker, H. W. (to E. I. du Pont de Nemours & Co.), U. S. Patent 1,847,711 (March 1, 1932).
9. Cox, H. L. (to Carbide and Carbon Chemicals Corp.), U. S. Patent 1,992,689 (Feb. 26, 1935).
10. Kiffer, A. D. (to Carbide and Carbon Chemicals Corp.), U. S. Patent 2,384,553 (Sept. 11, 1945).
11. Balcar, F. R. (to U. S. Industrial Chemicals, Inc.), U. S. Patents 2,386,182–3 (Oct. 9, 1945).
12. Heard, J. R., Jr. (to Wyandotte Chemicals Corp.), U. S. Patent 2,401,733 (June 11, 1946).
13. Britton, E. C., and Sexton, A. R. (to The Dow Chemical Co.), U. S. Patent 2,441,793–5 (May 18, 1948).
14. Sexton, A. R. (to The Dow Chemical Co.), U. S. Patent 2,441,848 (May 18, 1948).
15. Sexton, A. R., and Alquist, F. N. (to The Dow Chemical Co.), U. S. Patent 2,441,849 (May 18, 1948).

16. Keller, E. H. (to E. I. du Pont de Nemours & Co.), U. S. Patent 2,373,570 (April 10, 1943); Smith, W. R. (to The Texas Co.), U. S. Patent 2,524,484 (Oct. 3, 1950).
17. Conrad, F. H., Hill, E. F., and Ballman, E. A., *Ind. Eng. Chem.*, **32**, 542–3 (1940).
18. Romstatt, G., *Industrie chimique*, **25**, 517 (1938).
19. U. S. Army Specification No. 4-1116, June 15, 1943.
20. Clendenning, K. A. (to The Honorary Advisory Council for Scientific and Industrial Research), Canadian Patent 446,755 (Feb. 17, 1948).
21. Cunningham, J. P. (to Shell Development Co.), U. S. Patent 2,525,478 (Oct. 10, 1950).
22. Graves, G. D. (to E. I. du Pont de Nemours & Co.), U. S. Patent 1,900,014 (March 7, 1933).
23. "Dow Glycols," Midland, Michigan, The Dow Chemical Co., 1947.
24. Juggins, W. H. (to Chemical Research Laboratories), British Patent 578,847 (July 15, 1946).
25. Barab, J. (to The Commercial Research Co.), U. S. Patent 1,371,215 (March 15, 1921).
26. Perrott, G. St. J., and Tiffany, J. E., Dept. of Commerce, Serial No. 2935, May 1929.
27. Hibbert, H., U. S. Patents 1,213,367 (Jan. 23, 1917) and 1,231,351 (June 26, 1917).
28. Rinkenbach, W. H., *Ind. Eng. Chem.*, **18**, 1195 (1926); *Chem. & Met. Eng.*, **34**, 296 (1927).
29. Coates, A. B., and Perrott, G. St. J., Dept of Commerce, Serial No. 2923, April, 1929.
30. Shutt, R. S., and Mack, E., *Ind. Eng. Chem.*, **25**, 687 (1933).
31. Hodgins, T. S., and Hovey, A. G., *Ind. Eng. Chem.*, **31**, 673 (1939).
32. Hodgins, T. S., and Hovey, A. G. (to Reichhold Chemicals, Inc.), U. S. Patents 2,168,477 (Aug. 8, 1939) and 2,185,167 (Dec. 26, 1939).
33. Hodgins, T. S., Hewett, P. S., and Hovey, A. G. (to Reichhold Chemicals, Inc.), U. S. Patent 2,358,276 (Sept. 12, 1944).
34. Martin, S. R. W., P. B. Report No. 52858, 1946.
35. Atwood, F. C. (to National Dairy Products Corp.), U. S. Patent 2,418,688 (April 8, 1947).
36. Frank, G. W., *S. A. E. Journal*, **25**, 329 (1929).
37. Army Air Forces Tech. Order No. 24-25-1, May, 1947.
38. British Air Ministry Specification DTD 344, March, 1938.
39. Army Air Corps Specification No. 14108, Dec. 2, 1940.
40. Army Air Corps Specification AN-E-2a, April 1, 1944.
41. Britton, E. C., and Sexton, A. R. (to The Dow Chemical Co.), U. S. Patent 2,441,795 (May 18, 1948).
42. Abrahamson, G., *Chem. Eng. News*, **21**, 94 (1943).
43. Fain, J. M., *Chem. Inds.*, **59**, 1012 (1946).
44. Fulton, R. (to Puritan Co., Inc.), U. S. Patent 2,238,045 (April 15, 1941).
45. Tatter, J. W. (to Lewis Differential Co.), U. S. Patent 1,928,956 (Oct. 3, 1933).
46. Woodhouse, J. C., and Weber, A. G. (to E. I. du Pont de Nemours & Co.), U. S. Patent 2,232,581 (Feb. 18, 1941).
47. Muench, E., and Nicolai, F. (to I. G. Farbenindustrie A.-G.), U. S. Patent 1,989,564 (Feb. 21, 1933).
48. Paxton, B. (to Chicago Hydraulic Oil Co.), U. S. Patent 2,060,110 (Nov. 10, 1936).
49. Hodson, W. D., U. S. Patent 2,122,940 (July 5, 1938).
50. Bagley, T. J. (to R. M. Hollingshead Corp.), U. S. Patent 2,235,754 (March 18, 1941).

51. Cox, H. L., and Clapsadle, L. J. (to Carbide and Carbon Chemicals Corp.), U. S. Patent 2,003,662 (June 4, 1935).
52. Zisman, W. A., Spessard, D. R., and O'Rear, J. G., U. S. Patent 2,558,030 (June 26, 1951).
53. Sullivan, M. V., Wolfe, J. K., and Zisman, W. A., *Ind. Eng. Chem.*, **39,** 1614 (1947).
54. Walker, K. E. (to E. I. du Pont de Nemours & Co.), U. S. Patents 2,462,694 (Feb. 22, 1949) and 2,455,961 (Dec. 14, 1948).
55. Glavis, F. J., and Neher, H. T. (to Rohm & Haas Co.), U. S. Patents 2,435,950 (Feb. 10, 1948) and 2,455,117 (Nov. 30, 1948).
56. Katz, D. L., and Esterer, A. K. (to Hydraulic Brake Co.), U. S. Patent 2,390,258 (Dec. 4, 1945).
57. Böeseken, J., Vermaas, N., and Küchlin, A. T., *Rec. trav. chim.*, **49,** 711 (1930).
58. Ruben, S., U. S. Patent 1,710,073 (April 23, 1929).
59. Ruben, S. (to Ruben Condenser Co.), U. S. Patent 1,891,207 (Dec. 13, 1932).
60. Curtis, J. T. (to Curtis Continental Corp.), U. S. Patent 1,950,352 (March 6, 1934).
61. Lilienfeld, J. E. (to Ergon Research Laboratories, Inc.), U. S. Patent 1,986,779 (Jan. 1, 1935).
62. Fruth, H. F. (to P. R. Mallory and Co.), U. S. Patent 2,224,150 (Dec. 10, 1940).
63. Claassen, A. F. P. J., and Basart, J. C. M. (to N. V. Philips' Gloeilampenfabrieken), Dutch Patent 61,138 (June 15, 1948).
64. Georgiev, A. M., and Campbell, J. J. (to General Motors Corp.), U. S. Patent 2,505,180 (April 25, 1950).
65. Burnham, J. (to Sprague Electric Co.), U. S. Patent 2,444,725 (July 6, 1948).
66. Gresham, W. F. (to E. I. du Pont de Nemours & Co.), U. S. Patent 2,321,593 (June 15, 1943).
67. Rigby, G. W. (to the United States of America), U. S. Patent 2,445,366 (July 20, 1948).
68. Benjamin, M., and Osborn, A. B., *Trans. Faraday Soc.*, **36,** 287 (1940).
69. Thurber, E. A., and Wooten, L. A. (to Bell Telephone Laboratories, Inc.), U. S. Patent 2,385,313 (Sept. 18, 1945).
70. U. S. Army Air Corps Specification No. 20,025.
71. Goodman, H. G., Jr. (to Carbide and Carbon Chemicals Corp), U. S. Patent 2,302,760 (Nov. 24, 1942).
72. Berliner, J. F. T. (to E. I. du Pont de Nemours & Co.), U. S. Patent 2,137,830 (Nov. 22, 1938).
73. Urquhart, G. G. (to National Foam System, Inc.), U. S. Patent 2,413,667 (Dec. 31, 1946).
74. Sheffield, D. H. (to Hercules Powder Co.), U. S. Patent 2,347,337 (April 25, 1944).
75. Ganger, A. W., and Bereston, J. N., *J. Inst. Petroleum*, **33,** 687–94 (1947).
76. Sweeney, W. J., Fenske, M. R., and Cummings, G. H. (to Standard Oil Development Co. and Rohm & Haas Co.), U. S. Patent 2,396,299 (March 12, 1946).
77. Cummings, G. H., Sweeney, W. J., and Fenske, M. R. (to Standard Oil Development Co. and Rohm & Haas Co.), U. S. Patent 2,396,303 (March 12, 1946).
78. Shreve, R. N., and Pritchard, W. N., Jr., *Ind. Eng. Chem.*, **27,** 1488 (1935).
79. Arnold, G. B., and Coghlan, C. A., *Ind. Eng. Chem.*, **42,** 1217 (1950).
80. Souders, M., Jr. (to Shell Development Co.), U. S. Patent 2,449,793 (Sept. 21, 1948).
81. Strosacker, C. J. (to The Dow Chemical Co.), U. S. Patent 2,543,648 (Feb. 27, 1951).

82. Edmunson, R. W. (to The National Cash Register Co.), U. S. Patent 2,382,549 (Aug. 14, 1945).
83. Shawcross, O. L. (to Aluminum Co. of America), Canadian Patent 423,093 (Oct. 10, 1944).
84. Wiley, F. E. (to Plax Corp.), U. S. Patent 2,402,221 (June 18, 1946).
85. Reynolds, W. B., and Scully, S. A. (to Interchemical Corp.), U. S. Patent 2,382,441 (Aug. 14, 1945).
86. Gage, F. W., *Rubber Age*, **58,** 343–6, 351 (1945); *India Rubber World*, **112,** 590 (1945).
87. Pechukas, A. (to Pittsburgh Plate Glass Co.), U. S. Patent 2,537,908 (Jan. 9, 1951).
88. Kleinicke, W. E. (to the Johnson-March Corp.,) U. S. Patent 2,436,146 (Feb. 17, 1948).
89. Lauderman, V. A. (to The Champion Paper and Fibre Co.), U. S. Patent 2,468,633 (April 26, 1949).
90. Jefferson, G. D. (to The Atlas Powder Co.), U. S. Patent 2,538,199 (Jan. 16, 1951).
91. deNavarre, M. G. (to The Atlas Powder Co.), U. S. Patent 2,541,345 (Feb. 13, 1951).
92. Sharkey, W. H. (to E. I. du Pont de Nemours & Co.), U. S. Patent 2,541,839 (Feb. 13, 1951).
93. Scheibel, E. G., *Ind. Eng. Chem.*, **42,** 1497 (1950).

CHAPTER 5

ETHYLENE OXIDE

H. C. Schultze

Ethylene oxide (epoxyethane, oxirane, dimethylene oxide) has been known since 1859 when Wurtz,[1] first described its preparation and recognized this and other *alpha* oxides as members of a separate and distinct class of organic compounds. Berthelot[2] had previously prepared epichlorohydrin in 1854 by reacting glycerol and hydrochloric acid and adding potassium hydroxide to the product. However, the nature of the reaction occurring between alkali and a chlorohydrin remained unknown until Wurtz repeated Berthelot's work using ethylene glycol.

Wurtz's original work provided the foundation for the highly important chlorohydrin process by which much ethylene oxide is produced currently. A procedure whereby oxygen could be added directly to the ethylene bond was discovered by Lefort in 1931. His valuable research led to the development of a second major process for ethylene oxide manufacture and provided the impetus for a number of research investigations that have established ethylene oxide as a chemical compound of outstanding importance in many fields. It is the purpose of this chapter to summarize the commercial history, preparation, properties, reactions, and uses of this unusual organic intermediate.

Commercial History

Because ethylene oxide is utilized primarily as an intermediate in the production of ethylene glycol and ethylene glycol derivatives, its commercial history closely parallels that of the glycol. Carbide began large-scale manufacture of ethylene oxide through ethylene chlorohydrin in 1925 and by the direct oxidation of ethylene in 1937. As shown in Table 5.1, Dow, Jefferson, and Wyandotte entered the field later. The newest producer, Mathieson Chemical Corporation, commenced operations in November, 1951.

In 1950, ethylene oxide was approaching the stature of a heavy chemical, with 1949's production valued at 62 million dollars[3]. Production capacity (Table 5.2) more than doubled in the five years following World War II and was expected to be close to 600 million pounds in 1951. Consumption is estimated to have jumped from 108 million pounds in 1939 to 354 million pounds in 1949[4].

TABLE 5.1. ETHYLENE OXIDE PRODUCERS[4]

	Operating Date	Process
Carbide		
South Charleston, W. Va.	1925	Chlorohydrin
	1937	Oxidation
Texas City, Texas	1941	Oxidation
Whiting, Indiana	1950	Oxidation
Institute, W. Va.	1950	Oxidation
Dow		
Midland, Mich.	1939[a]	Chlorohydrin
Freeport, Texas	1941[b]	Chlorohydrin
Jefferson		
Port Neches, Texas	1948	Chlorohydrin
Wyandotte		
Wyandotte, Mich.	1948[c]	Chlorohydrin
Mathieson		
Doe Run, Kentucky	1951	Chlorohydrin

[a] Periodic production. [b] Late 1941 or early 1942. [c] Production in the ratio of four parts ethylene oxide and one part propylene oxide.

PREPARATION

Laboratory Methods

The alkaline hydroxides react with 2-chloroethyl acetate to produce ethylene oxide[5, 6, 7]. The alkaline hydroxide is added gradually to a solution of 2-chloroethyl acetate heated to a temperature between 40 and 150°C. An excess of unreacted base is avoided thereby in the reaction medium, and the reaction itself is made independent of the concentration of base employed[8].

$$\begin{array}{c} CH_2Cl \\ | \\ CH_2-O-\underset{\underset{O}{\|}}{C}-CH_3 \end{array} + 2KOH \rightarrow \begin{array}{c} CH_2 \\ \diagdown \\ | \quad O \\ \diagup \\ CH_2 \end{array} + KCl + CH_2COOK + H_2O$$

Attempts to prepare ethylene oxide by reaction of the halohydrins with zinc or lead oxide[9] or by the dehydration of ethylene glycol[10, 11, 12] have not been successful. The first reaction results in the formation of acetalde-

TABLE 5.2. ETHYLENE OXIDE CAPACITY[a] (IN MILLION POUNDS)[4]

	Capacity (Total)	Chlorohydrin			Oxidation		
		Capacity	Producers	Plants	Capacity	Producers	Plants
1951	593[b]	390	5	6	203	1	3
1950	440	320	4	5	120	1	3
1949	440	320	4	5	120	1	2
1948	302	242	4	5	60	1	2
1947	201	141	2	3	60	1	2
1946	201	141	2	3	60	1	2
1945	201	141	2	3	60	1	2
1944	201	141	2	3	60	1	2
1943	201	141	2	3	60	1	2
1942	201	141	2	3	60	1	2
1941	193	133	2	c	60	1	2
1940	148	133	2	2	15	1	1
1939	148	133	2	2	15	1	1
1938	155	140	1	1	15	1	1
1937	130	115	1	1	15	1	1
1936	115	115	1	1	0	0	0

[a] Exclusive of Du Pont glycol production deriving from HCHO; all cited include ethylene oxide, per se, as well as glycol equivalent. [b] Capacity frequently quoted at 750 million pounds and several estimate at 650 million; the Mathieson capacity based upon known available chlorine is slightly in excess of 30 million pounds; it is also probable that a present producer will increase capacity by about 50 million pounds in 1951—an amount not included here. [c] Dow plant at Freeport, Tex. began late this year or in 1942.

hyde since a higher temperature is required than that used with the alkaline oxides. Ethylene glycol, when heated alone or over zinc chloride or acids at 230°C., yields acetaldehyde or a polymer. The reaction to acetaldehyde is explained by assuming the intermediate formation of the unsaturated and unstable alcohol which transforms to the isomeric aldehyde.

$$
\begin{array}{c}
CH_2OH \\
| \\
CH_2OH
\end{array}
\xrightarrow{-H_2O}
\begin{array}{c}
CH_2 \\
\| \\
CHOH
\end{array}
\rightarrow
\begin{array}{c}
CH_3 \\
| \\
CHO
\end{array}
$$

Silver oxide may be reacted with ethylene diiodide or dibromide at 250°C. to form ethylene oxide[13].

$$
\begin{array}{c}
CH_2Br \\
| \\
CH_2Br
\end{array}
+ Ag_2O \rightarrow
\begin{array}{c}
CH_2 \\
\diagdown \\
\diagup \quad O \\
CH_2
\end{array}
+ 2AgBr
$$

In a similar manner the ethylene dihalides react with alkali oxides at a lower temperature of 180°C.[13]

$$
\begin{array}{c}
CH_2I \\
| \\
CH_2Cl
\end{array}
\;+\; Na_2O \;\rightarrow\;
\begin{array}{c}
CH_2 \\
\diagdown \\
\quad O \\
\diagup \\
CH_2
\end{array}
\;+\; NaI \;+\; NaCl
$$

Direct Oxidation of Ethylene

Ethylene oxide is prepared commercially either by the chlorohydrin process discussed in Chapter 2 ("Ethylene Glycol Production") or by the direct oxidation of ethylene.

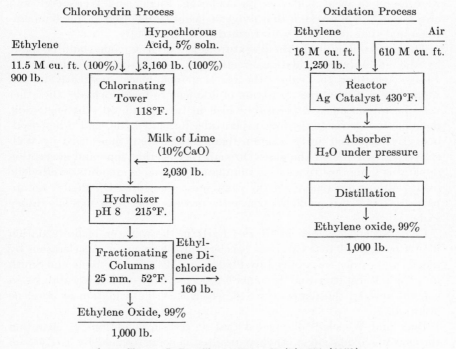

Chlorohydrin Process

Ethylene   Hypochlorous Acid, 5% soln.

11.5 M cu. ft. (100%)   3,160 lb. (100%)
900 lb.

Chlorinating Tower 118°F.

Milk of Lime (10%CaO)
2,030 lb.

Hydrolizer pH 8 215°F.

Fractionating Columns 25 mm. 52°F.

Ethylene Di-chloride
160 lb.

Ethylene Oxide, 99%
1,000 lb.

Oxidation Process

Ethylene   Air

16 M cu. ft. 1,250 lb.   610 M cu. ft.

Reactor Ag Catalyst 430°F.

Absorber H₂O under pressure

Distillation

Ethylene oxide, 99%
1,000 lb.

from Skeen, J. R., *Chem. Eng.*, **57** (7), 331 (1950)

The latter process has been the subject of considerable research in both industrial and academic laboratories.

Historical Aspects. *Uncatalyzed Oxidation of the Olefins.* The study of the reaction of olefins with oxygen began in 1879 when Schutzenberger[14] discovered that ethylene could be oxidized at approximately 400°C. to give recognizable quantities of formaldehyde. Studying this reaction, mostly in the absence of catalysts, Bone and Wheeler[15] found it to proceed slowly at temperatures below 500°C., yielding only traces of formaldehyde. Willstätter and Bommer[16, 17] in 1920 emphasized the distinction between catalyzed and uncatalyzed oxidation of ethylene in a study performed for the practical manufacture of formaldehyde. They found that it was possible to remove formaldehyde from the reaction zone if dilute ethylene was employed at an oxidation temperature of 600°C. and a short reaction time. The highest yield of aldehyde reported represented only 3 per cent of the ethylene introduced and 50 per cent of the ethylene reacted. Blair and Wheeler[18] in 1922 studied the same reaction and in general confirmed the earlier work of Willstätter and Bommer. Higher olefins than ethylene also were found to yield aldehydes on oxidation. Engler and Weissberg[19] and also Lewis[20] demonstrated that amylene could be oxidized at low temperatures and that peroxides were formed as intermediates.

The first intimation in the literature that ethylene oxide could be made by the uncatalyzed oxidation of ethylene was published by Lenher in 1931[21]. According to Lenher, the reaction took place apparently in two ways: one was the direct oxidation of ethylene to formaldehyde; the other was the formation of a peroxide which in turn produced ethylene oxide, dioxymethyl peroxide, hydrogen peroxide, formaldehyde, and other products. He employed lower reaction temperatures than those used by Willstätter and circulated the gases through the reaction zone and adsorption apparatus numerous times to accumulate appreciable amounts of ethylene oxide. Although a patent on the work was assigned to Du Pont[22], no apparent attempt was made to operate the process other than on a laboratory scale.

Catalyzed Oxidation of the Olefins. Early in the work on olefin oxidation it was recognized that catalysts accelerated the reaction. Acceleration by metals and oxides was noticed by Phillips in 1894[23] and by Bone and Smith in 1905[24]. Willstätter and Bommer[16] reported that oxidation catalysts in general lowered the temperature at which effective oxidation of ethylene occurred.

Blair and Wheeler[18] discovered that at certain conditions of operation the catalytic oxidation of ethylene resulted in some formaldehyde. Ryerson and Swearingen[25] stated in 1928 that the air-oxidation of ethylene over metallized silica gels as catalysts gave only carbon dioxide and water.

The first literature reference to the fact that ethylene oxide or the related substance, ethylene glycol, could be made from ethylene in a process em-ploying atmospheric oxygen for oxidation was published by Skärblom in 1929[26]. In his process ethylene reacted with iodine and with hypoiodous acid to form ethylene diiodide and ethylene iodohydrin. These were hydrolyzed to the glycol and hydriodic acid. The hydriodic acid reacted with free oxygen to regenerate iodine.

The addition of a single atom of oxygen to an ethylene bond by surface catalysis was discovered by T. E. Lefort. Patents for the process were granted in 1931 to the Société française de catalyze généralisée[27, 28, 29, 30]. Following this original work, noteworthy contributions to a knowledge of this important reaction were made by many. Carbide acquired the patents covering the Lefort work and elaborated these primary research efforts into a commercial process[31, 32, 33, 34, 35, 36]. Carter[37, 38, 39] of U. S. Industrial Chemicals, Inc., developed successful catalysts for laboratory- and commercial-scale processes. Langwell, Maddocks, and Short[40, 41] oxidized olefins to olefin oxides over silver and other metal catalysts in tubes of good heat-conducting material. Ryerson and Oppenheimer[42] studied the reaction over catalysts of finely divided silver and silver on fused alumina, altering the space velocity and using steam as a diluent gas to observe the effects of such on catalyst activity for ethylene oxide formation. McBee, Hass, and Wiseman[43] evaluated silver catalysts deposited on corundum to determine the most favorable operating conditions for the production of ethylene oxide. Twigg[44, 45] studied the chemisorption of oxygen on a silver catalyst and proposed an interesting hypothesis of the mechanism of the oxidation of ethylene over silver catalysts in a flow system. Others unmentioned herein contributed to information on this reaction and are cited so far as is known in the literature references given.

The Reaction Mechanism. Ethylene is oxidized in the vapor phase over certain catalysts, notably those containing silver, at 150 to 400°C., according to the following equation:

$$(1) \quad 2C_2H_4 + O_2 \rightarrow 2C_2H_4O$$

To a greater or lesser extent carbon dioxide and water are formed as by-products.

$$(2) \quad 2C_2H_4 + 6O_2 \rightarrow 4CO_2 + 4H_2O$$

$$(3) \quad 2C_2H_4O + 5O_2 \rightarrow 4CO_2 + 4H_2O$$

Sherwood[46] lists the heats of reaction at 291°C. for equations (1) and (2) as 56 kcal. and 631 kcal., respectively, and indicates that if a 50 per cent chemical efficiency is attained in the oxidation of ethylene, only 8 per cent of the total heat is due to the formation of ethylene oxide. Depending on the reaction conditions employed, the formation of carbon dioxide may account for greater or lesser amounts of the ethylene oxidized. Sherwood[46] demonstrates that the total heat of reaction changes rapidly as the yield of ethylene oxide decreases. By-products other than carbon dioxide and water are small, and little is known definitely of them. Traces of carbon monoxide are believed to be present, and at times traces of aldehyde have been found. Ethylene glycol does not appear to be formed under ordinary conditions employed for this oxidation reaction. Glycol can be prepared, however, by absorption of the oxide in water or by liquid-phase oxidation of ethylene.

The fundamental role of the catalyst in ethylene oxidation appears to be the activated adsorption of oxygen atoms on its extended surface. Ethylene then reacts with the adsorbed oxygen either to form ethylene oxide or to form carbon dioxide and water. The reactions occurring are complex, and an accurate kinetic interpretation of such is difficult. Twigg[44, 45] published a series of interesting articles discussing this problem. By employing static and flow systems to examine the oxidation, he deduced that the adsorption of oxygen is the slowest and, hence, the rate-controlling step of the entire series of reactions taking place at the surface of a silver catalyst. Carbon dioxide is produced by the direct oxidation of ethylene and also by the oxidation of ethylene oxide. In the latter reaction, the prior isomerization of ethylene oxide to acetaldehyde is believed to be a fundamental step[44, 45]. The mechanism for the oxidation of acetaldehyde is not clear because a surface reaction would require the adsorption of five oxygen atoms. The rate of oxidation of acetaldehyde is extremely rapid, and therefore no trace of this aldehyde is found during the formation of ethylene oxide when sufficient oxygen is present.

Twigg measured the electrical resistance of a silver catalyst tightly packed in a glass tube as oxygen was admitted to the system to find that the increase in resistance was directly proportional to the fraction of catalyst surface covered by adsorbed oxygen. The effect noticed was completely reversible. When the catalyst was treated with any gas to remove the oxygen, the resistance was lowered again to its initial value. This important discovery provided Twigg with a procedure to estimate directly the quantity of oxygen adsorbed and aided him appreciably in his study of the reactions occurring during the oxidation of ethylene.

Benton and Drake[47] studied the kinetics of reaction and adsorption in the silver-oxygen system. They found that oxygen reacts with finely divided silver at ordinary pressures and at temperatures as low as 160°C. to form silver oxide. The rate of formation is proportional to the pressure but practically independent of the extent of oxidation in the range 0.3 to 10 per cent. This may be expressed as

$$\text{cc. reacting per hour per mm. pressure} = 7.2 \times 10^7 e^{-22000/RT}$$

In a similar manner the decomposition rate is given by

$$1.9 \times 10^{17} e^{-35600/RT}$$

Benton and Drake found also that two types of adsorption occur at pressures below the dissociation pressure of silver oxide. One of these, the physical adsorption of oxygen, is large at $-183°C$. but decreases rapidly with increasing temperature. The other is an activated adsorption, whose limiting value is nearly independent of temperature over the range 150 to 200°C., and which proceeds slowly at 0°C. but increases rapidly at higher temperatures.

Most of the adsorbed oxygen on a silver catalyst surface is consumed in the direct oxidation reaction producing carbon dioxide from ethylene. Twigg[44, 45] states that the pressure increase occurring from this reaction is proportional to the quantity of oxygen removed from the catalyst surface and that an estimate of the adsorbed oxygen concentration at any time is made available therefrom. From work based on these facts he concluded that the rate of direct oxidation of ethylene was proportional to the square of the adsorbed oxygen concentration. The kinetics of the reaction involving the formation of ethylene oxide from ethylene could not be evaluated in a similar manner. He reasoned that since only one oxygen atom is involved, the rate should be proportional to the first power of the adsorbed oxygen atoms. The rate of the oxidation of ethylene oxide to carbon dioxide is controlled by the rate of isomerization of the oxide since the aldehyde, once formed, is oxidized with great rapidity.

A detailed discussion of the mechanism of the oxidation of olefins is presented by Ellis in his text "The Chemistry of Petroleum Derivatives"[12].

The Reaction Variables. *The Catalyst.* A literature survey indicates that silver in the elementary form is specific and is the preferred catalyst for the selective, vapor-phase oxidation of ethylene. Certain metallic oxides—notably those of chromium, nickel, cobalt, and similar metals—are active for the complete oxidation of ethylene at moderate temperatures of 250°C. or slightly higher. Other metallic oxides, such as the oxides of bismuth or cadmium, oxidize ethylene nonselectively at higher temperatures of operation. A third group of oxides—including those of barium, molybdenum, tantalum, and titanium—are practically inert towards the oxidation at temperatures to 450°C.

The patent literature reveals generally that active silver catalysts may be prepared by several varied procedures. The extent and nature of the catalytic surface prepared determines much of its activity. An extended, rough, and irregular surface is said to be more desirable than one which is smooth or than one which must be activated by chemical treatment after deposition. The activity of the irregular surface is attributed not only to the large area present but in many cases to the so-called "active-centers" which are present perhaps as peaks or valleys, as points or lines, or as abnormal spacings where adsorption characteristics are different from those found on smooth surfaces.

Twigg[44, 45] employed a catalyst prepared by plating glass-wool fibers with a thin coating (10⁻⁴ mm.) of silver. To accomplish this, he reduced an ammoniacal silver solution with sucrose, following a method used by Common[48]. Lefort[27, 28, 30] performed the selective ethylene oxidation reaction originally over silver catalysts prepared in a powder form or in the form of a wire gauze. These catalysts were activated by the introduction therein of small quantities of gold, copper, or iron. Francon[49] hammered silver foil to a very thin sheet, ground this into powder, and annealed it at 400°C. He mixed this material with cellulose acetate to deposit it on aluminum rods. The organic material was then removed by heating in a stream of air to 400°C.

The procedures most applicable for catalyst preparation appear to be those in which silver compounds are decomposed thermally or by chemical reaction. The catalysts differ in activity, depending on the nature of the procedure used. Silver compounds—such as the oxide, nitrate, carbonate, lactate, oxalate, acetate, cyanide, or chloride—are deposited on inert supports to be decomposed to elemental silver by heat, alcohol, hydrogen reduction, or otherwise. Van Peski[50] decomposed the silver salts of formic, acetic, oxalic, and other acids. Benton and Drake[47], to perform their oxygen-adsorption study, prepared active silver catalysts by precipitating silver oxide and reducing this to elemental silver with hydrogen at low temperatures. Carter[37] prepared active catalysts by reduction of a deposit of silver salt on an inert support with hydrogen. Ryerson and Oppenheimer[42] precipitated silver oxalate and decomposed it thermally.

Evans[51] combined silver oxalate and silver oxide precipitates to reduce them thermally. In later work he cited the preferred use of a catalyst containing silver metal and promoted with 0.5 to 5.0 per cent by weight sodium oxalate[52].

Cambron and McKim[53] used catalysts prepared from silver oxalate and calcium oxalate. They reduced their catalysts under water at 140 to 300°C. at superatmospheric pressures.

McBee, Haas, and Wiseman[43] coated corundum by evaporating a water slurry of silver oxide. They dried the catalyst at 110°C. and then used it without subsequent reduction.

Bergsteinsson and Finch[54] precipitated silver oxide and redissolved this material by use of ammonium hydroxide. They impregnated inert supports with the dissolved silver by reduction with glucose or other organic compounds and sodium hydroxide.

Bergsteinsson and Scheible[55] used a silver-on-aluminum catalyst for the oxidation of ethylene at approximately 320°C. and one atmosphere pressure, at a contact time of 25 seconds. The ethylene oxide was recovered by absorption at low temperatures in an aliphatic monohydric alcohol.

Aries[56] prepared an active silver catalyst for ethylene oxidation by impregnating a support with silver lactate solution and decomposing the salt to silver oxide-metallic silver at 400°C. in an inert gas atmosphere.

West and West[57] prepared silver catalysts by coprecipitating silver oxide and silver chloride, depositing the materials on a suitable carrier, and reducing them with ammonia at temperatures of 200 to 280°C., one atmosphere pressure. The use of air, oxygen, and water with ammonia is cited for the reduction step. The catalysts converted the ethylene to ethylene oxide in greater yields at a higher efficiency than did catalysts in which silver chloride was not used as a promoter.

Nevison and Lincoln[58] oxidized ethylene in air at 250 to 350°C. over catalysts containing 5 to 15 parts (by weight) of barium peroxide, 100 parts of finely divided silver, and 500 to 700 parts of a heat absorptive material to abstract the exothermic heat of reaction.

Becker[59] cited the oxidation of ethylene over fluidized granular silver catalysts at 100 to 400°C. He claimed that undesirable side reactions were inhibited by adequate temperature control in the fluid process.

Improved catalysts of metallic silver promoted with tin oxide, cadmium oxide, calcium carbonate, or calcium oxalate have been claimed[60], as have catalysts of crystalline silica treated successively with silver nitrate, ammonia, sodium hydroxide, ammonia, and a reducing solution[61]. Mitani and Kano[62] prepared a catalyst by etching silver wire with nitric acid or silver nitrate, immersing it in silver nitrate containing gold and cobalt salt promoters, and then reducing in a hydrogen-ethylene gas atmosphere.

Important information concerning ethylene oxidation work performed in Germany during the 1930's and 1940's is to be found in the "Bibliography of Scientific and Industrial Reports," a publication of the United States Department of Commerce. Reports of value include: PB 226; PB 485; PB 25,649; PB 60,950; PB 73,824; and PB 79,607.

Sherwood[46] states that, as far as is known, silver is the only catalyst used in the commercial manufacture of ethylene oxide by ethylene oxidation.

Catalyst Supports. Carriers preferred in this catalytic oxidation work are generally inert or noncatalytic materials possessing large and irregular surfaces. The chemical nature and physical state of the support can and does influence at times the activity of the catalyst appreciably. Refractory aluminum oxides or silicates in one form or another are favorably mentioned in the patent literature[37]. Silica, silicon carbide, or similar materials plus suitable bonding agents are generally strong and inert. Like aluminum oxide, these are particularly suitable as carriers[54]. Pumice, silica gel, activated carbon, activated alumina, charcoal, magnesia, and other materials are generally less desirable as supports, for these substances often adversely influence the oxidation reaction in one way or another. Sherwood[46] cites comparative activity data obtained over silver catalysts on pumice, glass, alundum, zeolite, and carborundum.

Catalyst Promoters. The literature reveals that a complete catalyst for selective ethylene oxidation usually includes a promoter or so-called modifying or activating agent. The addition of the promoter in very small quantities is reported to have the desirable effect of increasing the activity and prolonging the on-stream life of a catalyst. In addition, the catalyst is said to be more rugged and durable. Information available cites the preferred use of compounds of the alkali and alkaline earth series, notably the oxides or hydroxides of these elements[28, 31, 33, 39, 51, 53, 54, 58, 63]. Copper, gold, platinum, and other metals or their compounds are used also to advantage for work of this nature[27, 28, 29, 30, 40, 64, 65].

The manner whereby promoters enhance and prolong the activity of silver catalysts is obscure and no generally acceptable theory has been advanced to explain their behavior. It is possible that the promoter may effect the size and nature of the active silver material during decomposition or reduction. A finer state of division may be attained to increase activity, or the crystal growth of the active silver may be impeded favorably to contribute to the ruggedness and longevity of the promoted catalyst.

Reaction Inhibitors. Small quantities of organic compounds are often added to the reaction feed gases to achieve desirable results in ethylene oxidation. Prominent among these "anti-catalysts" or inhibitors are ethylene dichloride, ethylene dibromide, other alkyl halides, aliphatic alcohols, amines, aromatic hydrocarbons, and organo-metallic compounds[35, 36]. Sherwood[46] cites an ethylene oxidation process developed by the National Research Council of Canada in which ethylene dichloride inhibitor is used to suppress undesirable side reactions at rigorously controlled temperatures. It is said that over-oxidation of ethylene is restrained by the inclusion of such substances in the reaction feed in small amounts. The addition of too large a quantity of inhibitor is deleterious. Catalysts poisoned by the use of excessive ethylene dichloride inhibitor can be regenerated by continuing the reaction at a higher temperature in the absence of ethylene dichloride[43]. As is true with promoters, no acceptable theory has been propounded to explain the action of inhibitors on the reaction occurring at a catalyst surface, although the presence of silver chloride in the catalyst has been claimed beneficial (see page 83).

Reaction Temperature. Ethylene may be oxidized to ethylene oxide over active catalysts at temperatures below 200°C. However, the selective oxidation reaction generally assumes importance at temperatures above this. The relationship between temperature and the conversion of ethylene to ethylene oxide is dependent greatly on several other important process variables. The concentration of catalyst present on a support, the gas velocity employed, and the ratio of ethylene to oxygen in the reacting medium determine the extent and course of this oxidation. Ethylene conversion increases with temperature. The efficiency of this conversion to ethylene oxide is generally above that to carbon dioxide at temperatures to 250°C. At temperatures above 250°C. the conversion of ethylene and of ethylene oxide to carbon dioxide accelerates, and the selectivity of the oxidation reaction is thereby generally decreased.

Twigg[45] studied the effect of temperature on the rates of oxidation over a silver catalyst at temperatures of 190 to 360°C. He found that oxygen consumption over the catalyst began to increase sharply at temperatures above 230°C. Ethylene conversion to ethylene oxide increased at a moderate rate at temperatures to 300°C. and then decreased. Ethylene conversion to carbon dioxide was less than that to ethylene oxide at temperatures to 268°C., thus illustrating that the efficiency of the conversion was higher to the latter compound at temperatures below this. Above 268°C. the conversion to carbon dioxide accelerated to alter the efficiency balance, and the general over-all slope of a curve plotted for this particular conversion would be somewhat similar to that plotted for the consumption of oxygen.

McBee, Hass, and Wiseman[43] noted that the temperature for optimum ethylene oxide yields is somewhat lower than that for optimum conversion. They also noted that the optimum temperature of operation of the catalyst had to be increased with its age to maintain efficiency at the maximum level. Sherwood[46] states that as the temperature is raised, a point is eventually reached at which the carbon dioxide formation is unbearable economically and the catalyst must be replaced. A catalyst may be used satisfactorily for over a year.

Reaction Pressure. Little information of value is available in the literature concerning the effect of pressure on the ethylene oxidation reaction. Van Peski[50] and Evans[51] mention that pressures slightly in excess of atmospheric are desirable, but agree with others[54] that the reaction can be performed to advantage at atmospheric or subatmospheric pressures. The optimum pressure used is governed by the other conditions of operation and is related closely to the composition of the feed gases used. Either cyclic or noncyclic systems are used. In the noncyclic type of unit operated at low blow-off pressures, high production ratios of ethylene oxide require the use of large reaction velocities and perhaps high concentrations of reactants. Disadvantages of such operation include the excessive pressure drop across the catalyst bed resulting from the use of large gas velocities, the explosive hazard of high concentrations of ethylene and ethylene oxide in oxygen or air, and the loss of much unreacted ethylene.

Reaction Space Velocity, Contact Time. Twigg[45] studied the effect of contact time on reaction rates of ethylene oxidation over three separate catalysts of different activities at rather high temperatures to obtain information relative to the routes of formation of carbon dioxide. Reyerson and Oppenheimer[42] observed that reasonable changes in space velocity did not alter materially the yields of ethylene oxide attained over three different silver catalysts. McBee, Hass, and Wiseman studied the effect of contact time on the temperature at which optimum ethylene oxide efficiency and yield were obtained[43]. Their experimental results demonstrated that the temperature of operation of a silver catalyst must be increased as contact time is decreased to attain an optimum yield and that a deactivated catalyst, upon revival, requires a temperature of operation several degrees higher than that used for an untreated catalyst to attain optimum yields of ethylene oxide. Information relative to the relationship of contact time and reaction rate can be found also in the patent literature[37, 50, 51, 54].

Reactant and Product Concentrations. McBee, Hass, and Wiseman[43] performed a series of experiments at 268°C. and approximately constant contact time (1.04 to 1.13 seconds) in which they varied the air-to-ethylene feed ratios from 3.47:1 to 17.5:1 in order to determine the most favorable ratio for ethylene oxidation. The data obtained over a new silver catalyst, a catalyst two weeks old, and one four weeks old demonstrated that a high oxygen-to-ethylene ratio is most favorable for obtaining acceptable ethylene oxide efficiencies and yields. As the catalyst aged it was found that it became less efficient for ethylene oxidation and required a higher temperature of operation to maintain the maximum efficiency for the production of ethylene oxide. Twigg[45] varied the partial pressures of ethylene and oxygen in a reaction feed to a silver catalyst to show that the rate of oxidation of ethylene to ethylene oxide and to carbon dioxide is only slightly dependent on the ethylene concentration and is proportional approximately to the first power of the oxygen concentration.

The patent literature mentions generally the use of oxygen to ethylene in equal volume ratios or in ratios somewhat larger than 1 for ethylene oxidation. Patents assigned by Bergsteinsson and Finch and also by Evans to the Shell Development Company cite the use of equal volume ratios of oxygen and ethylene for oxidations performed over silver catalysts at atmospheric pressure[51, 54]. Bergsteinsson's and Finch's patent claims indicate that ethylene conversions of 20 or more per cent are obtained at operating temperatures of 250 to 290°C. and that ethylene oxide yields are 55 to 64 per cent. After periods of operation of 200 or more hours, no decline in catalyst activity is observed.

Each of the principal reaction products obtained in the ethylene oxidation reaction is an inhibitor for the reaction. However, neither ethylene oxide, carbon dioxide, nor water are selective in their action, and none of these influences the reaction rate in a manner comparable to that obtained by use of an inhibitor such as ethylene dibromide for reaction control.

PHYSICAL PROPERTIES

Ethylene oxide is a pleasant smelling compound that boils at 10.7°C. The vapors in all concentrations above 3 per cent are flammable and explosive; however, a nonflammable mixture may be prepared by addition of carbon dioxide to achieve a ratio of 7.15 parts of the latter to each part of ethylene oxide.

Below its boiling point, ethylene oxide is a mobile liquid that is completely miscible with water in all proportions. It forms azeotropic mixtures with many hydrocarbons boiling from -7 to $+36$°C.[66]

The principal impurities present in commercial ethylene oxide are water, ethylene chlorohydrin, and acetaldehyde. Because of the presence of any one or more of these or other substances, many of the properties reported in the literature are slightly erroneous. Reliable measurements of the more important physical properties of the substantially pure compound are summarized in Table 5.3 and expanded in the tables and charts that follow.

Explosive Limits

Pure Ethylene Oxide. Liquid ethylene oxide cannot be detonated, but *the pure vapor is flammable and explosive*. Within a closed vessel, 100 per cent ethylene oxide vapor at atmospheric pressure will explode with 45 per cent decomposition when ignited with a hot platinum wire coil; 90 per cent explosive decomposition will occur if the ignition is made with mercury fulminate[67].

Ethylene Oxide in Air. There is no upper explosive limit for ethylene oxide in air. A slight dilution of the pure vapor with air or a small increase in initial pressure provides ideal explosive conditions[67]. A value of 80 per cent was previously reported for the upper explosive limit[68, 69, 70, 71, 72]. The lower limit is 3 per cent.

Ethylene Oxide in Other Atmospheres. The limits of ethylene oxide in mixtures of air and carbon dioxide at atmospheric pressures are given by Jones[71] and at reduced pressures by Peters and Gauter[72]. From Jones' data it can be seen that all possible mixtures of ethylene oxide in air can be made nonflammable at atmospheric temperatures and pressures by adding at least 7.15 volumes or pounds of carbon dioxide to each volume or pound of ethylene oxide present[69]. Hess and Tilton[67] have reported the nonexplosive ranges of mixtures of ethylene oxide and several diluents at 30 to 35 pounds per square inch gauge for industrial handling of the compound.

TABLE 5.3. Physical Properties of Ethylene Oxide

$$H_2C \text{------} CH_2$$
$$\diagdown \diagup$$
$$O$$

Absorption spectra		see Fig. 5.1
Azeotropes		ref. 66
Boiling point at 760 mm.	10.7°C.	see Fig. 5.2, ref.
at 50 mm.	−44°C.	73
at 10 mm.	−66°C.	
Δb.p./Δp, 740–760 mm.	0.036°C./mm.	
Coefficient of expansion at 55°C.	0.00161	
at 55°C.	0.00170	
Critical pressure	1043 psia	
Critical temperature	195.8°C.	
Density (true) at 20°C.	0.8697 g./ml.	see Table 5.4
Dielectric constant at −1.0°C.	13.9 esu	ref. 74
Electric moment	1.88×10^{18}	ref. 75
Entropy at 10.5°C., 760 mm. (calc.)	57.38 cal./°C./ml.	ref. 76
at 25.0°C., 760 mm. (calc.)	57.94 cal./°C./ml.	ref. 76
Explosive limits in air at 760 mm. (upper)	100% by vol.	see page 87
(lower)	3% by vol.	
Flash point, Tag glass open cup	<0°F.	see Table 5.5
Freezing point	−111.3°C.	see Fig. 5.3, ref.
		73
Heat of combustion at 25°C., at 760 mm.	312.55 ± 0.20 kca./g. mol	ref. 77
Heat of formation (vapor)	17 kcal./g./mol	ref. 78
(liquid)	23.3 kcal./g. mol	ref. 78
Heat of fusion	1236.4 cal./mol	ref. 76
Heat of solution in water at constant pressure	1.5 kcal./mol	ref. 78
Heat of vaporization at 760 mm.		
10.7°C.	245 Btu/lb.	ref. 73
10.5°C.	6101 ± 6 cal./mol	ref. 76
10.5°C. (calc.)	6082 cal./mol	ref. 76
Ignition temperature in air at 760 mm.	429°C.	ref. 79
Isothermal compressibility		see Fig. 5.4
Melting point	−112.51°C.	ref. 76
Molal heat capacity		see Table 5.6
Molal volume at 10.7°C., 760 mm.	49.9	ref. 73
Molecular surface energy		see Table 5.7
Molecular weight	44.06	
Oxygen valence angle	77°	ref. 75
Parachor	112.2	ref. 73
Ramsey and Shields constant	1.79	ref. 73
Refractive index, n_D at 7°C.	1.3597	ref. 80
Solubility		see Table 5.8
Specific gravity (apparent) at 20/20°C.	0.8711	see Table 5.4
ΔSp. gr./Δt	0.00140	

Specific heat at 34°C., 760 mm.	0.268 cal./g./°C.	ref. 81
Spontaneous ignition temperature at 760 mm.	571°C.	ref. 68
Surface energy (total)	73.2 dynes	ref. 73
Surface tension at 20°C.	24.3 dynes/cm.	see Table 5.7
Thermal conductivity (vapor) at 25°C.	0.00002961 cal.-cm./ sec./cm.^{2}/°C.	see Table 5.9
Trouton's constant	21.14	ref. 73
Vapor-liquid equilibria		see Fig. 5.5
Vapor pressure at 20°C.	21.2 psia (1095 mm.)	see Table 5.10 and Fig. 5.6
Viscosity (absolute) at 0°C.	0.32 cp.	see Table 5.11

TABLE 5.4. DENSITY AND SPECIFIC GRAVITY OF ETHYLENE OXIDE

Temperature, °C.	True Density, g./ml.	Apparent Specific Gravity, t/20°C.
−40	0.9488	0.9505
−20	0.9232	0.9248
0	0.8969	0.8984
20	0.8697	0.8711
40	0.8413	0.8426
60	0.8108	0.8121
80	0.7794	0.7805
100	0.7443	0.7453
120	0.7052	0.7061
140	0.6609	0.6616
150	0.6357	0.6363

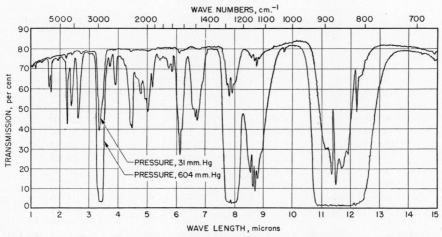

FIGURE 5.1. Infrared absorption spectra of ethylene oxide at 26°C. (cell thickness, 10 cm.).

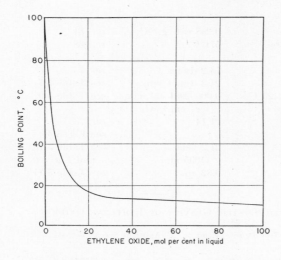

FIGURE 5.2. Boiling point of aqueous solutions of ethylene oxide at atmospheric pressure.[84]

TABLE 5.5. FLASH POINTS OF AQUEOUS SOLUTIONS OF ETHYLENE OXIDE

Ethylene Oxide, % by wt.	Flash Point, °F., Tag Closed Cup
1	87
3	38
5	28
10	28
15	28

TABLE 5.6. MOLAL HEAT CAPACITY OF ETHYLENE OXIDE[76, 80]

0°C. = 273.16°K.; mol. wt. = 44.052

Temperature, °K.	Molal Heat Capacity, cal./°C./mol	Temperature, °K.	Molal Heat Capacity, cal./°C./mol
15	0.60	160.65	16.35
20	1.43	melting point	
30	3.30	160.65	19.80
40	5.21	180	19.55
50	6.77	200	19.47
60	8.16	210	19.50
80	10.06	220	19.56
100	11.43	240	19.82
120	12.77	260	20.21
140	14.47	280	20.67
160	16.30	285	20.77
		307.18	11.76
		337.04	12.74
		371.23	13.89

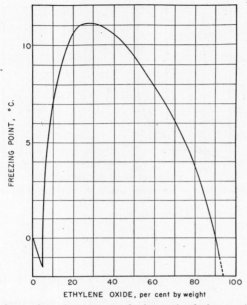

FIGURE 5.3. Freezing point of aqueous solutions of ethylene oxide. The maximum at approximately 29 per cent ethylene oxide concentration indicates the formation of a hydrate $C_2H_4O \cdot 6H_2O$. (Values above 6.9°C. were determined by Maass and Boomer.)

TABLE 5.7. SURFACE TENSION AND MOLECULAR SURFACE ENERGY OF ETHYLENE OXIDE[a73]

Temperature, °C.	Surface Tension, dynes/cm.	Molecular Surface Energy, $(Vm)^{2/3}$
−52.0	36.4	464.6
−50.8	35.5	453.5
−43.4	34.8	447.7
−39.2	33.8	436.5
−32.5	32.8	426.3
−26.2	31.9	417.0
−21.1	31.1	408.6
−15.0	30.3	400.3
−9.6	29.2	387.9
−5.0	28.4	378.8
−0.3	27.4	367.3
5.8	26.8	361.4
10.5	25.9	353.8
13.3	25.4	344.3
20.0	24.3	332.4

[a] Experimental data

GLYCOLS

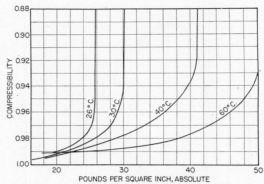

FIGURE 5.4. Compressibility of ethylene oxide at various temperatures.

$$\text{Compressibility} = \frac{P_2 V_2}{P_1 V_1}$$

where $P_1 = 14.4$ p.s.i.a.

TABLE 5.8. SOLUBILITY OF ETHYLENE OXIDE IN WATER AND IN DICHLOROETHANE[82]

Pressure, mm. Hg.	Solubility, cc. of Vapor[a] per cc. of Solvent					
	Water			Dichloroethane		
	5°C.	10°C.	20°C.	0°C.	10°C.	20°C.
150	45	33	20	99	50	22
200	60	46	29	130	80	42
300	105	76	49	380	199	101
400	162	120	74		365	180
500	240	178	101			274
600		294	134			412
700			170			506[b]
760			195			

[a] Reduced at 0°C. and 760 mm.   [b] 650 mm.

TABLE 5.9. THERMAL CONDUCTIVITY OF ETHYLENE OXIDE[83]

Temperature, °C.	Thermal Conductivity, cal.-cm./sec./cm.²/°C.
0	0.00002504
10.73	0.00002700
25	0.00002961
50	0.00003419
70	0.00003785

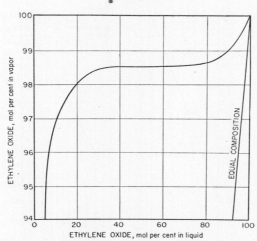

FIGURE 5.5. Vapor-liquid equilibria at atmospheric pressure for the system ethylene oxide-water[84].

TABLE 5.10. VAPOR PRESSURE OF ETHYLENE OXIDE

Temperature, °C.	Vapor Pressure, mm. Hg	Temperature, °C.	Vapor Pressure, mm. Hg
−57.0[a]	19.5	11.6	786.5
−50.3	32.7	12.8[a]	824.9
−43.4	50.9	30.0	1560
−37.4	74.5	45.0	2542
−30.4	110.6	50.0	2967
−24.2	155.7	59.9	3946
−18.9	207.5	69.8	5141
−14.6	257.6	79.6	6600
−10.5	312.7	89.5	8319
−7.8	352.8	97.9	10030
−5.8	388.2	109.8	12720
−3.3	431.7	119.6	15500
0.0	493.1	129.5	18690
2.0	537.0	139.3	22320
5.3	615.8	149.7	26730
7.9	682.2	159.7	31450
9.4	722.7	169.5	36780
10.6	756.6	179.3	42750
11.0	768.0	189.1	49840

Critical temperature, 195.8°C.

[a] −57 to 12.8°C., Maass and Boomer[73]; above 12.8°C., Carbide.

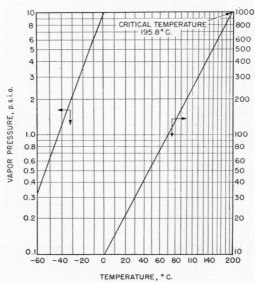

FIGURE 5.6. Vapor pressure of ethylene oxide.

TABLE 5.11. ABSOLUTE VISCOSITY OF ETHYLENE OXIDE[73]

Temperature, °C.	Absolute Viscosity, cps.
−49.8	0.5772
−49.0	0.5635
−45.7	0.5387
−38.2	0.4883
−32.2	0.4505
−21.0	0.3937
−13.6	0.3637
0.0	0.3202
9.3	0.2927

CHEMICAL REACTIONS

Ethylene oxide is very active chemically and adds to numerous organic substances having a labile hydrogen atom, thus serving to introduce the hydroxyethyl group (—CH_2CH_2OH) into a host of compounds. The addition of this group increases the water solubility of the resulting compounds and raises their boiling points 50 to 200°C. Reactions with ethylene oxide provide a convenient method for the introduction of this primary alcohol group, which, in turn, is a stepping stone to aldehydes, acids, esters, and other derivatives. The principal reactions of ethylene oxide may be described by the general equation

$$
\begin{array}{c}
CH_2 \\
| \quad \diagdown \\
| \qquad O \; + \; HA \; \rightarrow \\
| \quad \diagup \\
CH_2
\end{array}
\qquad
\begin{array}{c}
CH_2A \\
| \\
CH_2OH
\end{array}
$$

Some typical reaction products are listed as follows:

Reactant	Product
Water	Ethylene glycol
Hydrogen halides	Ethylene halohydrins
Hydrogen	Ethanol
Alcohols and phenols	Ethylene glycol monoethers
Acids	Ethylene glycol monoesters
Amines	Ethanolamines
Glycols	Di-, tri-, and polyglycols
Hydrogen cyanide	Ethylene cyanohydrin
Grignard reagent	Alcohol containing two more carbons than the alkyl halide used

Water

Wurtz[1] was the first to observe the reaction between ethylene oxide and water, heating these substances in a sealed tube to obtain ethylene glycol. Lourenco[85] noticed the simultaneous formation of diethylene glycol and triethylene glycol as by-products. Most of the ethylene glycol produced commercially is prepared by this reaction (see page 20).

The ethylene oxide hydration reaction is greatly accelerated by the presence of catalysts, in particular, mineral acids[86]. Brönsted, Kilpatrick, and Kilpatrick[87] obtained kinetic measurements of each of the following four reactions by which ethylene oxide disappears in a solution of hydrochloric acid:

$$C_2H_4O \;+\; H_2O \;\rightarrow\; C_2H_4(OH)_2 \tag{1}$$

$$C_2H_4O \;+\; H_2O \;\xrightarrow{H_3O^+}\; C_2H_4(OH)_2 \tag{2}$$

$$C_2H_4O \;+\; Cl^- \;+\; H_2O \;\rightarrow\; C_2H_4(OH)Cl \;+\; OH^- \tag{3}$$

$$C_2H_4O \;+\; Cl^- \;+\; H_3O^+ \;\rightarrow\; C_2H_4(OH)Cl \;+\; H_2O \tag{4}$$

Smith, Wode, and Widhe[88] published data for the rate of addition of water to ethylene oxide at 25°C. in solutions of nitric and perchloric acids of 0.01 to 0.5 molar concentration. The reaction was followed by analytical methods, and the authors state that they were unable to judge whether the reaction rate is proportional to the hydrogen ion concentration or to the hydrogen ion activity. From their experimental results they concluded that the nature of the anion of the catalyzing acid is relatively unimportant.

Brönsted, Kilpatrick, and Kilpatrick[87] mention that although ethylene oxide and its homologs exhibit basic properties in certain solutions, they are not bases or even pseudo-bases. The basicity is derived from the ability to take up acids, as shown above in reactions (3) and (4). As far as it is known experimentally, ethylene oxide is unable to show the function of a true base and add protons only. Whenever a proton is added, an anion is added also; and if no suitable anion is present, the ethylene oxide remains unchanged. The simultaneous addition of a proton and anion decreases the acidity of the solution, and ethylene oxide thereby appears to act as a base.

Considerable heat of reaction, 23 kilogram calories per mol[78], is liberated in the hydration of ethylene oxide in the presence of dilute sulfuric acid as a catalyst. Tasiro[89] obtained ethylene glycol in almost theoretical yields by reacting water and ethylene oxide in the presence of this acid. He observed that the reaction velocity depended on the temperature and on the amount of catalyst present. If sufficient water were not present, diethylene glycol was also formed during the hydration. Youtz[90] recommended the use of at least a 20 to 1 mol ratio of water to ethylene oxide in the reaction mixture to suppress polyethylene glycol formation, and a hydrolyzing catalyst and heating above the boiling point of ethylene oxide to obtain ethylene glycol.

Cartmell, Galloway, Olson, and Smith[91] studied the vapor-phase hydration of ethylene oxide to eliminate purification difficulties encountered in the acidic liquid-phase process. Over acid-type catalysts such as phosphoric acid on silica gel, alumina, thoria, etc., they obtained considerable amounts of aldehydes but no ethylene glycol. Silver oxide on alumina effectively catalyzed the hydration reaction to produce largely ethylene glycol. Ethylene oxide conversions (single pass yields) ranged from 20 to 30 per cent at ethylene glycol (ultimate) yields of about 80 and 40 per cent. The yield was found to be related to catalyst age. An approximately constant value of 80 per cent was attained after about five hours of operation. Reaction conditions for this experimental work included: temperature, 170 to 172°C.; contact time, 1.8 seconds; steam to ethylene oxide mol ratio, 13.5; and pressure, atmospheric. The authors suggest that the activity of the catalyst is due to its ability to adsorb water vapor. The adsorption complex then reacts with ethylene oxide to regenerate the original surface.

$$Ag_2O + H_2O(g) \rightarrow Ag_2O[H_2O]$$

$$Ag_2O[H_2O] + C_2H_4O \rightarrow [(CH_2OH)_2]Ag_2O$$

$$[(CH_2OH)_2]Ag_2O \rightarrow (CH_2OH)_2(g) + Ag_2O$$

Hydrogen Halides and Metallic Halides

Ethylene oxide reacts with the hydrogen halides to produce the corresponding halohydrins. The reaction is general, and ethylene chlorohydrin may be prepared by such a procedure[92]. Ethylene bromohydrin and iodohydrin are formed in a similar manner[93]. With certain metallic halides in aqueous solution, ethylene oxide reacts with the acid freed by dissociation and hydrolysis to precipitate the metallic hydroxide. This reaction serves as a basis of analysis for ethylene oxide and its homologs. Deckert[94] developed a qualitative test for ethylene oxide based on the reaction with aqueous sodium chloride which results in the formation of ethylene chlorohydrin and sodium hydroxide. Lubatti[95] developed a quantitative test using hydrochloric acid in a saturated solution of magnesium chloride.

The halides of aluminum, magnesium, iron, tin, zinc, and manganese in neutral aqueous solution react with ethylene oxide to precipitate the metallic hydroxides:

$$MgCl_2 + 2C_2H_4O + 2H_2O \rightarrow 2C_2H_4(OH)Cl + Mg(OH)_2$$

The halides of aluminum, chromium, iron, thorium, and zinc in dilute solution react also with ethylene oxide to form sols or gels of the metal-oxide hydrates and ethylene halohydrin which can be extracted from the solution with ethyl ether or by distillation[96]. If more than 90 per cent of the metal halide is converted to hydroxide, sols are formed which can be dried and then redissolved in water or concentrated alcohol or glycerol solutions. If more than 95 per cent of the halide is converted, the sol is unstable and a gel is slowly formed. Ribas and Tapia[97] observed that ethylene oxide in ether solution reacts with magnesium bromide to give the product $BrCH_2CH_2OMgBr \cdot (C_2H_5)_2O$. On hydrolysis, ethylene bromohydrin, magnesium bromide, and magnesium hydroxide are obtained.

Ethylene oxide may be condensed with aromatic hydrocarbons in the presence of aluminum chloride in a Friedel-Crafts reaction or by use of the appropriate Grignard reagent. The formation of intermediate double compounds between the oxide and metallic compound constitutes probably the first phase of the reactions cited. Schaarschmidt, Hermann, and Szemzö[98] passed ethylene oxide and hydrogen chloride into a mixture of benzene and aluminum chloride to obtain dibenzyl and a small amount of β-phenylethanol.

Grignard Reagents

Ethylene oxide reacts with alkyl or aryl magnesium halides to form primary alcohols containing two additional carbon atoms in their formulas. The reactions are not too important commercially but are used to prepare small samples of a variety of desirable compounds.

Grignard[99] proposed that an intermediate oxonium compound is formed when ethylene oxide is reacted with alkyl magnesium bromide:

$$
\begin{array}{ccc}
CH_2 & & R \\
& \diagdown \diagup & \\
& O & \\
& \diagup \diagdown & \\
CH_2 & & MgBr
\end{array}
$$

Blaise[100] reacted ethylene oxide and ethyl magnesium bromide to form ethylene bromohydrin. He explained the reaction by postulating the intermediate product, $BrCH_2CH_2OMgBr$.

Huston and Agett[101] studied the reaction of ethylene oxide with the Grignard reagent to obtain information that the intermediate product is $C_4H_8Br_2MgO_2$ without appreciable formation of $BrCH_2CH_2OMgBr$. With one or two mols of ethylene oxide, the following is stated to take place:

$$2RMgBr \rightleftharpoons MgBr_2 + R_2Mg$$

Ethylene oxide reacts with magnesium bromide as long as it is present.

$$MgBr_2 + 2C_2H_4O \rightarrow C_4H_8Br_2MgO_2$$

Primary and secondary R_2Mg react with $C_4H_8Br_2MgO_2$ only when heated, or on long standing, to give $(RCH_2CH_2)_2Mg$. The same product can be formed also by reaction of ethylene oxide with R_2Mg. The $(RCH_2CH_2O)_2Mg$ is hydrolyzed to a primary alcohol:

$$(RCH_2CH_2O)_2Mg + 2H_2O \rightarrow 2RCH_2CH_2OH + Mg(OH)_2$$

Benzylmagnesium chloride and ethylene oxide were reacted without heating or standing to obtain phenyl propyl alcohol. The amount of ethylene chlorohydrin produced was small.

Tertiary alkyl magnesium bromides, when reacted with one or two mols of ethylene oxide according to standard procedure, yield only ethylene bromohydrin, indicating a small reactivity of these compounds with either $(BrCH_2CH_2O)_2Mg$ or ethylene oxide. Homeyer, Whitmore, and Wallingford[102] reported ethylene chlorohydrin as the principal product from a reaction of tertiary butyl magnesium chloride with ethylene oxide. When the filtrate from the reaction of tertiary butyl magnesium bromide and two mols of ethylene oxide was allowed to stand for several months in the presence of light without heating, a small yield of 3,3-dimethylbutanol was obtained.

Yields of alcohols obtained by reacting ethylene oxide with Grignard reagents prepared from numerous alkyl and aryl halides are discussed by Huston and Agett[101].

Ammonia and Amines

When ethylene oxide is reacted with ammonia, a mixture of the ethanolamines is prepared. Knorr[103] has established that the presence of a small amount of water is essential to the reaction and that pure ethylene oxide will not react with anhydrous ammonia. The proportion of the three amines—mono-, di-, and triethanolamines—present in the reaction mixture depends on the ratio of reactants used. A large excess of ethylene oxide favors the formation of triethanolamine[104]. Germann and Knight[105] described the preparation of pure triethanolamine.

Schwoegler and Olin[106] disclosed that the hydroxyalkylamines may be prepared commercially by the passage of a mixture of ammonia or an amine and ethylene oxide through a heated chamber maintained at 120 to 275°C. The ammonia or amine is used in considerable excess to limit and absorb the heat of the exothermic reaction. Thus, ammonia and ethylene oxide in a 15 to 1 ratio are pumped into a reaction chamber at 130°C. and 1600 psig. pressure to obtain a reaction product consisting of 78.3, 16, and 4.4 per cent mono-, di-, and triethanolamines, respectively. Using monoethylamine and ethylene oxide in a 6 to 1 ratio at 150°C. and 485 psig. pressure, 78.3 and 19.6 parts of ethylmonoethanolamine and ethyldiethanolamine are formed.

Reid and Lewis[107] describe a method of producing the ethanolamines in which ethylene oxide and ammonia are reacted by passing a stream of a solution of one of the reacting substances at a temperature below 50°C. along a porous wall and diffusing the other reactant through the wall. Reid and Lewis[108] disclose also a procedure by which 2600 parts of ethylene oxide are added slowly to 3870 parts of 25 per cent aqueous ammonia at 25 to 30°C. to give a yield of more than 90 per cent triethanolamine. If only 352 parts of the oxide are added to 3400 parts of the above aqueous ammonia at 10°C., monoethanolamine is produced almost exclusively.

The three simple ethanolamines are produced by Carbide, Dow, and Jefferson. They are used largely where caustic alkalies are undesirable, particularly in the textile industry. They react with fatty acids to form surface-active agents of the anionic type, useful as detergents and as emulsifying agents for industrial oils, wax polishes, cosmetic preparations, and household cleaners[109]. The ethanolamines are employed for "sweetening" natural gas (Girbotol process), removing acidic gases from flue or other industrial waste gases, and concentrating carbon dioxide in the production of "dry ice." Triethanolamine, because of its desirable alkaline character and solvent properties, is used for the dispersion of dyes, casein, shellac, or rubber latex. It is useful for removing carbon and gum deposits from aluminum pistons of internal combustion engines. Its derivatives serve as corrosion inhibitors in engine coolants, special lubricating oils, and metal-cleaning compounds.

Complex nitrogen compounds can be formed by the reaction of ethylene oxide with the above ethanolamines, ammonia, or other amines. A mixture of the mono-, di-, and trihydroxyethyl ethers of triethanolamine is obtained by the action of excess ethylene oxide in aqueous ammonia[110]. Headlee, Collett, and Lazzell[111] reacted diethylamine and ethylene oxide at 100°C. for 5 to 180 minutes to obtain 81 to 87 per cent diethylaminoethanol. This compound boils at 160°C. and is employed chiefly for the synthesis of procaine, a valuable anesthetic for intradermal, neural, and spinal use. Ethylene oxide was reacted further with N,N-diethylaminoethanol in an autoclave to form a number of higher boiling compounds. From the product mixture, the mono-[2-(N,N-diethylamino)ethyl] ethers of ethylene glycol, diethylene glycol, triethylene glycol, and tetraethylene glycol were separated.

Horne and Shriner[112] observed that dry diethylamine does not react with ethylene oxide. However, in the presence of water, methanol, or ethanol, ethylene oxide reacts rapidly with the amine. The products obtained were similar to those outlined above.

Other amines prepared from ethylene oxide include complex structures similar to that shown below. They are obtained by reacting ethylenediamine and ethylene oxide in a 1 to 5 mol ratio[12].

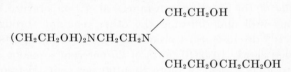

$$(CH_2CH_2OH)_2NCH_2CH_2N \diagup \begin{matrix} CH_2CH_2OH \\ \\ CH_2CH_2OCH_2CH_2OH \end{matrix}$$

Ethylene oxide adds to hydrazine to give N,N-bis(2-hydroxyethyl) hydrazine[12, 113, 114]:

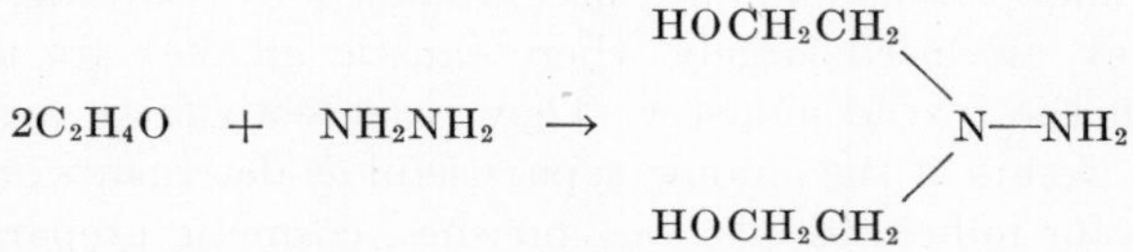

$$2C_2H_4O + NH_2NH_2 \rightarrow \begin{matrix} HOCH_2CH_2 \\ \\ HOCH_2CH_2 \end{matrix} \diagdown N—NH_2 \diagup$$

Phenylhydrazine and other derivatives react to yield more complex products[5, 12].

Ethylene oxide reacts with hydroxylamine on standing at 0°C. to form N,N-bis(2-hydroxyethyl) hydroxylamine and tris(2-hydroxyethyl)amine oxide[115].

$$2C_2H_4O + H_2NOH \rightarrow (HOCH_2CH_2)_2NOH$$

$$3C_2H_4O + H_2NOH \rightarrow (HOCH_2CH_2)_3NO$$

Gabel[116] heated equimolar quantities of dibenzylamine, water, and ethylene oxide in a sealed tube at 100°C. to obtain a 25 per cent yield of N,N-dibenzylaminoethanol. Ethylene oxide reacts thus with a large number of primary and secondary organic bases to produce the corresponding hydroxyethylamines.

2-Aminopyridine and dry ethylene oxide react in methanol at 15 to 20°C. to undergo rearrangement and form 1-(2-hydroxyethyl)pyridone-imine[117], which can be hydrolyzed in boiling 10 per cent caustic to the corresponding lactam, 1-(2-hydroxyethyl)pyridone:

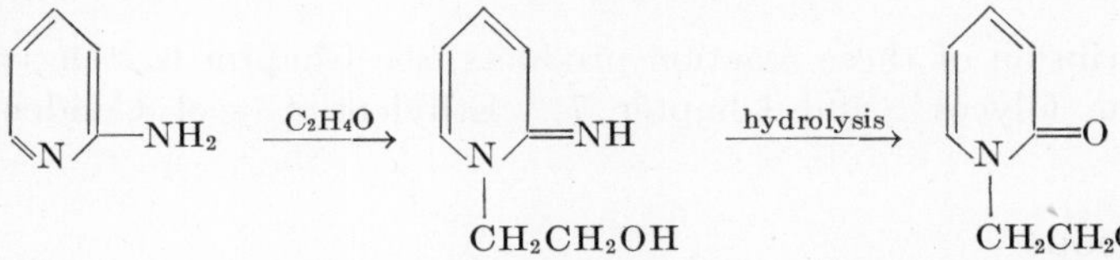

Ruberg and Shriner[118] condensed a number of aliphatic secondary amines with ethylene oxide at temperatures below 60°C. to obtain alcohol mixtures of the type $R_2NCH_2CH_2OH$ and $R_2N(CH_2CH_2O)_nH$.

Organic Acids and Anhydrides

Anhydrous organic acids react with ethylene oxide, particularly in the presence of a catalyst, to form the ethylene glycol monoesters of the acid used. The acid anhydrides react to form the ethylene glycol diesters. Thus, Wurtz[119] heated ethylene oxide with glacial acetic acid to obtain ethylene glycol monoacetate:

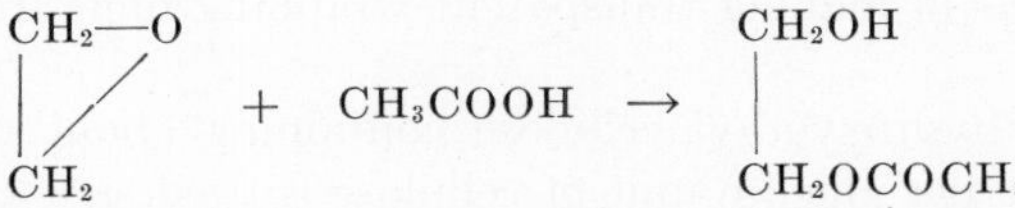

Heating ethylene oxide with acetic anhydride, he obtained ethylene glycol diacetate[120]:

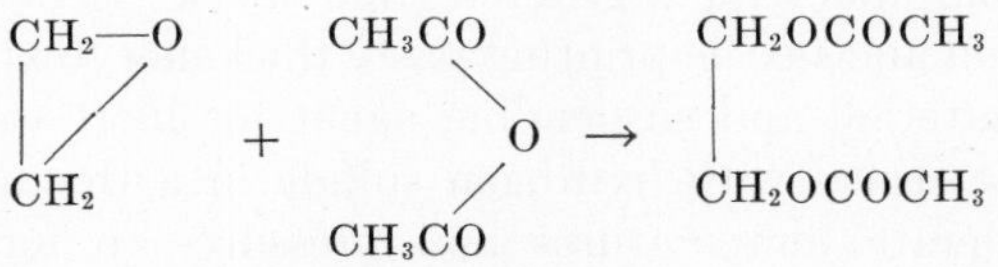

For a discussion of such reaction products, see Chapter 6, "Derivatives of Ethylene Glycol."

Alcohols, Glycols, and Phenols

Ethylene oxide reacts with alcohols or glycols in a manner analogous to its reaction with water. Alcohols and phenols react chiefly to form the well-known industrial solvents, the monoalkyl and aryl ethers of ethylene glycol:

$$H_2C\underset{\diagdown}{\overset{}{\rule{1.2em}{0.4pt}}}CH_2 \quad + \quad C_2H_5OH \quad \rightarrow \quad C_2H_5O\rule{0.8em}{0.4pt}CH_2CH_2OH$$
$$O$$

Glycols react to form di-, tri-, and polyethylene glycols:

$$H_2C\underset{\diagdown}{\overset{}{\rule{1.2em}{0.4pt}}}CH_2 \quad + \quad C_2H_4(OH)_2 \quad \rightarrow \quad HOCH_2CH_2OCH_2CH_2OH$$
$$O$$

For a description of these reaction products, see Chapter 6, "Derivatives of Ethylene Glycol," and Chapter 7, "Ethylene Glycol Condensation Polymers."

Miscellaneous

Nikitin and Rudneva[121, 122] studied the action of ethylene oxide on cellulose. They found that bleached cotton would react with ethylene oxide at 50°C. to give a reaction product containing only one hydroxyethyl group per 32 glucose units. In the presence of dilute alkalies the degree of etherification was increased to one ether group per four to eight glucose units. Lawrie, Reynolds, and Piggott[123] proposed the etherification of artificial cellulose textiles by olefin oxides in aqueous alkali of 11 per cent strength. The reaction of olefin oxides with cellulose was studied also by Dreyfus[124]. The production of hydroxyethyl ethers of cellulose is described in patents issued to Lilienfeld[125] and to Schorger[126], while Shoemaker[127] describes methods of making transparent wrapping films from these compounds.

Alkali-soluble hydroxyethyl cellulose containing about one-half a mol of ethylene oxide per glucose unit of cellulose is used as a sizing agent for textile fabrics. It is marketed as "Ceglin." A water-soluble hydroxyethyl cellulose containing about two and one-quarter mols of ethylene oxide per glucose unit is sold under the registered trade-mark "Cellosize." It is used as a resin emulsion and textile printing paste thickener, textile sizing agent, paper coating material, and suspending agent for inert solids.

Ethylene oxide reacts with hydrogen sulfide in a thiodiethylene glycol medium at moderate temperatures and pressures to form 2-mercaptoethanol and thiodiethylene glycol:

$$C_2H_4O \; + H_2S \rightarrow HOCH_2CH_2SH$$

$$2C_2H_4O + H_2S \rightarrow HOCH_2CH_2SCH_2CH_2OH$$

Chichibabin and Bestuzher[128] found that the first reaction would proceed in aqueous solutions at 8 to 10°C. and that after ten days a quantitative yield of product could be obtained. In the absence of proper cooling, higher and more viscous polyethylene glycol sulfides were obtained.

Tseou and Pan[129] synthesized thioethylene glycol by passing hydrogen sulfide and ethylene oxide through a Pyrex tube filled with iron or aluminum sulfide heated to 350°C. The yield was practically quantitative when the reaction was controlled.

Nenitzescu and Scarlatescu[130] prepared thiodiethylene glycol in a 90 per cent yield by reacting hydrogen sulfide and ethylene oxide vapors in a 1 to 2 mol ratio over glass beads moistened with the reaction product. They also prepared hydroxyethyl thioethers in good yields by reaction of mercaptans with ethylene oxide.

Headlee[131] also studied the reaction of ethylene oxide with hydrogen sulfide. A limited amount of 2-mercaptoethanol was obtained from reactions occurring in the presence of water at a temperature of 65°C. Other products were thiodiethylene glycol, ethylene glycol, and diethylene glycol. Similar results were obtained in benzene solution. In the absence of solvent, 2-mercaptoethanol and thiodiethylene glycol were obtained in an autoclave where the highest reaction pressure recorded was 940 cm. Hg. A subsequent experiment performed in an autoclave at −10°C. for 110 hours and then maintained at room temperature was discontinued by explosion after 50 hours' duration at the latter temperature. Headlee concluded that if the reactants were used in molar proportions, a high yield of mercaptoethanol was obtained. If ethylene oxide was present in excess, the yield to thiodiethylene glycol was favored.

Ethylene oxide reacts with hydrogen cyanide to form ethylene cyanohydrin[132, 133, 134], which is an important raw material in the manufacture of acrylonitrile and acrylic esters

$$C_2H_4O + HCN \rightarrow HOCH_2CH_2CN$$

Alkylene cyanohydrins are formed also by the reaction of olefin oxides with dispersions of the alkali or alkaline earth cyanides in water, alcohols, or mixtures of these at 10 to 30°C.[12]

Ethylene oxide may be passed over an alkali bisulfate catalyst at 120°C. to obtain dioxane[122].

A similar treatment in the presence of an alkali hydroxide yields highly polymerized substances of wax-like consistency. For a further discussion of these products, see Chapter 6, "Derivatives of Ethylene Glycol," and Chapter 7, "Ethylene Glycol Condensation Polymers."

Meerwein and Sönke[135] reacted ethylene oxide and trichloroacetic acid. They believed the product to be an *ortho*-ester because of its strongly acidic nature and because of its reaction with diazomethane. To confirm the structure, trichloroacetyl chloride was reacted with 2-methoxyethanol to prepare the straight-chain methoxyethyl trichloroacetate:

$$
\underset{\text{O}}{\overset{\text{O}}{\parallel}}\quad\quad\quad\quad\quad\quad\quad\quad\quad\quad\quad\underset{\text{O}}{\overset{\text{O}}{\parallel}}
$$

$$CCl_3\!-\!C\!-\!Cl \;+\; HOCH_2CH_2OCH_3 \;\rightarrow\; CCl_3\!-\!C\!-\!OCH_2CH_2OCH_3$$

This product differed in chemical properties from the supposed *ortho*-ester. Additional reactions of the compound showed it to be a tautomeric mixture of possible compounds in uncertain proportions[122]:

$$
CCl_3\!-\!\underset{}{\overset{\overset{\text{O}}{\parallel}}{C}}\!-\!OCH_2CH_2OH \;\leftrightarrows\;
$$

2-Hydroxyethyl trichloroacetate   2-Hydroxy-2-trichloro-methyl-1,3-dioxolane

Ethylene oxide adds to ethylene chlorohydrin to yield diethylene glycol chlorohydrin, $ClCH_2CH_2OCH_2CH_2OH$, and triethylene glycol chlorohydrin, $ClCH_2CH_2OCH_2CH_2OCH_2CH_2OH$[136]. Maass and Boomer[73] demonstrated that ethylene oxide reacts at low temperatures with bromine or chlorine to form the oxonium compounds: $C_2H_4O\cdot Cl$; $C_2H_4O\cdot 3Cl$; $C_2H_4O\cdot Br$; and $C_2H_4O\cdot 2Br$.

The nitration of ethylene oxide in the presence of sulfuric acid yields ethylene glycol dinitrate[137, 138]:

$$
\underset{H_2C}{\overset{H_2C\!-\!O}{\diagup}} \;+\; 2HNO_3 \;\xrightarrow{H_2SO_4}\; \underset{CH_2\!-\!ONO_2}{\overset{CH_2\!-\!ONO_2}{|}} \;+\; H_2O
$$

This compound is used with nitroglycerin as an explosive (see pages 65 and 130).

The olefin oxides are reduced in aqueous solution by sodium amalgam to the corresponding alcohol[12, 93]. Over a catalyst of nickel on barium oxide ethylene oxide is reduced in the vapor-phase under pressure at 80°C. to ethanol. With an excess of ethylene oxide the monoethyl ether of ethylene glycol is formed by reduction at temperatures of 130 to 150°C.[139]

Ethylene oxide and ketones react in the presence of tin tetrachloride[140] or boron trifluoride[141] to give cyclic ketals. Aldehydes react similarly to form acetals, but inert solvents must be used to prevent too much polymerization[142]. Ethylene oxide reacts with acetone to give 72 per cent polymer and 12 per cent 2,2-dimethyl-1,3-dioxolane (where R = methyl):

$$
\begin{array}{ccc}
\text{H}_3\text{C} & & \text{O} \\
\diagdown & \diagup & \diagdown \\
& \text{C} & \quad \text{CH}_2 \\
\diagup & | & | \\
\text{R} & \text{O}\!\!-\!\!-\!\!-\!\!\text{CH}_2
\end{array}
$$

With methyl ethyl ketone, 19 per cent 2-methyl-2-ethyl-1,3-dioxolane (where R = ethyl) is obtained. With methyl propyl ketone the product is 2-methyl-2-propyl-1,3-dioxolane (where R = propyl)[143].

Acetyl halides react with ethylene oxide to give 2-haloethyl acetates[143]. Acetyl iodide reacts in 20 hours at 25°C. to form 73.8 per cent 2-iodoethyl acetate. Acetyl chloride reacts after 45 days to form 2-chloroethyl acetate in a 95 per cent yield. If a drop of hydrochloric acid is added, the latter reaction is completed in two to three days. Small amounts of iodine also catalyze these reactions.

Twigg[44, 45] showed that ethylene oxide isomerizes to acetaldehyde over a silver catalyst at 323°C. In the presence of oxygen, the acetaldehyde is very quickly decomposed to carbon dioxide and water. The conversion of oxide to aldehyde observed by Twigg in an ethylene oxide-nitrogen atmosphere over this special silver catalyst was 2.2 and 12.2 per cent at the same temperature. Twigg ascribed the decrease in catalyst activity to the deposition of organic material on its surface.

Peytral[81] studied the action of heat on ethylene oxide to show that the compound decomposed at 570°C. to produce water, acetaldehyde, carbon monoxide, hydrogen, methane, acetylene, and butene. The decomposition reaction was found to be exothermic between 570 and 1200°C.

Travers[144] maintained that neither the reaction rate nor mechanism of ethylene oxide decomposition can be followed satisfactorily by measuring the rate of increase in pressure at constant volume. He considered that the reactions involve a chain mechanism and depend on the surface of the system. Travers and Seddon[145] indicated that complex changes were involved in the thermal decomposition of ethylene oxide.

Heckert and Mack[146] heated ethylene oxide in "Pyrex" chambers at 380 to 444°C. and found that the decomposition was a homogeneous gaseous reaction occurring in two steps, probably with acetaldehyde formation as an intermediate step. Their reaction products included carbon monoxide, methane, propylene, and aldehydes. Measuring the decomposition rate of ethylene oxide at 435 to 505°C., Thompson and Meissner[147] found their results to agree in general with those of Heckert and Mack.

The results of Sickman[148] indicate that an induction period is found in ethylene oxide pyrolysis and that the reaction is inhibited by the presence of inert gases. Fletcher[149] suggested the formation of free radicals and aldehydes at 400°C. to explain the mechanism of the changes occurring.

He found that at 443°C. acetaldehyde, exerting a pressure of 184 mm., is half decomposed in three minutes in the presence of ethylene oxide, exerting a partial pressure of 17 mm.

APPLICATIONS

Ethylene oxide is primarily a chemical intermediate. Its major outlets are indicated in Figure 5.7[4]. Estimated consumption is listed in Table 5.12[4].

Although used chiefly as a starting material in the synthesis of other compounds, ethylene oxide is also an excellent fumigant. It is generally noncorrosive to metals and apparently leaves no residual odor or taste in the most sensitive materials. In many cases a single fumigation destroys simultaneously insects, molds, and bacteria. This sterilizing action of ethylene oxide has been thoroughly studied and reviewed by Phillips and Kaye[150].

The biological activity of ethylene oxide was first noted by Cotton and

TABLE 5.12. ETHYLENE OXIDE CONSUMPTION (IN MILLION POUNDS)

	Glycols					Other Chemicals				
			Ethylene Glycol		Poly-ethyl-ene Glycols[3]	Sub-total	Ethyl-ene cyan-hydrin[4]	Etha-nol-amines[5]	Glycol-ethers[2]	Surface-active Agents and Miscel-laneous[6]	Anti-freeze, % of Total Oxide
	Total	Subtotal	Direct Use[1]	Chemi-cal[2]							
1950	413	325	277	21	27	88	26	25	26	11	61
1949	354	276	233	19	24	78	20	25	24	9	60
1948	286	228	188	18	22	58	14	18	21	5	58
1947	197	150	118	16	16	47	13	15	16	3	49
1946	160	119	90	15	14	41	12	13	14	2	44
1945	163	125	98	13	14	38	11	12	14	1	44
1944	173	128	100	13	15	45	17	11	16	1	40
1943	171	130	104	12	15	41	16	10	14	1	—
1942	165	137	110	11	16	28	9	9	9	1	—
1941	128	104	79	11	14	24	2	10	11	1	53
1940	115	97	76	9	12	18	1	7	10	1	60
1939	108	94	75	9	10	14	0	6	8	1	60

[1] See Chapter 4, "Commercial Applications of Ethylene Glycol."

[2] See Chapters 6, "Derivatives of Ethylene Glycol," and 7, "Ethylene Glycol Condensation Polymers."

[3] Includes polyglycol esters.

[4] Mostly acrylonitrile, but includes acrylate esters (not methacrylate).

[5] Includes derivatives (see Figure 5.7).

[6] See Figure 5.7.

[7] Estimated in two ways: (1) total ethylene glycol less chemical, export, and other uses and less production from formaldehyde, i.e., by differences; (2) from trade opinion and reviews previously reported.

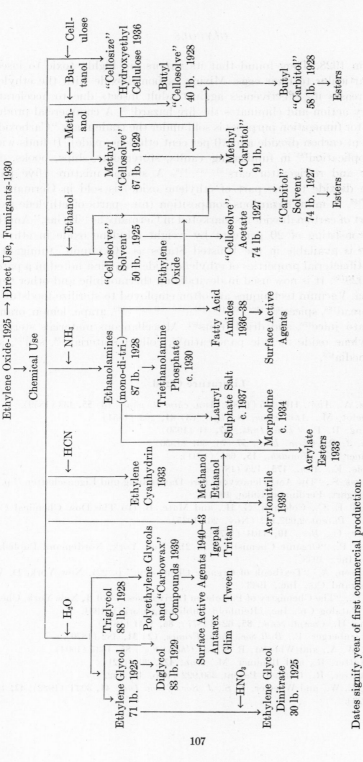

Ethylene Oxide-1925 → Direct Use, Fumigants-1930

Chemical Use

FIGURE 5.7

Dates signify year of first commercial production.
Lb. indicates number of pounds of ethylene oxide required to make 100 of indicated product.

Roark[151] in 1928. They found that its vapors are highly toxic to insects and in particular to their eggs. Mixing carbon dioxide with the ethylene oxide increases its effectiveness against adult insects due to accelerated respiratory action and eliminates the fire hazard[152]. A commercial product available for fumigation purposes is sold under the trade-mark "Carboxide" (90 per cent carbon dioxide and 10 per cent ethylene oxide). It finds wide-spread application[153] in fumigating vaults, storerooms, ships, books, and passenger and refrigerator cars[154, 155, 156]. A similar mixture (five parts of carbon dioxide to one part of ethylene oxide) is sold in Germany as "Cartox"[157]. A more hazardous composition (nine parts of ethylene oxide to one part of carbon dioxide) is marketed in Germany as "T-Gas." Another product consisting of 20 per cent by weight ethylene oxide in ethylene dichloride is available in the Unisted States as "Oxyfume" fumigant.

The antibacterial properties of ethylene oxide were first noted in a patent filed in 1929[158]. It is now used in devitalizing thermophilic and other types of bacteria. Vacuum techniques are often employed to sterilize foodstuffs[159] such as bread[160], spices[161, 162, 163, 164, 165, 166, 167, 168, 169], grape, lemon, orange, and tomato juice[170], and dried fruits[171]. Miscellaneous materials sterilized with ethylene oxide include pancreatin[172], colloid materials[173], soil[174], and culture media[175].

Literature Cited

1. Wurtz, A., *Ann.*, **110,** 125 (1859); *Ann. chim et. phys.*, (3) **55,** 433 (1859).
2. Berthelot, M., *Ann. chim. et phys.*, (3) **41,** 299 (1854).
3. Messing, R. F., *Chem. Inds.*, **67,** 41 (1950).
4. Skeen, J. R., *Chem. Eng.*, **57** (7), 331 (1950).
5. Roithner, E., *Monatsh.*, **15,** 665 (1894).
6. Demole, E., *Ann.*, **173,** 125 (1874).
7. Bodforss, S., "Die Aethylenoxyde, Ihre Darstellung und Eigenschaften," p. 12, Stuttgart, Ferdinand Enke, 1920.
8. Britton, E. C., Coleman, G. H., and Mate, B. (to The Dow Chemical Co.), U. S. Patent 2,022,182 (Noу. 26, 1935).
9. Wagner, G., *Ber.*, **10,** 1104 (1877).
10. Karrer, P., "Organic Chemistry," p. 219, New York, Nordemann Publishing Co., Inc., 1938.
11. Bernthsen, A., "Textbook of Organic Chemistry," p. 221, New York, D. Van Nostrand Co., Inc., 1943.
12. Ellis, C., "The Chemistry of Petroleum Derivatives," Vol. **I,** New York, Chemical Catalog Co., Inc. (Reinhold Publishing Corp.), 1934.
13. Greene, H., *Compt. rend.*, **85,** 624 (1877); **86,** 1141 (1878).
14. Schutzenberger, P., *Bull soc. chim. France*, (2) **31,** 482 (1879).
15. Bone, W. A., and Wheeler, R. V., *J. Chem. Soc.*, **85,** 1637 (1904).
16. Willstätter, R., and Bommer, M., *Ann.* **422,** 36 (1921).
17. Willstätter, R., German Patent 350,922 (Feb. 13, 1922).
18. Blair, E. W., and Wheeler, T. S., *J. Soc. Chem. Ind.*, **41,** 303T (1922); **42,** 415T (1923).

19. Engler, C., and Weissberg, J., *Ber.* **31,** 3050 (1898).
20. Lewis, J. S., *J. Chem. Soc.*, **1929,** 759.
21. Lenher, S., *J. Am. Chem. Soc.*, **53,** 2420, 3737, 3752 (1931).
22. Lenher, S. (to E. I. du Pont de Nemours & Co.), U. S. Patent 1,995,991 (March 26, 1935).
23. Phillips, F. C., *Z. anorg. Chem.*, **6,** 213 (1894); *Chem. Zentr.* **65, I,** 852 (1894).
24. Bone, W. A., and Smith, H. L., *J. Chem. Soc.*, **87,** 910 (1905).
25. Reyerson, L. H., and Swearingen, L. E., *J. Am. Chem. Soc.*, **50,** 2872 (1928).
26. Skärblom, K. E., U. S. Patent 1,982,545 (Nov. 27, 1934).
27. Lefort, T. E. (to Société française de catalyze généralisée), U. S. Patent 1,998,878 (April 23, 1935); (to Carbide and Carbon Chemicals Corp.), Re. 20,370 (May 18, 1937) and Re. 22,241 (Dec. 29, 1942).
28. Société française de catalyze généralisée, British Patent 402,438 (Dec. 4, 1933).
29. Société française de catalyze généralisée, British Patent 402, 749 (Dec. 4, 1933).
30. Société française de catalyze généralisée, French Patents 729,952 (March 27, 1931) and 739,562 (Oct. 3, 1931): Ad. 41,255; 41,474; 41,484; 41,810; and 41,811.
31. Law, G. H. (to Carbide and Carbon Chemicals Corp.), U. S. Patent 2,142,948 (Jan. 3, 1939).
32. Law, G. H. (to Carbide and Carbon Chemicals Corp.), U. S. Patent 2,187,882 (Jan. 23, 1940).
33. Law, G. H., and Chitwood, H. C. (to Carbide and Carbon Chemicals Corp.), U. S. Patent 2,194,602 (March 26, 1940).
34. McNamee, R. W., Chitwood, H. C., and Law, G. H. (to Carbide and Carbon Chemicals Corp.), U. S. Patent 2,219,575 (Oct. 29, 1940).
35. McNamee, R. W., and Blair, C. M. (to Carbide and Carbon Chemicals Corp.), U. S. Patent 2,238,474 (April 15, 1941).
36. Law, G. H., and Chitwood, H. C. (to Carbide and Carbon Chemicals Corp.), U. S. Patents 2,279,469–70 (April 14, 1942). British Patent 518,823 (March 8, 1940).
37. Carter, R. M. (to U. S. Industrial Alcohol Co.), U. S. Patent 2,125,333 (Aug. 2, 1938).
38. Carter, R. M. (to U. S. Industrial Alcohol Co.), U. S. Patents 2,177,361 (Oct. 24, 1939) and 2,294,383 (Sept. 1, 1942); British Patent 509,183 (July 12, 1939); Canadian Patent 387,564 (March 19, 1940); and French Patent 837,634 (Feb. 15, 1939.)
39. U. S. Industrial Alcohol Co., French Patent 837,792 (Feb. 20, 1939).
40. Langwell, H., Maddocks, C. B., and Short, J. F. (to The Distillers Co., Ltd.), British Patent 462,487 (March 10, 1937).
41. Langwell, H., Maddocks, C. B., and Short, J. F. (to The Distillers Co., Ltd.), British Patents 466,416 (May 24, 1937) and 472,629 (Sept. 24, 1937).
42. Reyerson, L. H., and Oppenheimer, H., *J. Phys. Chem.*, **48,** 290 (1944).
43. McBee, E. T., Hass, H. B., and Wiseman, P. A., *Ind. Eng. Chem.*, **37,** 432 (1945).
44. Twigg, G. H., *Trans. Faraday Soc.*, **42,** 284, 657 (1946).
45. Twigg, G. H., *Proc. Roy. Soc. (London)*, **188A,** 92 (1946).
46. Sherwood, P. W., *Petroleum Refiner*, **28** (3), 129 (1949).
47. Benton, A. F., and Drake, L. C., *J. Am. Chem. Soc.*, **56,** 255 (1934).
48. Common, A. A., *Proc. Roy. Inst.*, **13,** 171 (1890).
49. Francon, J. (to Carbide and Carbon Chemicals Corp.), U. S. Patent 2,143,371 (Jan. 10, 1939) and French Patent 794,751 (Feb. 25, 1936).
50. Van Peski, A. J. (to Shell Development Co.), U. S. Patent 2,040,782 (May 12, 1936).

51. Evans, T. W. (to Shell Development Co.), U. S. Patent 2,404,438 (July 23, 1946).
52. Evans, T. W. (to Shell Development Co.), U. S. Patent 2,446,132 (July 27, 1948).
53. Cambron, A., and McKim, F. L. W. (to The Honorary Advisory Council for Scientific and Industrial Research), U. S. Patent 2,426,761 (Sept. 2, 1947).
54. Bergsteinsson, I., and Finch, H. D. (to Shell Development Co.), U. S. Patents 2,424,083-6 (July 15, 1947).
55. Bergsteinsson, I., and Scheible, J. R. (to Shell Development Co.), U. S. Patent 2,437,930 (March 16, 1948).
56. Aries, R. S., U. S. Patent 2,477,435 (July 26, 1949).
57. West, T. J., and West, J. P. (to Allied Chemical and Dye Corp.), U. S. Patent 2,463,228 (March 1, 1949).
58. Nevison, J. A., and Lincoln, R. M., U. S. Patent 2,491,057 (Dec. 13, 1949).
59. Becker, S. B. (to Standard Oil Co.), U. S. Patent 2,430,443 (Nov. 11, 1947).
60. Honorary Advisory Council for Scientific and Industrial Research, British Patent 591,670 (Aug. 26, 1947).
61. Bergsteinsson, I., and Finch, H. (to Shell Development Co.), British Patent 590,479 (July 18, 1947).
62. Mitani, M., and Kano, H., *Mem. Faculty Eng., Hokkaido Imp. Univ.*, **8** (1), 75 (1947); *Chem. Abstracts*, **42,** 7246 (1948).
63. Société française de catalyze généralisée, French Patent 841,789 (May 26, 1939).
64. I. G. Farbenindustrie A.-G., British Patent 507,538 (June 16, 1938).
65. Société française de catalyze généralisée, French Patent 771,650 (Oct. 13, 1934).
66. Horsley, L. H., *Anal. Chem.*, **19,** 508 (1947); **21,** 842 (1949).
67. Hess, L. G., and Tilton, V. V., *Ind. Eng. Chem.*, **42,** 1251 (1950).
68. The Associated Factory Mutual Fire Insurance Companies, *Ind. Eng. Chem.,* **32,** 882 (1940).
69. Conrad, H. F., and Jones, C. W., "Limits of Inflammability in Vapors," U. S. Bureau of Mines, Bull. 279, Rev. Ed., 1938.
70. Jones, G. W., and Kennedy, R. E., *Ind. Eng. Chem.*, **22,** 146 (1930).
71. Jones, R. M., *Ind. Eng. Chem.*, **25,** 394 (1933).
72. Peters, G., and Gauter, W., *Angew. Chem.*, **51** (2), 30 (1938).
73. Maass, O., and Boomer, E. H., *J. Am. Chem. Soc.*, **44,** 1709 (1922).
74. Walden, P., *Z. physik. Chem.*, **70,** 569 (1910); "International Critical Tables," Vol. **6,** p. 84, 1929.
75. Hibbert, H., and Allen, J. S., *J. Am. Chem. Soc.*, **54,** 4115 (1932).
76. Giauque, W. F., and Gordon, J., *J. Am. Chem. Soc.*, **71,** 2176 (1949).
77. Crog, R. S., and Hunt, H., *J. Phys. Chem.*, **46,** 1162 (1942).
78. Bichowsky, F. S., and Rossini, F. D., "The Thermochemistry of Chemical Substances," p. 46, New York, Reinhold Publishing Corp., 1936.
79. Perkin, W. H., *J. Chem. Soc.*, **63,** 488 (1893).
80. Kistiakowsky, G. B., and Rice, W. W., *J. Chem. Physics*, **8,** 618 (1940).
81. Peytral, E., *Bull. soc. chim. France*, (4) **39,** 206 (1926).
82. Seidell, A., "Solubilities of Organic Compounds," New York, D. Van Nostrand Co., Inc., 1941.
83. Guseva, V., *Chem. Abstracts*, **34,** 3945 (1940).
84. Coles, K. F., and Popper, F., *Ind. Eng. Chem.*, **42,** 1434 (1950).
85. Lourenco, A., *Ann. chim. et phys.*, (3) **67,** 275 (1863).
86. Bigot, A., *Ann. chim. et phys.*, (6) **22,** 488 (1891).
87. Brönsted, J. N., Kilpatrick, M., and Kilpatrick, M., *J. Am. Chem. Soc.*, **51,** 428 (1929).
88. Smith, L., Wode, G., and Widhe, T., *Z. physik. Chem.*, **130,** 154 (1927).

89. Tasiro, Y., *Repts. Imp. Ind. Research Inst., Osaka, Japan*, **18** (3), 1–53 (1937); *Chem. Abstracts*, **33**, 1270 (1939).

90. Youtz, M. A. (to Standard Oil Co. of Indiana), U. S. Patent 1,875,312 (Aug. 30, 1932).

91. Cartmell, R. R., Galloway, J. R., Olson, R. W., and Smith, J. M., *Ind. Eng. Chem.*, **40**, 389 (1948).

92. Gebauer-Fuelnegg, E., and Moffett, E., *J. Am. Chem. Soc.*, **56**, 2009 (1934).

93. Wurtz, A., *Ann. chim. et phys.*, (3) **69**, 317, 355 (1863).

94. Deckert, W., *Angew. Chem.*, **45**, 559 (1932).

95. Lubatti, O. F., *J. Soc. Chem. Ind. (London)*, **54**, 424T (1935).

96. Ziese, W., *Ber.*, **66B**, 1965 (1933).

97. Ribas, I., and Tapia, E., *Brit. Chem. Abstracts*, **A 1933**, 48; *Anales fís. y quím. (Madrid)*, **30**, 778 (1932).

98. Schaarschmidt, A., Hermann, L., and Szemzö, B., *Ber.*, **58**, 1914 (1925).

99. Grignard, V., *Bull. soc. chim. France*, (3) **29**, 944 (1903); *Compt. rend.*, **136**, 1260 (1903).

100. Blaise, E. E., *Compt. rend.*, **134**, 551 (1902).

101. Huston, R. C., and Agett, A. H., *J. Org. Chem.*, **6**, 123 (1941).

102. Homeyer, A. H., Whitmore, F. C., and Wallingford, V. H., *J. Am. Chem. Soc.*, **55**, 4209 (1933).

103. Knorr, L., *Ber.*, **32**, 729 (1899).

104. Knorr, L., *Ber.*, **30**, 909 (1897).

105. Germann, F. E. E., and Knight, O. S., *J. Am. Chem. Soc.*, **55**, 4150 (1933).

106. Schwoegler, E. J., and Olin, J. F. (to Sharples Chemicals, Inc.), U. S. Patent 2,373,199 (April 10, 1945).

107. Reid, E. W., and Lewis, D. C. (to Carbide and Carbon Chemicals Corp.), Canadian Patent 298,851 (April 1, 1930).

108. Reid, E. W., and Lewis, D. C. (to Carbide and Carbon Chemicals Corp.), U. S. Patent 1,904,013 (April 18, 1933).

109. "Emulsions and Detergents," New York, Carbide and Carbon Chemicals Corp., 1949.

110. I. G. Farbenindustrie A.-G., British Patent 364,000 (July 25, 1930); French Patents 713,382 (March 17, 1931) and 713,998 (March 28, 1931).

111. Headlee, A. J. W., Collett, A. R., and Lazzell, C. L., *J. Am. Chem. Soc.*, **55**, 1066 (1933).

112. Horne, W. H., and Shriner, R. L., *J. Am. Chem. Soc.*, **54**, 2925 (1932).

113. Knorr, L., and Brownsdon, H. W., *Ber.*, **35**, 4474 (1902).

114. Barnett, E. de B., *Proc. Chem. Soc.*, **28**, 259 (1912).

115. Jones, L. W., and Burns, G. R., *J. Am. Chem. Soc.*, **47**, 2966 (1925).

116. Gabel, G., *Bull. soc. chim. France*, (5) **1**, 1006 (1934).

117. Knunjanz, I. L., *Ber.*, **68**, 397 (1935).

118. Ruberg, L. A., and Shriner, R. L., *J. Am. Chem. Soc.*, **57**, 1581 (1935).

119. Wurtz, A., *Ann.*, **116**, 249 (1860).

120. Wurtz, A., *Ann.*, **113**, 255 (1860).

121. Nikitin, N. I., and Rudneva, T. I., *J. Applied Chem. (U.S.S.R.)*, **8**, 1023 (1935); *Chem. Abstracts*, **30**, 5408 (1936).

122. Ellis, C., "The Chemistry of Petroleum Derivatives," Vol. **II**, New York, Reinhold Publishing Corp., 1937.

123. Lawrie, L. G., Reynolds, R. J. W., and Piggott, H. A. (to Imperial Chemical Industries, Ltd.), British Patent 439,880 (Dec. 17, 1935).

124. Dreyfus, H., British Patent 397,116 (Aug. 14, 1933).

125. Lilienfeld, L., U. S. Patents 1,722,927–8 (July 30, 1929).
126. Schorger, A. W. (to C. F. Burgess Laboratories, Inc.), U. S. Patent 1,863,208 (June 14, 1932).
127. Shoemaker, M. J. (to Carbide and Carbon Chemicals Corp.), U. S. Patent 2,029,131 (Jan. 28, 1936).
128. Chichibabin, A. E., and Bestuzher, M. A., *Compt. rend.*, **200,** 242 (1935).
129. Tseou, H., and Pan, T., *J. Chinese Chem. Soc.*, **7,** 29 (1939); *Chem. Abstracts,* **34,** 1970 (1940).
130. Nenitzescu, C. D., and Scarlatescu, N., *Ber.*, **68,** 587 (1935).
131. Headlee, A. J., "A Study of Ethylene Oxide and Some of Its Derivatives," Thesis, West Virginia University Graduate School, 1932.
132. Erlenmeyer, E., *Ann.*, **191,** 269 (1878).
133. Hörmann, J. V., *Ber.*, **12,** 23 (1879).
134. Carpenter, E. L. (to American Cyanamid Co.), U. S. Patent 2,453,062 (Nov. 2, 1948).
135. Meerwein, H., and Sönke, H., *Ber.*, **64B,** 2375 (1931).
136. Fourneau, E., and Ribas, I., *Bull. soc. chim. France (4)*, **41,** 1046 (1927).
137. Matthews, F. E., and Strange, E. H., British Patent 12,770 (May 30, 1912).
138. Lawrie, J. W., "Glycerol and the Glycols—Production, Properties, and Analyses," A. C. S. Monograph No. 44, p. 389, New York, Chemical Catalog Co., Inc. (Reinhold Publishing Corp.), 1928.
139. Kathol, J. (to Reinische Kampfer-Fabrik G.m.b.H.), German Patent 563,625 (March 20, 1931).
140. Bogert, M. T., and Roblin, R. O., Jr., *J. Am. Chem. Soc.*, **55,** 3741–5 (1933).
141. Petrov, A. A., *J. Gen. Chem. (U.S.S.R.)*, **10,** 981 (1940).
142. Bersin, T., and Willfang, G., *Ber.*, **70B,** 2167 (1937).
143. Gustus, E. L., and Stevens, P. G., *J. Am. Chem. Soc.*, **55,** 374 (1933).
144. Travers, M. W., *Nature*, **136,** 909 (1935).
145. Travers, M. W., and Seddon, R. V., *Nature*, **137,** 906 (1936).
146. Heckert, W. W., and Mack, E., Jr., *J. Am. Chem. Soc.*, **51,** 2706 (1929).
147. Thompson, H. W., and Meissner, M., *Nature*, **137,** 870 (1936); *Trans. Faraday Soc.*, **32,** 1451 (1936).
148. Sickman, D. V., *J. Chem. Phys.*, **4,** 297 (1936).
149. Fletcher, C. J. M., *J. Am. Chem. Soc.*, **58,** 534 (1936).
150. Phillips, C. R., and Kaye, S., *Am. J. Hyg.*, **50,** 270–306 (1949).
151. Cotton, R. T., and Roark, R. C., *Ind. Eng. Chem.*, **20,** 805 (1928).
152. Cotton, R. T., and Young, H. D., *Proc. Entomol. Soc.*, **31,** 97–102 (1929).
153. Young, H. D., and Busbey, R. L., "References to the use of ethylene oxide for pest control," U. S. Department of Agriculture, Bureau of Entomology and Plant Quarantine, April, 1935.
154. Russ, J. M., Jr., *Ind. Eng. Chem.*, **22,** 328, 844 (1930).
155. Brown, E. W., *U. S. Naval Med. Bull.*, **32,** 294 (1934).
156. Kimberly, A. E., *Chemist*, **15,** 236 (1938).
157. Kilgore, L. B., *Soap Sanit. Chemicals*, **22** (2), 122 (1946).
158. Schrader, H., and Bossert, E. (to Union Carbide and Carbon Corp.), U. S. Patent 2,037,439 (April 14, 1936).
159. Prickett, P. S., *Proc. Inst. Food Technol.*, **1941,** 160.
160. Kirby, G. W., Atkin, L., and Frey, C. N., *Food Inds.*, **8,** 450 (1936).
161. Jensen, L. B., Wood, I. H., and Jansen, C. E., *Ind. Eng. Chem.*, **26,** 118–20 (1934).
162. Hall, L. A., *Food Inds.*, **10,** 424 (1938).
163. James, L. H., *Food Inds.*, **10,** 428 (1938).

164. McBride, R. S., *Food Inds.*, **10,** 430 (1938).
165. Smith, H. W., *Food Inds.*, **12** (11), 50 (1940).
166. Yesair, J., and Williams, O. B., *Food Research*, **7,** 118 (1942).
167. Griffith, C. L., and Hall, L. A. (to The Griffith Laboratories, Inc.), U. S. Patent 2,189,947 (Feb. 13, 1940).
168. Baer, J. M. (to The Guardite Corp.), U. S. Patent 2,229,360 (Jan. 21, 1941).
169. Angla, B., *Compt. rend. acad. agr. France*, **25,** 73 (1939).
170. Whelton, R., Phaff, H. J., Mrak, E. M., and Fisher, C. D., *Food Inds.*, **18,** 23, 174, 318 (1946).
171. Baerwald, F. K. (to Rosenberg Brothers & Co.), U. S. Patent 2,370,768 (March 6, 1945).
172. Griffith, C. L., and Hall, L. A. (to The Griffith Laboratories, Inc.), U. S. Patent 2,189,948 (Feb. 13, 1940).
173. Griffith, C. L., and Hall, L. A. (to The Griffith Laboratories, Inc.), U. S. Patent 2,189,949 (Feb. 13, 1940).
174. Roberts, J. L., Allison, L. E., Prickett, P. S., and Riddle, K. B., *J. Bact.*, **45,** 40 (1943).
175. Hansen, H. N., and Snyder, W. C., *Phytopathology*, **37,** 369 (1947).

CHAPTER 6

DERIVATIVES OF ETHYLENE GLYCOL

A. B. Boese, Jr., C. K. Fink, and H. G. Goodman, Jr.

Ethylene glycol is important chemically for the derivatives that can be produced by its etherification, esterification, condensation, and oxidation. These reaction products are described in this chapter under the general headings monoethers, diethers, dioxane, acetals and ketals, glyoxal, esters, alkyd resins, and ether-esters.

Monoethers

Since their first commercial production in 1926, the monoethers of ethylene glycol have become important as industrial solvents and chemical intermediates. Carbide sells them in the United States under the trademark "Cellosolve." In Germany, Anorgana G.m.b.H. markets the methyl, ethyl, and butyl monoethers as Methyl Glycol, Ethyl Glycol, and Butyl Glycol, respectively. The same compounds are sold in England by Oxirane, Ltd., as Methyl Oxitol, Oxitol, and Butyl Oxitol, respectively.

Preparation

The glycols react in much the same way as monohydric alcohols in ether formation. The first reaction to produce an ethylene glycol ether was carried out in 1859 by Wurtz[1], who heated a mixture of the mono- and disodium derivatives of ethylene glycol with ethyl iodide. Wurtz described only the diethyl ether and did not isolate or characterize the monoethyl ether. Later, Demole[2] and Palomaa[3] prepared various monoethers by reacting the monosodium derivative of ethylene glycol with alkyl iodides. Cretcher and Pittenger[4] reported the reaction of ethylene oxide with sodium alcoholates dissolved in an excess of the corresponding alcohol. Ethylene chlorohydrin may be used in place of ethylene oxide.

Industrially the monoalkyl ethers of ethylene glycol are usually produced by reacting ethylene oxide with alcohols[5, 6] under various conditions of temperature, pressure, and catalytic influences:

$$\begin{array}{c} CH_2 \\ | \quad\quad\searrow O \\ | \quad\quad\nearrow \\ CH_2 \end{array} + C_2H_5OH \longrightarrow C_2H_5O—CH_2CH_2OH$$

Ethylene oxide   *Ethanol*   *Ethylene glycol monoethyl ether*

Among the catalysts which have been employed with aliphatic alcohols are sulfates of metals having a valence greater than one such as nickel sulfate[7], active hydrosilicates such as "tonsil"[8], tertiary amines such as triamylamine or trimethylamine[9], diethyl sulfate[10], acidified hydrosilicates such as aluminum hydrosilicate[11] or aluminum fluosilicate[12], boron trifluoride[13], and acid and basic catalysts in general[14]. High ratios of alcohol to ethylene oxide favor the formation of ethers of ethylene glycol while lower ratios produce monoethers of diethylene, triethylene, and higher polyglycols[15].

Ethylene glycol monoethers can also be produced by reacting ethylene chlorohydrin or glycol with sodium hydroxide and a dialkyl sulfate such as diethyl sulfate[16]:

$$
\begin{array}{c}
CH_2OH \\
| \qquad\qquad + \quad (C_2H_5)_2SO_4 \quad + \quad NaOH \quad \longrightarrow \\
CH_2OH
\end{array}
$$

Ethylene   *Diethyl*
glycol   *sulfate*

$$C_2H_5O—CH_2CH_2OH \quad + \quad NaC_2H_5SO_4 \quad + \quad H_2O$$

Ethylene glycol   *Sodium ethyl*
monoethyl ether   *sulfate*

They are likewise obtained from the reaction of ethylene glycol with an alcohol in the presence of normal metallic sulfates such as zinc, nickel, or chromium sulfate[17].

Aryl and alkaryl ethers of ethylene glycol are formed by reacting phenol or its derivatives with ethylene oxide usually under superatmospheric pressure or by reacting the sodium derivative of the phenol with ethylene chlorohydrin. In general, better yields are obtained by the first method[18]. Boyd, Marle, and Thomas[19, 20] studied the reaction of ethylene oxide with substituted sodium phenolates and found the reactivity of the sodium phenolate to be enhanced by the presence of alkyl groups and diminished by the presence of negative groups. Alkaryl derivatives such as the benzyl ether of ethylene glycol have been described[21, 22].

The condensation of secondary olefins with ethylene glycol in the presence of sulfuric acid as a condensing agent has been employed by Evans and Bullard[23] to produce other ethers such as the secondary butyl ether of ethylene glycol. Evans and Edlund[24] describe the preparation of the tertiary butyl and tertiary amyl derivatives by condensing tertiary olefins with ethylene glycol.

According to Dreyfus[25], the vinyl ether of ethylene glycol can be produced by heating vinyl chloride with sodium glycolate in an autoclave at 80 to 100°C. This monomer, when refluxed with benzoyl peroxide or exposed to ultraviolet radiation, gives a water-soluble polymer. Hill, Pidgeon, and Potter[26, 27] describe the preparation of various vinyl ethers of ethylene glycol and note that these compounds cyclize to substituted 1,3-dioxolanes with traces of sulfuric acid. The allyl ether was prepared by Hurd and Pollack[28] from the sodium alcoholate of ethylene glycol and allyl bromide.

Properties

Ethylene glycol monoethers are colorless, mobile, almost odorless liquids. Their boiling points and refractive indices increase with molecular weight; their specific gravities decrease. They are miscible with the majority of organic solvents. The lower members up to the butyl ether are completely miscible with water. With increasing molecular weight, however, their solubility in water decreases. Physical properties of commercially available ethylene glycol monoethers are summarized in Table 6.1.

The glycol monoethers undergo the usual chemical reactions of primary

TABLE 6.1. PHYSICAL PROPERTIES OF SOME COMMERCIAL ETHYLENE
GLYCOL MONOETHERS

	Ethylene Glycol Monoether							
	Methyl	Ethyl	Butyl	Phenyl	2-Ethylbutyl	2-Ethyl-hexyl	p-tert-Amyl-phenyl[a]	di-tert-Amyl-phenyl[a]
Boiling point								
at 760 mm, °C.	124.5	135.1	171.2	244.7	196.8	228.3	297–310	315–225
at 50 mm, °C.	55	64	94	157	116	141	(range)	(range)
at 10 mm, °C.	27	35	61	118	84	108		
Δb.p./Δp, °C./mm.	0.043	0.042	0.046	0.052	0.050	0.053	—	—
Coefficient of expansion								
at 20°C.	0.00095	0.00097	0.00092	0.00077	0.00089	—	—	—
at 55°C.	0.00099	0.00101	0.00095	0.00079	0.00092	—	—	—
Flash point (open cup), °F.	115	130	165	250	180	230	280	300
Freezing point, °C.	−85.1	—	—	14	−90 (sets to a glass)	—	−55	−35
Heat of vaporization, Btu/lb.	239	234	171	124	150	133	—	—
Molecular weight	76.09	90.12	118.17	138.16	146.22	174.28	208.3	278.4
Refractive index, n_D at 20°C.	1.4021	1.4076	1.4193	1.5386	1.4304	1.4362	1.519	1.507
$\Delta n_D/\Delta t$	0.00040	—	—	—	0.00040	—	—	—
Solubility in water at 20°C., % by wt.	∞	∞	∞	2.7	1.2	0.09	—	—
Solubility of water in, at 20°C., % by wt.	∞	∞	∞	10.8	10.0	5.4	—	—
Specific gravity (apparent) at 20/20°C.	0.9663	0.9311	0.9019	1.1094	0.8954	0.8859	1.018	0.960
Δsp.gr./Δt	0.00092	0.00090	0.00083	0.00085	0.00080	0.00078	—	—
Specific heat at 20°C., cal./g./°C.	0.534	0.555	0.583	—	—	—	—	—
Vapor pressure at 20°C., mm.	6.2	3.8	0.6	0.03	0.17	0.02	—	—
Viscosity (absolute) at 20°C., cp.	1.7	2.1	6.4	30.5	5.9	7.5	95(25)	410(25)

[a] "Synthetic Organic Chemicals," 14th Ed., Philadelphia, Sharples Chemicals, Inc., 1946.

alcohols such as esterification with organic and inorganic acids (see page 128), oxidation or dehydrogenation, dehydration, formation of acetals with aldehydes, and addition of acrylonitrile. When dehydrogenated in the vapor phase, ethylene glycol monomethyl ether yields methoxy acetaldehyde, which can be further oxidized to methoxy acetic acid[29]. Formal type condensation products are produced in the usual manner by condensing glycol monoethers with formaldehyde, paraldehyde, or other aldehydes[30, 31]. The addition of acrylonitrile to ethylene glycol monoallyl ether gives 3-(2-allyloxyethoxy) propionitrile[32]. A large number of ethylene glycol ether urethanes have been prepared and examined for their narcotic properties[33, 34]. None of these appeared to be superior to urethane itself as a narcotic or hypnotic.

Because of their ether linkage, the glycol monoethers show a slight tendency to deteriorate on storage due to the formation of peroxides. This deterioration is prevented by the addition of small quantities of a hydroxyalkylamine, such as triethanolamine, or certain metals, such as copper, aluminum, chromium, or nickel[35, 36].

Applications

Ethylene glycol monoethers—notably the methyl, ethyl, and butyl ethers—are widely used in the protective coatings industry. They act as solvents in lacquer and thinner formulations and are components of quick drying varnishes and enamels[37, 38, 39, 40, 41, 42]. These same compounds are used in the textile industry for dyeing and printing[43]. They also act as coupling agents in dry cleaning soaps, soluble oils, metal-cutting compositions, and insecticide mixtures[44]. With higher ketones, water, and an amine soap, they form compositions which are effective for removing sludge deposits from internal combustion engines[45]. These glycol ethers are also solvents for nonaqueous wood stains[46, 47], and for dyestuffs used on leather, in printing inks, and for miscellaneous materials[48, 49, 50, 51].

Ethylene glycol monomethyl ether is widely used for sealing moistureproof cellophane[52, 53]. It has been employed as a nonaqueous solvent for the potentiometric titration of the acidity of materials insoluble in water[54]. It has also been suggested as an entrainer in the azeotropic distillation of styrene obtained by the catalytic dehydrogenation of ethylbenzene or from the coking of coal[55, 56].

Ethylene glycol monoethyl ether has been successfully used in place of ethyl alcohol as a dehydrating agent in histological and cytological work[57]. This ether and the ethyl ether of diethylene glycol, when present to the extent of 0.005 to 0.045 per cent, are effective aids in the hydraulic grinding of cement clinker[58].

Tertiary butyl and isopropyl ethylene glycol ethers, as well as similar glycol diethers, are claimed to be anti-knock agents for liquid fuels in the gasoline boiling range[59].

In combination with tritolyl phosphate and tributyl phosphate, ethylene glycol monobenzyl ether forms a synthetic low-temperature, high-temperature lubricant which functions well in the temperature range from -90 to $150°F.$[60]. A combination of the same ether, tritolyl phosphate, and triethylene glycol dihexanoate has been patented as a lubricant for gyro instruments for aircraft[61].

Ethylene glycol monophenyl ether, known as "Phenoxethol," has been found to have a high bacteriostatic and bactericidal effect in infections with *Pseudomonas pyocyaneus*[62, 63, 64, 65]. It can be used alone or in combination with quaternary ammonium germicides. It is also claimed to be useful in the treatment of pediculosis, being effective against both nits and adult lice. The same ether is also sold commercia'ly as a fixative in perfumes under the name "Arosol"[66].

Substituted ethylene glycol phenyl ethers—such as the 2-hydroxy-3-chlorobiphenyl and the *p-tert*-butylphenyl ethers—are useful as insecticidal compounds[67]. Ethylene glycol 2,4-dichlorophenyl ether[68] has been tested for various insecticidal and botanical applications[69, 70]. It possesses about 75 per cent of the activity of 2,4-dichlorophenoxy acetic acid (2,4-D) as a growth regulating substance when tested for its inhibiting action against germinating corn[71].

The di-*tert*-amylphenyl and *p-tert*-amylphenyl ethers have been found to be excellent foam inhibitors when employed in amounts ranging from 0.01 to 0.05 per cent of the solution[72].

DIETHERS

The dialkyl ethers of ethylene glycol are colorless liquids with ethereal odors. Physical properties of three of these compounds are listed in Table 6.2.

The dialkyl ethers of ethylene glycol are obtained to some extent as by-products in the reaction of ethylene oxide with monohydric alcohols in the presence of sulfuric acid as a catalyst. However, they are prepared to advantage by reacting the sodium alcoholate of an ethylene glycol ether with an alkyl halide

$$
\begin{array}{ccccc}
CH_2OH & & CH_2ONa & & CH_2OR' \\
| & \xrightarrow{Na} & | & \xrightarrow{R'X} & | \\
CH_2OR & & CH_2OR & & CH_2OR
\end{array}
$$

or by reacting dialkyl sulfate with the ethylene glycol monoalkyl ether

$$
\begin{array}{ccc}
CH_2OH & & CH_2OR' \\
| & \xrightarrow{R_2'SO_4} & | \\
CH_2OR & & CH_2OR
\end{array}
$$

TABLE 6.2. PHYSICAL PROPERTIES OF ETHYLENE GLYCOL DIETHERS

	Ethylene Glycol Diether		
	Dimethyl	Diethyl	Dibutyl
Boiling point, °C., at 760 mm.	85.2	121.4	203.3
at 50 mm.	16	49	117
at 10 mm.	−14	20	84
Δb.p./Δp, °C./mm.	0.042	0.044	0.052
Coefficient of expansion at 20°C.	0.00127	0.00121	0.00100
at 55°C.	0.00131	0.00126	0.00105
Flash point (open cup), °F.	40	95	185
Freezing point, °C.	−71.0	−74.0	−69.1
Heat of vaporization, Btu/lb.	161	178	118
Molecular weight	90.12	118.17	174.28
Refractive index, n_D at 20°C.	—	1.3922	1.4131
$\Delta n_D/\Delta t$	—	—	0.00043
Solubility in water at 20°C., % by wt.	∞	21.0	0.2
Solubility of water in, at 20°C., % by wt.	∞	3.4	0.6
Specific gravity (apparent) at 20/20°C.	0.8692	0.8417	0.8374
Δsp.gr./Δt	0.00109	0.00102	0.00085
Specific heat at 20°C., cal./g./°C.	—	—	0.48
Vapor pressure at 20°C., mm.	61.2	9.4	0.2
Viscosity (absolute) at 20°C., cp.	—	0.7	1.3

Because of their combination of hydrocarbon and ether groups, the dialkyl ethers of ethylene glycol are stable compounds, useful as inert reaction media. They are excellent mutual solvents, and when added to colloidal systems such as detergents and wetting agents of limited solubility, they permit dilution with water with less tendency to gel or cloud.

DIOXANE

Dioxane is a cyclic diether with the structural formula

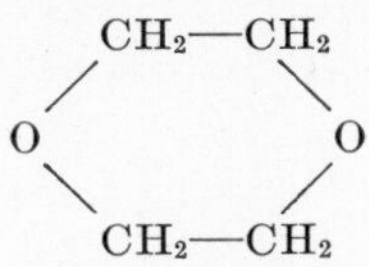

$$
\begin{array}{c}
CH_2 \!-\! CH_2 \\
/ \qquad \backslash \\
O \qquad\qquad O \\
\backslash \qquad / \\
CH_2 \!-\! CH_2
\end{array}
$$

Also known as diethylene-1,4-dioxide, it has unusual solvent powers because of the two ether-oxygen atoms in the molecule.

Preparation

Dioxane was first prepared in 1863 by Lourenco,[73] who heated ethylene glycol with ethylene dibromide in sealed tubes for several days at 160°C.[73] At about the same time, Wurtz[74] obtained it by treating the dibromide of dioxane with hydrogen sulfide or mercury at room temperature. The dibromide of dioxane resulted from the reaction of one mol of bromine with two mols of ethylene oxide at low temperatures[75].

More modern and commercially feasible methods for the production of dioxane include: (a) the dehydration of ethylene glycol, polyethylene glycols, or their ethers using catalysts such as sulfuric acid, hydrochloric acid, zinc chloride, phosphoric acid, benzenesulfonic acid, or ferrous sulfate[76, 77, 78, 79, 80, 81]; (b) the dimerization of ethylene oxide in the vapor phase over catalysts such as sodium sulfate, aluminum sulfate, acid phosphates, or aluminum hydrosilicate[82, 83]; and (c) the reaction of bis(2-chloroethyl) ether or 2-chloroethyl-2'-hydroxyethyl ether with strong aqueous sodium hydroxide[84, 85]. Dreyfus[86] has claimed the production of dioxane and its homologs by passing aldehydes such as formaldehyde or acetaldehyde over catalysts favoring etherification reactions. Among these are mentioned sulfuric acid, ferric chloride, benzenesulfonic acid, phosphoric acid, and acid phosphates.

Properties

Dioxane is a colorless, mobile liquid of mild, not unpleasant, odor. It is completely miscible with water and is a solvent for most resins, waxes, oils, and organic and inorganic compounds[87, 88]. Its physical properties are listed in Table 6.3. From considerations of the Raman spectrum, dipole moment, and electron-diffraction, the plane, chair, and boat forms have been proposed for the structure of the dioxane ring[89, 90, 91].

Dioxane forms a minimum boiling azeotrope with water at 87.8°C. and atmospheric pressure. It contains 81.6 per cent dioxane by weight. At 260

TABLE 6.3. PHYSICAL PROPERTIES OF DIOXANE

Boiling point at 760 mm.	101.3°C.
at 50 mm.	31°C.
Δb.p./Δp	0.043°C./mm.
Coefficient of expansion at 20°C.	0.00108/°C.
at 55°C.	0.00113/°C.
Flash point (open cup)	65°F.
Freezing point	11.8°C.
Heat of vaporization	177 Btu/lb.
Molecular weight	88.10
Refractive index, n_D at 20°C.	1.4224
$\Delta n_D/\Delta t$	0.00058
Specific gravity (apparent) at 20/20°C.	1.0356
Δsp.gr./Δt	0.00112
Specific heat at 20°C.	0.410 cal./g.
Vapor pressure at 20°C.	29 mm.
Viscosity (absolute) at 20°C.	1.3 cp.

mm. this azeotrope boils at 60°C. and contains 84.6 per cent dioxane by weight. Physical properties of the system have been studied[92, 93].

Dioxane shows the characteristic inert properties of aliphatic ethers. It is stable in the presence of acids, alkalies, metallic sodium, ammonia, or mild oxidizing agents. However, because of its ether linkages and hygroscopicity, dioxane forms peroxides, acetaldehyde, ethylene acetal, and acidic materials on standing. Consequently, when used as a solvent in precise physical measurements or in processes where these impurities would be deleterious, it must be carefully purified and then protected from moisture and air. Under these conditions it is stable indefinitely. For most purposes where the concentration of aldehydes is relatively low, treatment of dioxane with sodium hydroxide and sodium is sufficient[94, 95, 96]. Aldehydes, when present in appreciable quantities, can be first destroyed by treatment with a volatile inorganic acid such as hydrochloric, hydrobromic, or sulfurous[96, 97, 98, 99]. Peroxides can be removed by passage of the liquid through columns of activated alumina[100].

When thermally decomposed at temperatures between 459 and 534°C. under pressures between 50 and 600 mm, dioxane decomposes according to the equation

$$C_4H_8O_2 \rightarrow 2CO + C_2H_6 + H_2$$

The reaction velocity is practically independent of the ratio of surface to volume in the reaction vessel[101, 102].

Dioxane is oxidized by potassium permanganate to oxalic acid and carbon dioxide. Heating dioxane with hydrogen iodide at 140°C. gives iodine, ethyl iodide, and acetic acid[103].

Under the proper conditions the dioxane ring can be ruptured by acid anhydrides or acid chlorides to yield the corresponding diesters of ethylene glycol or diethylene glycol. Macleod[104] has shown that ring cleavage occurs when dioxane reacts with acetic anhydride, the products being ethylene glycol diacetate and diethylene glycol diacetate. According to Varvoglis[105], ethylene glycol diacetate and ethylene glycol dibenzoate are formed by the reaction of dioxane with acetyl chloride and benzoyl chloride, respectively, in the presence of zinc.

By virtue of its ether linkages, dioxane forms addition complexes[106, 107, 108, 109, 110, 111, 112, 113, 114, 115, 116] with many organic and inorganic molecules. These oxonium compounds are usually well-defined crystalline materials of varying degrees of stability; some lose dioxane on heating or exposure to air while others can be sublimed unchanged. Many are dissociated into their components when dissolved in organic solvents. Typical examples of these dioxane addition compounds are the zinc, cadmium, and cobalt halide complexes $ZnCl_2 \cdot C_4H_8O_2$, $CdBr_2 \cdot C_4H_8O_2$, and $CoI_2 \cdot 3C_4H_8O_2$.

Dioxane reacts with one or two mols of sulfur trioxide to give compounds of the coordination type which are powerful and convenient sulfonating and sulfating reagents[117, 118, 119]. Thus, with benzene and naphthalene the corresponding sulfonic acids are formed.

Dioxane reacts with chlorine to give 2,3-dichlorodioxane[120]. On further chlorination four isomeric tetrachlorodioxanes are formed[121]. The reactions of 2,3-dichlorodioxane have been studied[122, 123, 124, 125, 126, 127].

Toussaint and MacDowell[128] report an unusual transformation of dioxane involving its simultaneous reaction with chlorine and ethylene. In this reaction the dioxane ring is broken, producing as the principal product triethylene glycol dichloride ($ClCH_2CH_2OC_2H_4OC_2H_4Cl$) along with smaller quantities of bis(2-chloroethyl) ether. Homologous compounds are similarly obtained from dioxane, chlorine, and propylene or higher olefins.

Applications

Dioxane has excellent solvent properties for cellulose nitrate, cellulose acetate, cellulose ethers, natural resins including the oil- and alcohol-soluble types, vegetable and mineral oils, and oil-soluble dyes. Accordingly, it has been suggested for use as a solvent in the manufacture of lacquers containing cellulose esters or ethers, as a degreasing and wool scouring agent, and as a component of dye baths[129, 130, 131, 132, 133]. Actual utilization has been limited, however, because of the toxicological hazards involved (see page 315).

Dioxane is reported to be an efficient selective solvent for unsaturated hydrocarbons[134], being used, for instance, in the separation of acetylene from other gases[135]. It is claimed to be an effective solvent for the purification of aspirin by recrystallization[136]. Dioxane also serves as a solvent in the determination of molecular weights[137, 138, 139, 140], but because of its highly hygroscopic nature and slow decomposition with time, dioxane of unquestionable purity must be used in order to obtain results that are reliable[141].

According to Adkins[142], there is no solvent more useful than dioxane as a medium for the catalytic hydrogenation of organic compounds. Its chief disadvantages lie in the difficulty of separating it from liquids boiling below 150°C. and *its instability over Raney nickel at temperatures above 200°C.* A number of explosions during hydrogenation have been attributed to this property with the result that dioxane is seldom recommended for this use.

Dioxane was first employed in place of alcohols and clearing oils used in paraffin embedding and the staining of tissue sections by Graupner and Weissberger[143] in 1931. Since then, the Dioxane Technic has been critically investigated, and the use of dioxane for this purpose has been firmly established[144, 145, 146, 147].

ACETALS AND KETALS

Ethylene glycol condenses with aldehydes and ketones in the presence of acidic catalysts to form 1,3-dioxolane and its homologs.

(5)   (1)
CH_2——O R_1
       (2)
       C
CH_2——O R_2
(4)   (3)

In the above formula, R_1 and R_2 may be hydrogen or alkyl or aryl groups, depending on the carbonyl compound used in the condensation process.

Preparation

1,3-Dioxolane, the simplest of these cyclic diethers, was first described by Trillat and Cambier[148], who obtained it by heating ethylene glycol with paraformaldehyde in the presence of anhydrous ferric chloride. Verley[149] prepared it by heating ethylene glycol with aqueous formaldehyde in the presence of phosphoric acid. Similar processes employing other acidic catalysts such as sulfuric acid have been patented[150, 151, 152].

1,3-Dioxolanes substituted in the 2-position are prepared by condensing glycols with aldehydes or ketones in the presence of acidic catalysts:

CH_2OH + CH_3CHO → CH_2—O
                                        CH—CH_3 + H_2O
CH_2OH CH_2—O

Ethylene glycol   *Acetaldehyde*   *2-Methyl-1,3-dioxolane*

In the case of the higher boiling carbonylic compounds, a solvent such as benzene or toluene can be used as an entraining agent to remove the water of reaction[153, 154, 155, 156]. 2-(2-Haloalkyl)-1,3-dioxolanes are formed by condensing glycols with unsaturated aldehydes, such as acrolein and crotonaldehyde, by the action of a hydrogen halide[157, 158]. Other general methods for the preparation of 2-substituted dioxolanes include the reaction of ethylene oxide with aldehydes and ketones (see page 104) and the addition of acetylene and substituted acetylenes to ethylene glycol:

                                   $H_{11}C_5$ O—CH_2
                     CH_2OH
C_5H_{11}—$C\equiv CH$ +   → C
                     CH_2OH
                                     H_3C O—CH_2

Amylacetylene   *Ethylene*   *2-Amyl-2-methyl-1,3-*
                        glycol   *dioxolane*

In the latter reaction mercuric oxide, mercuric sulfate, sulfuric acid, and boron trifluoride have been used as catalysts[159, 160, 161, 162, 163].

2-Ethoxy-1,3-dioxolane can be prepared by the reaction of ethyl orthoformate with ethylene glycol in the presence of toluenesulfonic acid. From this compound the corresponding 2-menthyloxy and 2-bornyloxy derivatives were obtained by reaction with menthol and borneol, respectively, using the same catalyst[164].

2-Hydroxymethyl-1,3-dioxolane can be produced by the simultaneous dehydrogenation and dehydration of ethylene glycol in the vapor phase at 200 to 350°C. over a supported copper-chromium catalyst[165]:

$$2\ \begin{array}{c} CH_2OH \\ | \\ CH_2OH \end{array} \rightarrow \begin{array}{c} CH_2-O \\ \\ CH_2-O \end{array}\!\!\!\!\!\Bigg\rangle CH-CH_2OH \ + \ H_2 \ + \ H_2O$$

Ethylene glycol   *2-Hydroxymethyl-1,3-dioxolane*

The product is the cyclic acetal of glycolic aldehyde and ethylene glycol.

Interesting cyclic acetals are obtained when ethylene glycol reacts with dialdehydes. For example, ethylene glycol reacts with glyoxal to yield 1,4,5,8-naphthodioxane:

$$2\ \begin{array}{c} CH_2OH \\ | \\ CH_2OH \end{array} + \begin{array}{c} CHO \\ | \\ CHO \end{array} \rightarrow \begin{array}{ccc} & O \quad\quad O & \\ H_2C & CH & CH_2 \\ | & | & | \\ H_2C & CH & CH_2 \\ & O \quad\quad O & \end{array} + \ 2H_2O$$

Ethylene glycol   *Glyoxal*   *1,4,5,8-Napthodioxane*

This substance, which exists in two stereoisomeric forms, also can be synthesized from 2,3-dichlorodioxane and ethylene glycol[166].

Properties

The physical properties of some representative 2-substituted 1,3-dioxolanes are presented in Table 6.4. 1,3-Dioxolane itself is a limpid, colorless liquid, completely miscible with water. The water solubility of the 2-substitued 1,3-dioxolanes decreases with increasing length of the carbon chain of the substituents in the 2-position. The lower members of the 1,3-dioxolane series are considerably more volatile than ethylene glycol and have excellent solvent properties for natural and synthetic resins and cellulose esters.

TABLE 6.4. PHYSICAL PROPERTIES OF 2-SUBSTITUTED 1,3-DIOXOLANES

Compound	Boiling Point at 760 mm., °C.	Specific Gravity, 20/20°C.	Refractive Index, n_D at 20°C.	Melting Point, °C.	Ref.
1,3-Dioxolane	74–75	1.065	—	−95	167
2-Methyl	81–82	0.982	—	—	159
2-Ethyl	105	0.954 (25/20)	—	—	
2-Propyl	130–131	0.943	—	—	
2-(1-Ethylpentyl)	202	0.913	—	—	
2-Ethoxy	120–123	1.053 (20/4)	1.4000	—	164
2-Chloromethyl	57 (13)	—	—	—	168
2-Bromomethyl	175	—	—	—	154
2-p-Nitrophenyl	—	—	—	89–89.5	169
2-Furfuryl	87 (9)	—	—	—	170
2,2-Dimethyl	92.5	0.9417 (20/4)	1.4000	—	171
2-Methyl-2-ethyl	118–118.5	0.9353 (20/4)	1.4110	—	156, 171
2-Methyl-2-propyl	140–140.5	0.9246 (20/4)	1.4174	—	171
2-Methyl-2-phenyl	88–89 (11)	0.8970 (20/4)	1.4289	—	156
2-Methyl-2-butyl	62–63 (20)	0.922 (21/4)	1.4232 (21°)	—	161
2-Butyl-2-amyl	103–105 (10)	0.8862 (25/25)	1.4339 (25°)	—	162
2-Methyl-2-acetyl	75–77 (17)	—	—	—	172
2,2-Dipropyl	172.5–174	—	—	—	153

Like other acetals 1,3-dioxolanes are fairly stable under alkaline conditions, but in the presence of dilute acids they hydrolyze rapidly to their components. Because of their ether linkages, 1,3-dioxolane and its polymers deteriorate when exposed to air due to the formation of peroxides. They may be stabilized by the addition of antioxidants, such as hydroquinone, p-aminophenol, diphenylamine, and condensation products of aromatic amines with carbonylic compounds[173].

The dioxolane ring can be split with acid anhydrides to form ethylene glycol diesters[174]. Acid chlorides react to give viscous, high molecular weight polyethers claimed to be useful in the textile and rubber industries[175]. Friedel-Crafts type catalysts polymerize them to polyethers which can be employed as intermediates for surface-active agents[176]. Unsaturated compounds, such as ethylene, copolymerize to form waxes useful as paper sizes, moistureproofing agents, and constituents of wax polishes[177, 178, 179, 180].

GLYOXAL

Oxidation of ethylene glycol leads to a variety of products such as acetaldehyde, glyoxal, formaldehyde, glycolic acid, and oxalic acid, depending on the nature of the oxidizing agent and the reaction conditions. Although it was thought for many years that the principal products of ethylene glycol oxidation in the animal body were glycolic acid and oxalic acid[181], more recent work shows that only very small amounts of the latter are formed[182, 183].

The dialdehyde glyoxal, CHO—CHO, is one of the most important of the ethylene glycol oxidation products. It can be produced by the careful oxidation of ethylene glycol, ethanol, or acetaldehyde with nitric acid[184, 185] or by the saponification of acetylene tetrachloride with fuming sulfuric acid[186]. Glyoxal is obtained commercially by the vapor-phase oxidation of ethylene glycol over a supported copper catalyst[187, 188]:

$$\begin{array}{ccccc}
CH_2OH & & & CHO & \\
| & + & O_2 \rightarrow & | & + \quad 2H_2O \\
CH_2OH & & & CHO &
\end{array}$$

Properties

Pure glyoxal is a yellow crystalline solid which melts at 15°C., boils at 51°C., and has a specific gravity of 1.14 at 20/4°C. The commercial product is supplied as a 30 per cent aqueous solution which contains small amounts of chemically related substances such as ethylene glycol, formaldehyde, formic acid, and glycolic acid.

Glyoxal undergoes most of the reactions typical of aldehydes. It will reduce mildly alkaline solutions of silver salts such as Tollen's reagent, precipitating a metallic mirror. Reaction with two mols of sodium bisulfite yields a characteristic addition product, and diacetals and tetra-acetals may be formed by reaction with alcohols. Condensations occur with compounds containing reactive hydrogen atoms such as hydroxylamine, ammonia, amines, and hydrocyanic acid. High molecular weight compounds are formed by condensing glyoxal with phenols, aromatic amines, urea, or melamine. Glyoxal can be oxidized to formic acid or, under controlled conditions, to glyoxalic acid. When mixed with dilute alkali, it is converted almost immediately to a solution of the glycolic acid salt, or if an aqueous glyoxal solution is subjected to prolonged heating under pressure, a solution of free glycolic acid is formed.

When an aqueous solution of pure glyoxal at pH of 4 to 5 is distilled at 60°C. under a pressure of 150 mm., a solid still residue remains which is a mixture of polymers $(C_2H_2O_2)_n \cdot (H_2O)_m$, where n averages 3 to 4[189]. The combined water is within one mol of the same value as n. These polymers are converted largely to the monomer upon heating or dissolving in a sufficient amount of cold water. Polymerized glyoxal may also be depolymerized by boiling with anethole, phenetole, safrole, methyl nonyl ketone, benzaldehyde, or acetic anhydride[190].

Polymeric glyoxal is often referred to as "trimeric glyoxal." The constitution of "trimeric glyoxal" has been the subject of a discussion between

Raudnitz[191] and Dyson[192]. The former suggested the formula of 2,3,6,7-tetrahydroxy-1,4,5,8-naphthodioxane, partly because it forms a diisopropylidene compound[193] from three mols of glyoxal and two mols of acetone. This derivative contains neither hydroxyl nor keto groups and decomposes into its components upon heating with mineral acids. Dyson contested the naphthodioxane formula. He proposed instead a quinone formula because of the compound's ready conversion to tetrahydroxyquinone by atmospheric oxidation in alkaline solution[194]. Reduction of tetrahydroxyquinone to inositol is readily carried out by the use of palladium and hydrogen.

Raudnitz defended his proposed naphthodioxane structure with the evidence that the diisopropylidene compound gives no reactions for carbonyl, for phenolic —OH, or for unsaturation. He claimed also that the quinone formula does not explain the ready depolymerization of "trimeric glyoxal." He explained the formation of tetrahydroxyquinone as due to depolymerization, then condensation under mild alkaline conditions to hexahydroxybenzene[195], which is easily oxidized to tetrahydroxybenzoquinone[196].

Applications

The industrial utilization of glyoxal is largely based on the advantage which may be taken of its two aldehyde groups, its lack of volatility from the aqueous solution, and its inoffensive odor. The uses of commercially available aqueous glyoxal solutions have been reviewed[188, 197].

Insolubilization of protein matter[198, 199, 200] such as animal glue, gelatine, casein, zein, or albumin with glyoxal depends on the ability of glyoxal to react with the amino and imino groups of the protein. This property of glyoxal, as well as its ability to combine with hydroxyl groups, makes it a valuable agent for modifying certain animal and synthetic fibers. Thus, glyoxal enters into an important process for the stabilization of rayon that results in the elimination of excessive shrinkage or stretch[201]. Glyoxal reacts with urea in the presence of hydrochloric acid to form acetylene diureine, which condenses with formaldehyde to yield resins useful for such purposes. Likewise, the treatment of wool with glyoxal and glyoxal bisulfite modifies the fiber to allow it to resist dyes[202].

Water-soluble hydroxyethyl cellulose is capable of reaction with glyoxal to provide water-resistant films[203]. By condensing urea with glyoxal in the presence of water-soluble cellulose ethers or other highly polymeric carbohydrates, water-soluble colloidal products are obtained. These are useful as adhesives, binding, thickening, impregnating, and dressing agents, or as additives to soap and washing agents[204, 205].

Plastic compositions containing polyvinyl partial acetal resins may be modified by adding 2 to 30 per cent of glyoxal to their solutions and then evaporating them[206]. This has the effect of raising their melting points and rendering them water-insoluble.

A process for improving the wet tensile and wet rub strength of paper has been developed[200]. It comprises sizing the paper by applying animal glue to the surface and subsequently treating the sized paper with an aqueous glyoxal solution.

Resins that harden on heating may be prepared by refluxing glyoxal, or substances generating it, with furfuryl alcohol or its resins in aqueous acid solutions[207]. Formaldehyde condenses with glyoxal diureine (glycoluril) in the presence of alcohol to give resins which are likewise capable of being hardened[208]. Hard, tough resins are also prepared by refluxing aqueous glyoxal with ketones, such as methyl ethyl ketone[209]. They may be used as baking lacquers alone or in combination with other resins, such as those of the alkyd type.

ESTERS

Organic Esters

Ethylene glycol esters of organic acids can be prepared by the conventional methods employed for esterifying acids with primary alcohols[210]. These include the acid-catalyzed reaction of ethylene glycol with acids, acid anhydrides, and acid chlorides, interchange reactions between ethylene glycol and organic esters and amides, and the reaction of ethylene dihalides with metallic salts of acids. Mono- or diesters are formed, depending on the molar ratio of acid to ethylene glycol employed. More specialized procedures include the addition of ethylene oxide to acids[211, 212] and the cleavage of the dioxane ring with acid anhydrides or acid chlorides[104, 105, 213].

The mono- and diesters of simple organic acids are easily distillable liquids with relatively high solvent power. Physical properties of the ethylene glycol esters of the more common organic acids are summarized in Table 6.5. Of the lower members of the series, ethylene glycol diformate and ethylene glycol diacetate are available commercially. Ethylene glycol diformate is a colorless liquid completely soluble in water, in which it slowly hydrolyzes to produce formic acid. Hence, its use has been suggested in reactions and processes where a gradual release of formic acid is desirable. Ethylene glycol diacetate is similar to glyceryl triacetate except that it is slightly more volatile. In the absence of water it is quite stable and is useful as a fairly high-boiling, slow-evaporating solvent in cellulose ester printing inks and lacquers. It is a solvent for fluorinated refrigerant gases and can be used in solvent mixtures for the refining of lubricating oils and for the removal of free fatty acids from oils and fats.

A number of ethylene glycol diesters are described in the patent literature as plasticizers for nitrocellulose, cellulose acetate, cellulose ethers, and

TABLE 6.5. PHYSICAL PROPERTIES OF COMMON ETHYLENE GLYCOL ESTERS

Ethylene Glycol Ester	Boiling Point at 760 mm., °C.	Melting Point, °C.	Specific Gravity, 20/20°C.	Refractive Index, n_D at 20°C.	Ref.
Monoesters					
Formate	119–180.5		1.1989 (15/4)		214
Acetate	182.0		1.106	1.4224	
Butyrate	220.0				215
Benzoate	173.0 (21)		1.0937 (15/15)		216
Salicylate	172.0 (12)	37	1.2537 (15/15)		216
Diesters					
Diformate	177.1		1.2277	1.4153	
Diacetate	190.5		1.1063	1.4159	
Dipropionate	210.3		1.0484		
Dibutyrate	240.0		1.024 (15/15)		217
Dibenzoate		73			218
Disalicylate		83			219

natural and synthetic resins. Among these are butoxyethoxyacetate[220], acetylglycolate[221], haloaryloxyacetates[222], aryloxyacetates[223], and phenoxy-acetoxyacetate[224].

A series of glycol carbonate esters having the general formulas $ROCOOC_2H_4OCOOR$ and $[ROCOOC_2H_4O]_2CO$ is derived from ethylene glycol and phosgene or chlorocarbonic acid esters[225, 226, 227]. The reaction products are high-boiling esters claimed to be useful as plasticizers, solvents, resin intermediates, and heat transfer media.

The preparation, properties, and industrial uses of the ethylene glycol esters of fatty acids from C_{12} to C_{20} have been thoroughly discussed by Goldsmith[228] in a paper on the polyhydric alcohol esters of fatty acids. Table 6.6, taken from Goldsmith's review, presents the available data on the physical properties of some of the more common fatty acid esters. These compounds, particularly the partially esterified glycols because of their position between hydrophilic and lyophilic materials, have interface modifying properties. Consequently, they are useful as emulsifying, stabilizing, dispersing, wetting, foaming, and suspending agents. In most cases they are not used alone but as auxiliary agents along with other surface-active materials[229, 230, 231, 232, 233, 234, 235, 236, 237, 238, 239, 240, 241, 242, 243].

Inorganic Esters

Inorganic esters of the glycols may be prepared by procedures completely analogous to those employed to produce the corresponding esters of the monohydric aldohols. The refining of the glycol derivatives is not easily accomplished, especially in the case of the dibasic or polybasic inorganic acids, because of the low volatility and thermal instability of the esters.

TABLE 6.6. PHYSICAL PROPERTIES OF ETHYLENE GLYCOL ESTERS OF SOME COMMON FATTY ACIDS

Glycol Ester	Melting Point, °C.	Boiling Point at 0 mm., °C.	Density at Melting Point, g./ml.	Refractive Index
Monesters				
Laurate	27.5			1.4440
Margarate (heptadecanoate)	50.2; 53.2			
Palmitate	47.5; 48; 49; 51–52.5; 51.5		0.8786	1.4411
Stearate	56; 58.5		0.8780	1.4310
Oleate	1	190–200 (0.05)		1.4600 (27)
Diesters				
Dilaurate	49; 52; 54	188		
Dimyristate	63; 64	208		
Dimargarate (heptadecanoate)	65.5; 70.4		0.8605	1.4392
Dipalmitate	65; 68.7–68.9; 69; 70; 70.5; 72	226	0.8594	1.4378
Distearate	73; 75–76.5; 75.8; 76; 77; 79	241	0.8581	1.4385
Dioleate		183–185 (3)	0.90 (25°C.)	1.4492 (70)

Ethylene Glycol Dinitrate. Ethylene glycol dinitrate represents the largest industrial outlet for ethylene glycol with the exception of anti-freeze compostions (see Chapter 4, "Commercial Applications of Ethylene Glycol"). It is used in conjunction with nitroglycerin in high explosives (dynamites and permissible explosives) as a low-freezing ingredient, the amounts constituting about 25 per cent of the oil. Such mixtures have lower freezing points than those made with mixtures of nitroglycerin and nitropolyglycerin and are safer for use under ordinary winter conditions[244, 245, 246, 247, 248, 249].

Preparation

In 1869, Kekule[250] passed ethylene through a cooled mixture of concentrated sulfuric and nitric acids and obtained an unstable oil which he formulated as ethylene glycol nitrate-nitrite. Later, Wieland and Sakellarios[251] demonstrated that this product was a mixture of ethylene glycol dinitrate and the nitric acid ester of 2-nitroethyl alcohol.

Pure ethylene glycol dinitrate was first prepared and characterized by Henry[252], who carefully introduced ethylene glycol into a mixture of sulfuric acid and nitric acid cooled to 0°C. Similar procedures have been described by Champion[253] and Nef[254]. Other methods described for its production include the nitration of ethylene glycol[255], ethylene oxide[256], sulfoglycol, $SO_2(OCH_2)_2$[257], mixtures of glycols[258], ethylene[259], or the condensation product of ethylene glycol with nitrochlorobenzene[260]. It has also been produced by the electrolysis of mixtures of the salts of various dibasic organic acids and nitrates[261, 262, 263, 264].

The ethylene glycol dinitrate used by Rinkenbach[244, 245, 246, 247] for determining physical properties was prepared by slowly adding 20 g. of ethylene glycol to a mixture of 70 g. of nitric acid (specific gravity 1.42) and 130 g. of sulfuric acid (specific gravity 1.84) at a temperature of 23°C. Forty-nine grams of the dinitrate separated. After washing with 300 cc. of water in small portions, 39.6 g. of acid-free material remained. The low yield so obtained could be improved by maintaining a lower temperature and using a different nitrating mixture. Analysis of the product after standing in a sulfuric acid desiccator for four months gave a nitrogen content of 18.37 per cent (theoretical, 18.43 per cent).

Physical and Explosive Properties

Pure ethylene glycol dinitrate is a colorless, mobile liquid at ordinary temperatures. It is completely miscible with ether, benzene, toluene, acetone, carbon tetrachloride, chloroform, bromoform, aniline, nitrobenzene, glacial acetic acid, furfural, ethylene glycol diacetate, nitroglycerin, and methanol. In ethyl, isopropyl, and normal butyl alcohols it is less soluble as the molecular weight of the alcohol increases. It is immiscible or only slightly soluble in carbon disulfide, ethylene glycol, and glycerol. It is only slightly soluble in water but more so than nitroglycerin. Pure ethylene glycol dinitrate is practically nonhygroscopic[265].

The physical properties of ethylene glycol dinitrate are summarized in Table 6.7 and its explosive properties in Tables 6.8 and 6.9. Additional information is given in the text.

Sensitivity to Impact. Tests made by dropping a 500-gram weight on drops of the liquid showed that ethylene glycol dinitrate and nitroglycerin detonated when the weight fell distances of 110 and 70 cm., respectively[245].

Velocity of Detonation. With picric acid boosters and No. 8 detonators, the mean velocities of detonation of nitroglycerin and ethylene glycol dinitrate were found to be 8484 m./sec. and 8266 m./sec., respectively. With No. 8 detonators alone, values as low as 6000 to 7800 m./sec. were obtained[270].

The Effect of Substituting Ethylene Glycol Dinitrate in Permissible Explosives. Comparisons between samples of permissible explosive in which 25 per cent of the explosive oil had been replaced by 25 per cent of ethylene glycol dinitrate and samples in which no change had been made showed that the substitution does not have any marked effect on the properties of the explosive[248]. There are, however, certain well-marked tendencies

TABLE 6.7. PHYSICAL PROPERTIES OF ETHYLENE GLYCOL DINITRATE

		Ref.
Boiling point at 19 mm.	105.5°C.	250
at 760 mm.	114–116°C. (explodes)	266
Explosion temperature at 760 mm.	215°C. (approx.)	265
Freezing point	−22.3°C.	245
Heat of combustion at constant volume[a]	1763.9 cal./g.	245
at constant pressure	1752.5 cal./g.	
Heat of formation[b]	365.5 cal./g.	245
Magnetic rotation at 12.6°C.		267
Specific rotation	0.6686	
Molecular rotation	3.768	267
Refractive index, n_D at 20°C.	1.4473	245
Specific gravity at 15/15°C.	1.4962	245
at 20/15°C.	1.4890	
Vapor pressure at 20°C.[c]	0.0490 mm.	268
at 50°C.	0.665 mm.	
Viscosity at 20°C.[d]	0.0421 poises	269
at 50°C.	0.0214 poises	

[a] The heat of combustion of nitroglycerin
     at constant volume is 1630.4 cal./g.
     at constant pressure is 1622.1 cal./g.
[b] The heat of formation of nitroglycerin is 359.8 cal./g.
[c] The vapor pressure of nitroglycerin at 20°C. is 0.00038 mm.
                                      at 50°C. is 0.0081 mm.
[d] The viscosity of nitroglycerin at 20°C. is 0.360 poises
                                    at 50°C. is 0.0938 poises

TABLE 6.8. EXPLOSIVE CONSTANTS OF ETHYLENE GLYCOL DINITRATE AND
NITROGLYCERIN[245]

Compound	Tempera-ture of Explosion (t), °C.	Gas Produced from 1 Kg. at 760 mm., liters		Pressure When 1 Kg. is Exploded in 1 Liter, kg./sq. cm.	Energy Developed on Exploding 1 Kg., meter-kg.
		(0°C.)	(t)		
Ethylene glycol dinitrate	4209	736.93	12,099	12,498	695.7×10^6
Nitroglycerin	4177	715.53	11,663	12,048	647.8×10^6

which may be summarized as follows. The substitution of ethylene glycol dinitrate tends (1) to increase the rate of detonation, (2) to increase the sensitiveness by the halved cartridge method, (3) not to affect the unit deflective charge, and (4) not to affect the limit charge to an extent such that the samples containing ethylene glycol dinitrate should be considered any less safe for use in coal mines.

TABLE 6.9. SAND BOMB TESTS[245]

Charge of Mixture, grams	Explosive in Charge, grams	Sand Crushed by 0.300 g. Mercury Fulminate and	
		Nitroglycerin, grams	Glycol Dinitrate, grams
0.150	0.090	20.15	20.1
0.250	0.150	26.85	27.7
0.333	0.200	33.9	34.9
0.500	0.300	44.25	47.3
0.833	0.500	68.0	70.3

Mixtures of exactly 40 per cent of kieselguhr and 60 per cent of liquid explosive were made up, diluted with ether, and stirred until all the ether had been evaporated and an even mixture remained. Weighed charges of each of these mixtures were pressed into No. 8 detonator shells (0.300 gram of mercury fulminate was added in each case) and the whole was surmounted by a reinforcing cap. After being subjected to a pressure of 50 pounds (91,700 grams per square centimeter), the detonator was fired in the No. 2 standard test bomb. The amount of sand crushed was determined by sieving and weighing.

Ageing Properties. Studies on the relative ageing properties of gelatin dynamites containing nitroglycerin and ethylene glycol dinitrate showed that the propulsive strength is unaffected by age for both types of explosive[249]. With respect to detonation rates, the dynamites containing ethylene glycol dinitrate showed better ageing properties than straight nitroglycerin dynamites.

Miscellaneous. Ethylene glycol dinitrite (b.p. 96–98°C., specific gravity at 0°C. 1.2156) is a toxic liquid obtained by distilling glycerol trinitrite with somewhat more than the theoretical quantity of ethylene glycol[271]. It is insoluble in water, but reacts with ethanol to form ethyl nitrite. On standing, it decomposes to oxalic acid.

Ethylene glycol mononitrate, prepared from ethylene bromohydrin and silver nitrate[272], is a water-soluble liquid (specific gravity at 11°C. 1.31).

The mono- and disulfuric acid esters of ethylene glycol have been prepared by the reaction of ethylene glycol with sulfuric acid or chlorosulfonic acid. They are syrups which decompose in water to ethylene glycol and sulfuric acid[273, 274, 275].

Mono- and dithiosulfuric acid esters of ethylene glycol in the form of their sodium salts have been described by Purgotti[276]. He obtained them by reacting sodium thiosulfate with ethylene chlorohydrin and ethylene dichloride, respectively.

Ethylene glycol reacts with thionyl chloride to give the cyclic ester, ethylene glycol sulfite (b.p. at 38 mm. 86–88°C.)[277, 278]. Ethylene chlorohydrin and ethylene dichloride, which may be regarded loosely as esters, can be formed from ethylene glycol in classical ways, but since the products so obtained can be synthesized much more readily by other methods, these syntheses are of no commercial importance.

Ethylene glycol esters of phosphorous and phosphoric acids have been reported[279], and a number of such esters are claimed to be useful for reduction of tackiness and flammability in regenerated cellulose[280]. Bailly and Gaumé[281] describe the preparation of ethylene glycol monophosphate by reacting sodium hydrogen phosphate, Na_2HPO_4, with ethylene halohydrins. According to Atherton, Openshaw, and Todd[282], glycol monophosphate can also be prepared by the addition of ethylene oxide to sodium hydrogen phosphate. The general reaction of ethylene oxide with phosphorous and phosphoric acids has been described in the patent literature[283]. Although the products were not definitely characterized, they were reported to be useful as oil additives.

Cyclic esters of glycol obtained by the reaction of phenyl phosphonyl chloride on glycol are disclosed in a patent and are claimed to be useful as plasticizers and oil addition agents[284].

Trihydroxyethyl borate, a crystalline solid (m.p. 161.7°C.), has been obtained by reacting ethylene glycol with boron trichloride. It is hydrolyzed by water to ethylene glycol and boric acid[285]. Boron trifluoride readily combines with ethylene glycol to form a stable addition product[286]. When heated with boric acid or boric anhydride, ethylene glycol forms nonvolatile vitreous polymeric products[287, 288]. The ester obtained by reacting ethylene glycol with ammonium borate and boric acid is a viscous syrup containing suspended solid particles[289]. It is used in electrolytic condensers (see Chapter 4, "Commercial Applications of Ethylene Glycol"). Mixed organic orthoborates are obtained by reacting ethylene glycol and an alcohol or phenol with boric anhydride[290]. Thus, boric anhydride, cyclohexanol, and ethylene glycol give cyclohexyl ethylene borate (b.p. at 10 mm. 119°C.). On standing, these esters are transformed to vitreous polymers, probably through disproportionation.

Arsenious acid esters have been prepared by reacting ethylene glycol with arsenious acid in the presence of a water carrier[291]. A series of spirane-type derivatives has been obtained by the reaction of glycol with substituted arsonic acids[291].

ALKYD RESINS

Alkyd resins are polyesters prepared by reacting polyhydric alcohols with polybasic acids or their derivatives. Although glycerol is the polyhydric alcohol most commonly used in the preparation of alkyds, glycols are employed in the manufacture of soft resins or balsams useful for plasticizing nitrocellulose and other synthetic resins.

Glycol alkyd resins are obtained commercially by heating the glycol and a dibasic acid together at temperatures ranging from 180 to 250°C. under an inert atmosphere such as nitrogen. The reactions involved are simple esterification, with only minor side reactions[293, 294, 295, 296, 297, 298, 299, 300, 301, 302, 303]. Kinetics of the reactions using dibasic acids, anhydrides, acid chlorides, and esters have been studied[304].

These glycol alkyd resins are of two types: nonconvertible polyesters which remain thermoplastic and soluble on being heated or exposed to air; and convertible polyesters, which may become insoluble and infusible on heating or air drying. When the acid is bifunctional, nonconvertible resins are formed. When the acid has a functionality of three or more, convertible resins are formed.

Nonconvertible Alkyds

Either intermolecular reactions to form polymers or intramolecular reactions to form cyclic esters may occur when a glycol is reacted with a bifunctional acid. Five-membered rings are formed when the structural unit contains five atoms:

$$HOCH_2CH_2OH \; + \; C_2H_5O\overset{\overset{O}{\|}}{C}OC_2H_5 \; \rightarrow \quad \begin{array}{c} CH_2-O \\ | \qquad\qquad \diagdown \\ | \qquad\qquad\quad C=O \\ | \qquad\qquad \diagup \\ CH_2-O \end{array} \; + \; 2C_2H_5OH$$

Either a six-membered ring or a linear polymer is formed when the structural unit contains six atoms:

$$HOCH_2CH_2CH_2OH \; + \; C_2H_5O\overset{\overset{O}{\|}}{C}OC_2H_5 \; \rightarrow \quad \begin{array}{c} CH_2-O \\ \diagup \qquad\qquad \diagdown \\ CH_2 \qquad\qquad C=O \\ \diagdown \qquad\qquad \diagup \\ CH_2-O \end{array} \; + \; 2C_2H_5OH$$

$$-OCH_2CH_2CH_2O\overset{\overset{O}{\|}}{C}- \; + \; 2C_2H_5OH$$

Polymers are formed exclusively when the structural unit contains seven or more atoms:

$$HOCH_2CH_2CH_2CH_2OH \; + \; C_2H_5O\overset{\overset{O}{\|}}{C}OC_2H_5 \; \rightarrow$$

$$-OCH_2CH_2CH_2CH_2O\overset{\overset{O}{\|}}{C}- \; + \; 2C_2H_5OH$$

Larger cyclic esters, although not formed as primary products, can be obtained by depolymerizing polyesters under high vacuum at temperatures just below their decomposition points and in the presence of an alkaline ester interchange catalyst[305, 306]. Super polyesters with average molecular weight above 10,000 can be produced by heating polyesters with molecular weights up to 5000 in a molecular still[307]. With oxalic and malonic acids, the course of the esterification reaction is somewhat different, leading to the formation of glycol diformates and diacetates (see page 128) with the elimination of carbon dioxide[308].

A large number of nonconvertible polyesters have been prepared and studied by Carothers and his co-workers. The most outstanding property exhibited by many of the polyesters is crystallinity. Although this property is not highly developed, the polymers melt sharply and exhibit well-defined x-ray patterns. Crystallinity in polyester copolymers (from more than one glycol or dibasic acid) is less pronounced or fails to appear[309].

Production of nonconvertible linear glycol alkyds is small compared to that of the glycerol alkyds. Nonconvertible cyclic glycol polyesters are only of academic interest.

Convertible Alkyds

Alkyds prepared from acids with a functionality of three or more are convertible[293, 295, 296, 310, 311, 312, 313]. When the acid used is saturated (citric, tartaric, malic), the resin will convert with heat[314, 315, 316, 317]. When the acid used is unsaturated (maleic, fumaric), the resin will convert not only with heat but also by polymerization in the presence of benzoyl peroxide or by copolymerization in the presence of benzoyl peroxide and vinyl acetate, styrene, or other vinyl monomers[310, 318, 319, 320, 321, 322].

The unsaturated glycol polyesters are generally amorphous compounds whose properties vary according to the dibasic acid and the type and degree of modification. Linear polyesters with a low degree of modification may be more or less crystalline, but become noncrystalline when converted.

Ethylene Glycol Alkyds

Many types of ethylene glycol resins are produced commercially[323]. They were first used in 1932 when ethylene glycol appeared as a regular component of commercial alkyd varnish resins[324]. A 1:1 molar ratio of a glycol to pentaerythritol is equivalent to glycerol in functionality in the preparation of convertible-type polyesters. Such a replacement is of interest in periods of glycerol shortages, as during World War II. In normal times the practicality of this replacement would depend entirely on economics.

The most important ethylene glycol resins are the unsaturated polyesters. Polymerizable mixtures of a maleic or fumaric polyester of the glycol with vinyl monomers and a peroxide catalyst are useful as low-pressure laminating resins for glass, cloth, rayon, and paper[325]. Resins of this type were used in the United States during World War II in fabricating certain aircraft parts and a highly efficient body armor[326]. Another application is as an adhesive for cementing optical elements[327]. Polymerizable esters prepared from acrylic acid and substituted acrylic acids[328], glycol bis-allyl and methallyl carbonates[329], and glycol bis-allyl oxalate[330] find similar applications. Convertible polyesters that are modified with drying oil fatty acids[310, 315, 331] or with allyl or methallyl alcohol[332, 333, 334] are suitable for air-dry and baking coatings, adhesives, impregnants, and laminating resins. Fumarate resins formed in the presence of acyclic terpene adducts are useful for electrical insulating materials[335], as are also wire enamel resins from ethylene glycol and aryl polycarboxylic acids[336]. The use of polymerizable olefins such as styrene[337] and alloöcymene[335] along with polymerizable alkyds from glycol has been described.

Polyesters prepared from ethylene glycol, a long-chain dibasic acid, and maleic anhydride can be vulcanized to rubber-like products. "Paracon" rubber is an example of this type of material[338]. Other vulcanizable products have been prepared from ethylene glycol and polymerized linseed oil, soybean oil, and tall oil[339, 340, 341, 342, 343, 344]. These materials are soft and sticky but can be compounded on rubber rolls after partial curing. Although the products are inferior to natural rubber in tensile strength and elastic properties, they retain their elasticity at low temperatures and exhibit good resistance to oxidation. The compounded products may be calendered onto cloth and are suitable for molding operations. Rubber-like polymers can also be formed by vulcanizing a polyester derived from an ω-hydroxy aliphatic acid and a glycol ester of unsaturated dicarboxylic acid such as maleic and fumaric acids[345]. Leather-like materials have been reported from the reaction of a glycol, monoalkanolamine, and an aliphatic dicarboxylic acid[346]. Ethylene glycol polyesters of mercaptosuccinic acid are also useful in vulcanizable resins[347].

Adhesive products for incorporation into natural and synthetic resins are prepared by heating together rosin, triethanolamine, and an ethylene glycol-dimerized soybean oil acid polyester[348]. Among a group of commercially available rosin esters for use as plasticizers and in adhesives, lacquers, and enamels are "Flexalyn" C (ethylene glycol diabietate), "Stabelite" Ester No. 1 (ethylene glycol ester of hydrogenated rosin), and "Poly-pale" Ester No. 1 (ethylene glycol ester of polymerized rosin)[349].

Ethylene glycol ethers and esters of lac have been studied extensively as laminating resins[350, 351, 352, 353, 354] and as plasticizers[355]. They reportedly perform well as substitutes for conventional materials, but their dark color imposes a limitation on their practical applications.

The nonconvertible ethylene glycol polyesters are stabilized against marked changes in molecular weight by the addition of alkyl phosphite or alkyl phenyl phosphite esters[356]. A coating resistant to high octane gasoline consists of a cellulose ester and a polyester derived from ethylene glycol, glycerol, and succinic anhydride[357]. A synthetic textile fiber, known as "Dacron," is a super polymer prepared by condensing terephthalic acid or its derivatives with ethylene glycol or its derivatives[358, 359, 360, 361, 362, 363].

ETHER-ESTERS

A large number of ethylene glycol monoether-esters of mono- and polybasic organic and inorganic acids have been described in the literature. They are usually prepared by the esterification of ethylene glycol monoethers with acids, acid anhydrides, or acyl halides.

Physical properties of typical ether-esters of ethylene glycol are summarized in Table 6.10. The more volatile compounds have found use as solvents, while the higher boiling compounds have been employed as plasticizers, softening agents, resin solvents, and for a wide variety of applications.

TABLE 6.10. PHYSICAL PROPERTIES OF SOME COMMERCIAL ETHYLENE GLYCOL ETHER-ESTERS

	Ethylene Glycol Ether-Ester					
	Methyl Ether Acetate	Ethyl Ether Acetate	Butyl Ether Acetate	Phenyl Ether Acetate	Di(2-ethyl-butyl ether) Succinate	Di(hexyl ether) Adipate
Boiling point at 760 mm., °C.	144.5	156.4	191.5	259.7	decomposes	decomposes
at 50 mm., °C.	70	80	109	168	278	—
at 10 mm., °C.	37	49	76	131	234	265
Δb.p./Δp, °C./mm.	0.043	0.046	0.049	0.058	—	—
Coefficient of expansion at 20°C.	0.00109	0.00112	—	—	—	—
at 55°C.	0.00114	0.00117	—	—	—	—
Flash point (open cup), °F.	140	150	190	290	385	390
Freezing point, °C.	−65.1	−61.7	−64.6	−2.7	−80 (sets to a glass)	−3.1
Heat of vaporization, Btu/lb.	166	145	130	138	—	—
Molecular weight	118.13	132.16	160.21	180.20	374.50	402.56
Refractive index, n_D at 20°C.	1.4019	1.4058	1.4200	1.5076	1.4387	1.4460
$\Delta n_D/\Delta t$	—	0.00052	—	0.00043	0.00023	0.00033
Solubility in water at 20°C., % by wt.	∞	22.9	1.1	0.17	<0.01	<0.01
Solubility of water in, at 20°C. % by wt.	∞	6.5	1.6	0.92	0.6	0.66
Specific gravity (apparent) at 20/20°C.	1.0067	0.9748	0.9422	1.1084	0.9856	0.9706
Δsp. gr./Δt	0.00110	0.00109	0.00098	0.00098	0.00083	0.00081
Specific heat at 20°C.	0.496 (30)	0.494	—	—	—	—
Vapor pressure at 20°C., mm.	3.3	1.2	0.3	<0.01	<0.01	<0.01
Viscosity (absolute) at 20°C., cps.	1.1	1.3	1.8	9.4	15.3	17.8

Applications

The glycol ether-esters of acetic acid[364] are outstanding solvents for cellulose esters. They are used in the formulation of lacquers and dopes, in textile printing, in making photographic film, and in the compounding of solution coatings and adhesives.

Rodman[365] prepared the azelaic diester of ethylene glycol monobutyl ether. It is employed as a plasticizer for vinyl resins used for coating fabrics. Ethylene glycol monoethyl ether sebacate and ethylene glycol monobutyl ether sebacate have the same application[366]. The ethylene glycol methyl and butyl ether-esters of oleic acid are suitable materials for plasticizing nitrocellulose and similar resins[367, 368].

Ethylene glycol ether phthalates[369, 370, 371, 372] are useful plasticizers for cellulosic and other resins. Hot-melt compositions containing glycol ether phthalates as plasticizers have been described by Salo and Vivian[373].

Cox and Carruthers[374] have prepared a series of ethylene glycol ether-esters of acylated hydroxy acids, such as tri-(methoxyethyl) acetyl citrate, di-(butoxyethyl) diacetyl tartrate, and ethoxyethoxyethyl butyl lactate. Compounds of this type are useful as solvents and plasticizers for vinyl resins and cellulosic derivatives. Carruthers[375] also describes the preparation of the methyl, butyl, and phenyl ether-esters of acetyl ricinoleic acid by a process involving reaction of the ethylene glycol ether with castor oil, followed by esterification of the free hydroxyl group with acetic anhydride.

Hunter[376] prepared a series of ethylene glycol ether-esters of 12-hydroxystearic acid. A timepiece lubricant of low pour point containing ethylene glycol monoethyl ether ricinoleate has been patented by Morgan and Lowe[377]. Sulfonated ricinoleic acid esters of ethylene glycol ethers are used as wetting, foaming, and dispersing agents[378].

Grether and DuVall[379] describe a series of plasticizers prepared by esterifying nuclear substituted salicylic acids with glycol monoethers. Among these are the ethylene glycol ether-esters of salicylic acid and its 5-bromo, 4-iodo, 5- or 6-chloro, 3-methyl, 4-phenyl, and 4-propoxy derivatives. Grether[380] has also prepared the ethylene glycol ethyl and butyl ether-esters of various phenoxyacetic acids such as 2-chlorophenoxyacetic acid, 2-phenylphenoxyacetic acid, phenoxyacetic acid, and naphthoxyacetic acid. He claimed their use as plasticizers for cellulose derivatives. Other ether-esters useful as plasticizers have been derived from adipic acid[381], lauric acid[382], o-benzoyl benzoic acid[383], endomethylene tetrahydrophthalic acids[384], 4-acetyl-4-methylpimelic acid[385], and levulinic acid[386].

Glycol monoether-esters of glycolic acid[387, 388] are claimed to be useful as plasticizers, softeners, penetrating agents for printing pastes, frothing agents, and sizing agents. Similar esters have been prepared from glycol monoethers and alkoxy acetic acids, such as methoxyacetic acid[389, 390].

Ethylene glycol monophenyl ether propionate, ethylene glycol monophenyl ether butyrate, ethylene glycol monobenzyl ether isobutyrate, and ethylene glycol o-tolyl ether isobutyrate have been prepared and recommended for use in perfumes[391]. Burger and Maglio[392] prepared di-(ethylene glycol phenyl ether) oxalate, and in view of its high melting point, 114°C., suggested its use as a synthetic wax.

Ethylene glycol alkyl and aryl ethers readily form esters with lactic acid[393]. Ethylene glycol ether acrylates have been prepared from the acetates of the corresponding lactates by thermal decomposition[394]. Polymers of these acrylates have been found useful as adhesives in laminated fabrics[395].

Several ethylene glycol ether-esters of carbonic acid have been reported by Drake and Carter[396]. A series of unsaturated esters of the same acid prepared by reacting phosgene with unsaturated glycol ethers such as ethylene glycol monovinyl ether and ethylene glycol monoallyl ether has been prepared by Pollock[397]. These may be polymerized to high molecular weight products by treatment with peroxides. From ethylene glycol monoallyl ether, Muskat[398] prepared bis(allyloxyethyl) carbonate and allyl allyloxyethyl carbonate. These compounds are useful as plasticizers and solvents.

Ether-esters of phosphoric[399] and of phenylphosphonic[400] acids have been prepared from the reaction of ethylene glycol ethers with phosphorus oxychloride and phenyl phosphonyl chloride, respectively. These phosphate derivatives have been found to have outstanding properties as low-temperature plasticizers for "Perbunan"[401].

The p-toluenesulfonates of ethylene glycol methyl, ethyl, butyl, benzyl, and phenyl ethers have been prepared and characterized by Tipson[402]. These compounds have been employed to introduce the alkoxyethyl or aryloxyethyl group into the cinchona alkaloids and quinoline derivatives[403, 404, 405, 406]. Nair and Peacock[407] report the reaction of ethyl acetoacetate with the p-toluenesulfonate of ethylene glycol monophenyl ether to give ethyl 2-(2-phenoxyethyl)acetoacetate. Similarly, Peacock and Tha[408] alkylated malonic ester to obtain diethyl 2-phenoxyethylmalonate.

Ethylene glycol methyl, ethyl, and butyl ether-esters of methylene malonic acid have been described by D'Alelio[409]. When copolymerized with unsaturated alkyd resins, these compounds give products which are useful for molded articles, adhesives, and protective coatings.

Russell[410] claims the barium and strontium alcoholates of ethylene glycol diamyl phenyl ether and ethylene glycol methyl isopropyl phenyl ether as useful oil additives. Hill[411] describes the vanadic acid triesters of ethylene glycol ethyl and phenyl ethers as being employed to improve the burning properties of fuel oils.

A series of ethylene glycol ether nitrates was prepared and characterized by Desseigne[412]. Tri-(ethylene glycol alkyl ether) borates can be prepared in the usual manner by esterification of boric acid with an ethylene glycol alkyl ether[413, 414]. Dyestuffs for acetate rayons ranging from orange to brown shades have been prepared by acylating a glycol ether such as ethylene glycol monomethyl ether with substituted anthraquinone carboxylic acid halides[415].

Literature Cited

1. Wurtz, A., *Ann. chim. et phys.*, (3) **55**, 429 (1859).
2. Demole, E., *Ber.*, **9**, 745 (1876).
3. Palomaa, M. H., *Ber.*, **35**, 3299 (1902).
4. Cretcher, L. H., and Pittenger, W. H., *J. Am. Chem. Soc.*, **46**, 1503–4 (1924).
5. Young, C. O., Jr. (to Carbide and Carbon Chemicals Corp.), U. S. Patent 1,696,874 (Dec. 25, 1928).
6. Wittwer, M. (to I. G. Farbenindustrie A.-G.), U. S. Patent 1,976,677 (Oct. 9, 1934).
7. Gibson, W., and Payman, J. B. (to Imperial Chemical Industries, Ltd.), U. S. Patent 1,774,089 (Aug. 26, 1930).
8. I. G. Farbenindustrie A.-G., German Patent 558,646 (March 14, 1930).
9. Stanley, H. M., and Youell, J. E. (to Distillers Co., Ltd.), British Patent 467,228 (July 8, 1937).
10. Birch, S. F., and Scott, W. D. (to Anglo-Persian Oil Co., Ltd.), U. S. Patent 1,882,564 (Oct. 11, 1932).
11. Dehnert, H., and Krey, W. (to I. G. Farbenindustrie A.-G.), U. S. Patent 1,996,003 (March 26, 1935).
12. Ashburn, H. V., Collett, A. R., znd Lazzell, C. L., *J. Am. Chem. Soc.*, **58**, 1549–51 (1936).
13. Petrov, A. A., *J. Gen. Chem. (U. S. S. R.)*, **10**, 981–96 (1940).
14. I. G. Farbenindustrie A.-G., British Patent 271,169 (Feb. 22, 1926).
15. Zimakov, P., and Churakov, A., *Org. Chem. Ind. (U. S. S. R.)*, **1**, 329–32 (1936).
16. Davidson, J. G. (to Carbide and Carbon Chemicals Corp.), U. S. Patents 1,614,883 (Jan. 18, 1927) and 1,732,356 (Oct. 22, 1929).
17. Imperial Chemical Industries, Ltd., French Patent 684,126 (Aug. 5, 1929).
18. Smith, R. A., *J. Am. Chem. Soc.*, **62**, 994 (1940).
19. Boyd, D. R., and Marle, E. R., *J. Chem. Soc.*, **105**, 2117–39 (1914).
20. Boyd, D. R., and Thomas, D. F., *J. Chem. Soc.*, **115**, 1239–43 (1919).
21. I. G. Farbenindustrie A.-G., French Patent 655,871 (June 11, 1928).
22. Kayser, F., and Schranz, K. (to Winthrop Chemical Co., Inc.), U. S. Patent 1,651,458 (Dec. 6, 1927).
23. Evans, T. W., and Bullard, E. F. (to Shell Development Co.), U. S. Patent 2,067,385 (Jan. 12, 1937).
24. Evans, T. W., and Edlund, K. R., *Ind. Eng. Chem.*, **28**, 1186–8 (1936); (to Shell Development Co.), U. S. Patent 1,968,033 (July 31, 1934).
25. Dreyfus, H., British Patent 398,173 (Sept. 1, 1933).
26. Hill, H. S., and Pidgeon, L. M., *J. Am. Chem. Soc.*, **50**, 2718–25 (1928).
27. Hill, H. S., and Potter, G. J. C., *J. Am. Chem. Soc.*, **51**, 1509–14 (1929).

28. Hurd, C. D., and Pollack, M. A., *J. Am. Chem. Soc.*, **60,** 1905–11 (1938).
29. Drake, N. L., (to Carbide and Carbon Chemicals Corp.), U. S. Patent 2,170,854 (Aug. 29, 1939).
30. British Celanese, Ltd., British Patent 556,756 (Oct. 20, 1943).
31. Seymour, G. W., and Baggett, J. L. (to Camille Dreyfus), Canadian Patent 390,733 (Aug. 13, 1940).
32. Schwoegler, E. J. (to Wyandotte Chemicals Corp.), U. S. Patent 2,403,686 (July 9, 1946).
33. Emerson, G. A., and Abress, B. E., *Univ. California Berkeley Pubs.*, *Pubs. Pharmacol.*, **1,** 93–100 (1938).
34. Ashburn, H. V., Collett, A. R., and Lazzell, C. L., *J. Am. Chem. Soc.*, **60,** 2933–4 (1938).
35. Cox, H. L., and Greer, P. S. (to Carbide and Carbon Chemicals Corp.), U. S. Patent 1,992,292 (Feb. 26, 1935).
36. Cox, H. L. (to Carbide and Carbon Chemicals Corp.), U. S. Patent 2,035,383 (March 24, 1936).
37. Davidson, J. G., *Ind. Eng. Chem.*, **18,** 669 (1926).
38. Davidson, J. G., and Reid, E. W., *Ind. Eng. Chem.*, **20,** 199 (1928).
39. Reid, E. W., *Ind. Eng. Chem.*, **26,** 21 (1934).
40. Reid, E. W., and Davidson, J. G., *Ind. Eng. Chem.*, **19,** 977 (1927); *Paint, Varnish Production Mgr.*, **33,** 6 (1929).
41. Reid, E. W., and Hofmann, H. E., *Ind. Eng. Chem.*, **20,** 497 (1928).
42. Hofmann, H. E., and Reid, E. W., *Ind. Eng. Chem.*, **21,** 247, 955 (1929).
43. Harvey, N. D., Jr., *Am. Dyestuff Reptr.*, **19,** 242 (1930); **24,** 508 (1935).
44. McClure, H. B., *Ind. Eng. Chem., News Ed.*, **17,** 149 (1939).
45. Skinner, G. M. (to National Carbon Co., Inc.), U. S. Patent 2,403,618 (July 9, 1946).
46. Moore, C. G., and Zucker, M. (to The Glidden Co.), U. S. Patent 1,977,345 (Oct. 16, 1934).
47. Dove, L. P., U. S. Patent 2,093,424 (Sept. 21, 1937).
48. Ottley, G. B., U. S. Patent 1,897,071 (Feb. 14, 1933).
49. Wallach, R. N., and Morgan, W. L. (to Sylvania Industrial Corp.), U. S. Patent 2,183,948 (Dec. 19, 1939).
50. Wolfe, H. J., and Greubel, P. W. (to American Can Co.), U. S. Patent 2,361,442 (Oct. 31, 1944).
51. Kritchevsky, W. (to Ninol, Inc.), U. S. Patent 2,158,627 (May 16, 1939).
52. Snyder, J. E. (to Dupont Cellophane Co., Inc.), U. S. Patent 1,815,365 (July 21, 1931).
53. Caprio, A. F. (to Celluloid Corp.), U. S. Patent 1,981,141 (Nov. 20, 1934).
54. Ruehle, A. E., *Ind. Eng. Chem., Anal. Ed.*, **10,** 130–1 (1938).
55. Schneider, R. E. (to The Lummus Co.), U. S. Patent 2,385,235 (Sept. 18, 1945).
56. Blummer, W. J. (to The Lummus Co.), U. S. Patent 2,398,689 (April 16, 1946).
57. Derby, J. T., *Microscope and Entomol. Monthly*, **3,** 243–6 (1939).
58. The Master Builders Co., British Patent 561,510 (May 23, 1944).
59. Standard Oil Development Co., British Patent 507,246 (June 13, 1939).
60. Morgan, J. D., and Lowe, R. E. (to Cities Service Oil Co.), U. S. Patent 2,395,380 (Feb. 19, 1946).
61. Morgan, J. D., and Lowe, R. E. (to Cities Service Oil Co.), U. S. Patent 2,409,443 (October 15, 1949).
62. Davis, W. A., *J. Am. Med. Assoc.*, **123,** 825–6 (1943).

63. Berry, H., *Lancet*, **1944, II,** 175.
64. Boehm, E. (to Nipa Laboratories), U. S. Patent 2,451,149 (Oct. 12, 1948).
65. Roy, D. N., and Ghosh, S. M., *Indian Med. Gaz.*, **82,** 199 (1947).
66. *Drug & Cosmetic Ind.*, **35** (1), 79 (1934).
67. Coleman, G. H., and Zemba, J. W. (to The Dow Chemical Co.), U. S. Patents 2,130,526 (Sept. 20, 1938) and 2,158,957 (May 16, 1939).
68. Newman, M. S., Fones, W., and Renoll, M., *J. Am. Chem. Soc.*, **69,** 718–23 (1947).
69. Weinman, C. J., and Decker, G. C., *J. Econ. Entomol.*, **40,** 74–8 (1947).
70. Linduska, J. P., Cochran, J. H., and Morton, F. A., *J. Econ. Entomol.*, **39,** 767–9 (1946).
71. Thompson, H. E., Swanson, C. P., and Norman, A. G., *Botan. Gaz.*, **107,** 476–507 (1946).
72. Tremain, H. E., and Bacon, L. R. (To Wyandotte Chemicals Corp.), U. S. Patent 2,407,589 (Sept. 10, 1946).
73. Lourenco, A., *Ann. chim. et phys.*, (3) **67,** 288 (1863).
74. Wurtz, A., *Ann. chim. et. phys.*, (3) **69,** 324 (1863).
75. Wurtz, A., *Ann.*, **122,** 354 (1862).
76. Knorr, A. (to I. G. Farbenindustrie A.-G.), German Patent 500,223 (Dec. 24, 1924).
77. I. G. Farbenindustrie A.-G., German Patents 507,761 (May 7, 1926) and 570,674 (Feb. 20, 1933).
78. Knorr, A., and Steimmig, G. (to I. G. Farbenindustrie A.-G.), U. S. Patent 1,681,861 (Aug. 21, 1928).
79. Steimmig, G., and Hambsch, O. (to I. G. Farbenindustrie A.-G.), U. S. Patent 1,939,189 (Dec. 12, 1933).
80. Dreyfus, H., U. S. Patent 2,072,101 (March 2, 1937).
81. Van Alphen, J., *Rec. trav. chim.*, **49,** 1040–4 (1930).
82. Webel, F. (to I. G. Farbenindustrie A.-G.), German Patents 597,496 (May 25, 1934) and 598,952 (June 22, 1934).
83. I. G. Farbenindustrie A.-G., British Patent 346,550 (March 20, 1930).
84. Webel, F. (to I. G. Farbenindustrie A.-G.), German Patent 526,478 (March 29, 1929).
85. Carbide and Carbon Chemicals Corp., British Patent 363,895 (Feb. 20, 1930) and French Patent 711,595 (Feb. 19, 1931).
86. Dreyfus, H., French Patent 772,154 (Oct. 24, 1934).
87. Williams, J. W., *J. Am. Chem. Soc.*, **52,** 1831–37 (1930).
88. Jones, G. W., Seaman, H., and Kennedy, R. E., *Ind. Eng. Chem.*, **25,** 1283–6 (1933).
89. Kohlrausch, K. W. F., and Stockmair, W., *Z. physik. Chem.*, **31B,** 382–401 (1936).
90. Sutton, L. E., and Brockway, L. O., *J. Am. Chem. Soc.*, **57,** 473–83 (1935).
91. Robles, H. de V., *Rec. trav. chim.*, **59,** 184–90 (1940).
92. Gillis, J., and Delaunois, A., *Rec. trav. chim.*, **53,** 186–90 (1934).
93. Hovorka, F., Schaefer, R. A., and Dreisbach, D., *J. Am. Chem. Soc.*, **58,** 2264 (1936).
94. Scatchard, G., and Benedict, M. A., *J. Am. Chem. Soc.*, **58,** 837 (1936).
95. Harned, H. S., and Morrison, J. O., *Am. J. Sci.*, **33,** 161 (1937).
96. Hess, K., and Frahm, H., *Ber.*, **71B,** 2627–36 (1938).
97. Ebert, L., and Büll, R., German Patent 651,111 (Oct. 7, 1937).
98. Eigenberger, E., *J. prakt. Chem.*, **130,** 75–8 (1931).
99. Haardt and Co. A.-G., British Patent 442,540 (Feb. 10, 1936).

100. Dasler, W., and Bauer, C. D., *Ind. Eng. Chem., Anal. Ed.*, **18,** 52–4 (1946).
101. Gross, P., and Suess, H., *Monatsh.*, **68,** 207–14 (1936).
102. Küchler, L., and Lambert, J. D., *Z. physik. Chem.*, **B37,** 285–306 (1937).
103. Paterno, E., and Spallino, R., *Atti. accad. naz. Lincei, Classe sci. fis. mat. e nat.*, (5) **16,** 87 (1907).
104. Macleod, M., *J. Chem. Soc.*, **1928,** 3092.
105. Varvoglis, G. A., *Praktika Akad. Athenon*, **13,** 42–4 (1938); *Chem. Abstracts*, **34,** 5050 (1940).
106. Juhasz, R., and Yntema, L. F., *J. Am. Chem. Soc.*, **62,** 3522 (1940).
107. Kelley, C. J., and McCusker, P. A., *J. Am. Chem. Soc.*, **65,** 1307–9 (1943).
108. Doak, G. O., *J. Am. Pharm. Assoc.*, **23,** 541–3 (1934).
109. Brand, K., and Türck, T., *Pharm. Zentralhalle*, **77,** 591–3 (1936).
110. Crenshaw, J. L., Cope, A. C., Finkelstein, N., and Rogan, R., *J. Am. Chem. Soc.*, **60,** 2308–11 (1938).
111. Meerwein, H., *Ber.*, **66B,** 411–4 (1933).
112. Rheinboldt, H., and Luyken, A., *J. prakt. Chem.*, **133,** 284–8 (1932).
113. Heines, U., and Yntema, L. F., *Trans. Kentucky Acad. Sci.*, **7,** 85–9 (1938).
114. Reiff, F., *Z. anorg. u. allgem. Chem.*, **208,** 321–47 (1932).
115. Rheinboldt, H., and Boy, R., *J. prakt. Chem.*, **129,** 268–77 (1931).
116. Rheinboldt, H., Luyken, A., and Schmittmann, H., *J. prakt. Chem.*, **148,** 81–7 (1937); **149,** 30–54 (1937).
117. Suter, C. M., Evans, P. B., and Kiefer, J. M., *J. Am. Chem. Soc.*, **60,** 538–40 (1938).
118. Suter, C. M., and Malkemus, J. D., *J. Am. Chem. Soc.*, **63,** 978–81 (1941).
119. Bordwell, F. G., Suter, C. M., and Webber, A. J., *J. Am. Chem. Soc.*, **67,** 827–32 (1945).
120. Böeseken, J., Tellegen, F., and Henriquez, P. C., *J. Am. Chem. Soc.*, **55,** 1284–8 (1933); *Rec. trav. chim.*, **50,** 909 (1931).
121. Butler, C. L., and Cretcher, L. H., *J. Am. Chem. Soc.*, **54,** 2987–92 (1932).
122. Summerbell, R. K., and Christ, R., *J. Am. Chem. Soc.*, **54,** 3777–8 (1932).
123. Christ, R., and Summerbell, R. K., *J. Am. Chem. Soc.*, **55,** 4547–8 (1933).
124. Summerbell, R. K., and Bauer, L. N., *J. Am. Chem. Soc.*, **57,** 2364–8 (1935).
125. Summerbell, R. K., and Umhoefer, R. R., *J. Am. Chem. Soc.*, **61,** 3016–9 (1939).
126. Britton, E. C., and Slagh, H. R. (to The Dow Chemical Co.), U. S. Patent 2,195,386 (March 26, 1940).
127. Slagh, H. R. (to The Dow Chemical Co.), U. S. Patents 2,190,907 (Feb. 20, 1940) and 2,164,355–6 (July 4, 1939).
128. Toussaint, W. J., and MacDowell, L. G., Jr. (to Carbide and Carbon Chemicals Corp.), U. S. Patent 2,383,091 (Aug. 21, 1945).
129. Reid, E. W., and Hofmann, H. E., *Ind. Eng. Chem.*, **21,** 695 (1929).
130. Jordan, O. (to I. G. Farbenindustrie A.-G), U. S. Patent 1,919,727 (July 25, 1933).
131. I. G. Farbenindustrie A.-G., British Patents 275,652–3 (Dec. 23, 1924).
132. Staud, C. J., and Webber, C. S. (to Eastman Kodak Co.), U. S. Patents 1,954,336 (April 10, 1934) and 1,957,868 (May 8, 1934).
133. McNally, J. G., and Schmitt, J. J. (to Eastman Kodak Co.), U. S. Patent 1,991,109 (Feb. 12, 1935).
134. Robey, R. F., and Rosen, R. (to Standard Oil Development Co.), U. S. Patent 2,338,600 (Jan. 4, 1944).
135. Hamill, W. H., and Vogt, R. R. (to E. I. du Pont de Nemours & Co.), U. S. Patents 2,383,547 (Aug. 28, 1945) and 2,405,693 (Aug. 13, 1946).

136. Slagh, H. R. (to The Dow Chemical Co.), U. S. Patent 2,209,019 (July 23, 1940).
137. Anschütz, L., and Broeker, W., *Ber.*, **59**, 2844 (1926).
138. Herz, W., and Lorentz, E., *Z. physik. Chem.*, **140A**, 406 (1929).
139. Oxford, A. E., *Biochem. J.*, **28**, 1325–9 (1934).
140. Kraus, C. A., and Vingee, R. A., *J. Am. Chem. Soc.*, **56**, 511–6 (1934).
141. Roth, W. A., and Meyer, I., *Z. Elektrochem.*, **39**, 35 (1933).
142. Adkins, H., "Reactions of Hydrogen," p. 27, Madison, University of Wisconsin Press, 1937.
143. Graupner, H., and Weissberger, A., *Zool. Anz.*, **96**, 204–6 (1931); **102**, 39–44 (1933).
144. Miller, B. J., *Mendel Bull.*, **10**, 5–9 (1937).
145. Huber, P., *Mikrokosmos*, **35**, 179–81 (1942).
146. Mossman, H. W., *Stain Technol.*, **12** (4), 147 (1937).
147. Hall, W. B., *Am. J. Clin. Path., Tech. Sect.*, **7**, 98–100 (1943).
148. Trillat, A., and Cambier, R., *Compt. rend.*, **118**, 1279 (1894).
149. Verley, A., *Bull. soc. chim. France*, (3) **21**, 275–7 (1899).
150. Squires, L. (to E. I. du Pont de Nemours & Co.), U. S. Patent 2,350,940 (June 6, 1944).
151. Dreyfus, H., U. S. Patent 2,095,320 (Oct. 12, 1937).
152. Société Nobel Française, French Patent 804,714 (Oct. 31, 1936).
153. Dworzak, R., and Hermann, K., *Monatsh.*, **52**, 83–106 (1929).
154. Hibbert, H., and Hill, H. S., *J. Am. Chem. Soc.*, **45**, 734–51 (1923).
155. Salmi, E. J., *Ber.*, **71B**, 1803–8 (1938).
156. Salmi, E. J., and Rannikko, V., *Ber.*, **72B**, 600–4 (1939).
157. Hill, H. S., and Potter, G. J. C., *J. Am. Chem. Soc.*, **51**, 1509–14 (1929).
158. Hibbert, H., and Whelen, M. S., *J. Am. Chem. Soc.*, **51**, 3115–23 (1929).
159. Hill, H. S., and Hibbert, H., *J. Am. Chem. Soc.*, **45**, 3108–16 (1923).
160. Walter, H. (to Verein für Chemische Industrie A.-G.), British Patent 288,707 (Jan. 11, 1927).
161. Killian, D. B., Hennion, G. F., and Nieuwland, J. A., *J. Am. Chem. Soc.*, **58**, 1658–9 (1936).
162. Bried, E. A., and Hennion, G. F., *J. Am. Chem. Soc.*, **60**, 1717–9 (1938).
163. Hennion, G. F., and Murray, W. S., *J. Am. Chem. Soc.*, **64**, 1220–2 (1942).
164. Mkhitaryan, V. G., *J. Gen. Chem. (U. S. S. R.)*, **10**, 667–9 (1940).
165. McNamee, R. W., and Blair, C. M. (to Carbide and Carbon Chemicals Corp.), U. S. Patent 2,140,938 (Dec. 20, 1938).
166. Baker, W., and Shannon, A., *J. Chem. Soc.*, **1933**, 1598.
167. Baker, W., and Field, F. B., *J. Chem. Soc.*, **1932**, 86–91.
168. Hallonquist, E. G., and Hibbert, H., *Can. J. Research*, **8**, 129–36 (1933).
169. Fieser, L. F., Fields, M., and Lieberman, S., *J. Biol. Chem.*, **156**, 191–201 (1944).
170. Hinz, A., Meyer, G., and Schücking, G., *Ber.*, **76B**, 676–89 (1943).
171. Petrov, A. A., *J. Gen. Chem. (U. S. S. R.)*, **10**, 981–96 (1940).
172. Böeseken, J., and Tellegen, F., *Rec. trav. chim.*, **57**, 133–43 (1938).
173. Gresham, W. F. (to E. I. du Pont de Nemours & Co.), U. S. Patent 2,376,354 (May 22, 1945).
174. Senkus, M., *J. Am. Chem. Soc.*, **68**, 734–6 (1946).
175. Gresham, W. F. (to E. I. du Pont de Nemours & Co.), U. S. Patent 2,377,878 (June 12, 1945).
176. Gresham, W. F. (to E. I. du Pont de Nemours & Co.), U. S. Patents 2,395,265 (Feb. 19, 1946), 2,394,910 (Feb. 12, 1946), and 2,382,938 (Aug. 14, 1945).
177. Peterson, M. D., and Weber, A. G. (to E. I. du Pont de Nemours & Co.), U. S. Patent 2,395,292 (Feb. 19, 1946).

178. Hanford, W. E., and Roland, J. R. (to E. I. du Pont de Nemours & Co.), U. S. Patent 2,402,137 (June 18, 1946).
179. Howk, B. W., Roland, J. R., and Hoehn, H. H. (to E. I. du Pont de Nemours & Co.), U. S. Patent 2,409,683 (Oct. 22, 1946).
180. E. I. du Pont de Nemours & Co., British Patent 583,181 (Dec. 11, 1946).
181. Dakin, H. D., *J. Biol. Chem.*, **3,** 57 (1907).
182. Wiley, F. H., Hueper, W. C., Bergen, D. S., and Blood, F. R., *J. Ind. Hyg. Toxicol.*, **20,** 269 (1938).
183. Mulinos, M. G., Pomerantz, L., and Lojkin, M. E., *Am. J. Pharm.*, **115,** 51 (1943).
184. Ljubavin, N., *Ber.*, **14,** 2685 (1881).
185. DeForcrand, R., *Ber.*, **17R,** 168 (1884).
186. Ott, K. (to Chemische Fabr. u. Weiler-Ter Meer), German Patent 362,743 (Sept. 25, 1922).
187. McNamee, R. W., and Dunn, J. T. (to Carbide and Carbon Chemicals Corp.), U. S. Patents 2,339,282; 2,339,346; and 2,339,348 (Jan. 18, 1944).
188. Bohmfalk, J. F., Jr., McNamee, R. W., and Barry, R. P., *Ind. Eng. Chem.*, **43,** 786 (1951).
189. Walker, J. F. (to E. I. du Pont de Nemours & Co.), U. S. Patent 2,379,555 (July 3, 1945).
190. Hess, K., and Ubrig, C., *Ber.*, **50,** 365 (1917).
191. Raudnitz, H., *Chemistry & Industry*, **1944,** No. 37, 327; No. 42, 366.
192. Dyson, G. H. *Chemistry & Industry*, **1944,** No. 39, 342.
193. Fischer, H. O. L., and Taube, C., *Ber.*, **59,** 854 (1926).
194. Homolka, B. (to Farbwerke v. Meister Lucius and Brünig), German Patents 368,741 (Dec. 11, 1922) and 370,222 (Jan. 8, 1923).
195. Nietzki, R., and Benckiser, T., *Ber.*, **18,** 507, 1837 (1885).
196. Homolka, B., *Ber.*, **54,** 1393 (1921).
197. Field, J. A., *Chem. Inds.*, **60,** 960 (1947).
198. Hansen, D. W. (to Prolamine Products, Inc.), U. S. Patent 2,102,623 (Dec. 21, 1937).
199. Ernst, A., and Sponsel, K. (to I. G. Farbenindustrie A.-G.), U. S. Patent 1,841,797 (Jan. 19, 1932).
200. Davidson, P. B. (to Strathmore Paper Co.), U. S. Patent 2,414,858 (Jan. 28, 1947).
201. Pfeffer, E. C., Jr., and Epelberg, J. (to Cluett, Peabody and Co.), U. S. Patent 2,412,832 (Dec. 17, 1946).
202. Elliott, G. H., and Speakman, J. B., *J. Soc. Dyers Colourists*, **59,** 185 (1943).
203. Broderick, A. E. (to Carbide and Carbon Chemicals Corp.), U. S. Patent 2,285,490 (June 9, 1942).
204. Kalle and Company A.-G., British Patent 488,686 (July 12, 1938) and French Patent 827,217 (April 21, 1938).
205. Sponsel, K. (to Kalle and Co. A.-G.), German Patent 712,561 (Sept. 25, 1941).
206. Cogan, H. D., and Quarles, R. W. (to Carbide and Carbon Chemicals Corp.), U. S. Patent 2,387,831 (Oct. 30, 1945).
207. Harvey, M. T., and Durst, R. F. (to Harvel Research Corp.), U. S. Patent 2,383,793 (Aug. 28, 1945).
208. Scheuermann, H., and Haarer, E. (to I. G. Farbenindustrie A.-G.), German Patent 719,394 (March 12, 1942).
209. Rust, J. B. (to Montclair Research Corp.), U. S. Patent 2,388,086 (Oct. 30, 1945).
210. Hilditch, T. P., and Rigg, J. G., *J. Chem. Soc.*, **1935,** 1774.
211. I. G. Farbenindustrie A.-G., British Patents 292,059 (Jan. 31, 1927) and 265,233 (Jan. 29, 1926).

212. Fraenkel-Conrat, H., and Olcott, H. S., *J. Am. Chem. Soc.*, **66,** 1420 (1944).
213. Gol'dfarb, Y. L., and Smorgonskii, L. M., *J. Gen. Chem.* (*U. S. S. R.*), **8,** 1516 (1938); *Chem. Abstracts,* **33,** 4593 (1939).
214. Palomaa, M. H., *Chem. Zentr.*, **84, II,** 1956 (1913).
215. Lourenco, A., *Ann. chim. et phys.*, (3) **67,** 267 (1863).
216. Cretcher, L. H., and Pittenger, W. H., *J. Am. Chem. Soc.*, **47,** 2560–3 (1925).
217. Wurtz, A., *Ann. chim. et phys.*, (3) **55,** 436 (1859).
218. Heim, H. C., and Poe, C. F., *J. Org. Chem.*, **9,** 299–301 (1944).
219. Gilmer, L., *Ann.*, **123,** 377 (1862).
220. Hubacher, M. H. (to Herbert S. Kreighbaum), U. S. Patent 2,010,154 (Aug. 6, 1935).
221. Carruthers, T. F., and Blair, C. M. (to Carbide and Carbon Chemicals Corp.), U. S. Patent 2,158,107 (May 16, 1939).
222. Grether, E. F., Shawver, W. R., and Du Vall, R. B. (to The Dow Chemical Co.), U. S. Patent 2,121,226 (June 21, 1938).
223. Grether, E. F., Shawver, W. R., and Du Vall, R. B. (to The Dow Chemical Co.), U. S. Patent 2,170,995 (Aug. 29, 1940).
224. Ernsberger, M. L., and Pinkney, P. S. (to E. I. du Pont de Nemours & Co.), U. S. Patent 2,424,652 (July 29, 1947).
225. Muskat, I. E. (to Pittsburgh Plate Glass Co.), U. S. Patents 2,379,249 (June 26, 1945) and 2,403,112 (July 2, 1946).
226. Muskat, I. E., and Strain F. (to Pittsburgh Plate Glass Co.), U. S. Patents 2,370,567 (Feb. 27, 1945); 2,370,571–2 (Feb. 27, 1945); 2,379,250–1 (June 26, 1945); and 2,384,115 (Sept. 4, 1945).
227. Strain F. (to Pittsburgh Plate Glass Co.), U. S. Patent 2,397,630 (April 2, 1946).
228. Goldsmith, H. A., *Chem. Revs.*, **33,** 284–6 (1943).
229. Ellis, C. (to Ellis-Foster Co.), U. S. Patent 2,221,674 (Nov. 12, 1940).
230. Pungs, W., and Jahrstorfer, M. (to I. G. Farbenindustrie A.-G.), U. S. Patent 1,737,975 (Dec. 3. 1929); British Patent 350,992 (Dec. 16, 1929); and French Patent 703,792 (Oct. 17, 1930).
231. Schmaltz, D., *Kolloid-Z.*, **71,** 234–5 (1935).
232. Putt, E. B. (to H. Theaman), U. S. Patent 2,042,359 (May 26, 1936).
233. Johnston, E. C. (to Robert A. Johnston Co.), U. S. Patent 2,211,209 (Aug. 13, 1940).
234. Franz Ströher A.-G., British Patents 463,481 (March 30, 1937) and 486,086 (May 26, 1938).
235. Harris, B. R., Epstein, A. K., and Cahn, F. J., *Oil & Soap*, **18,** 179–82 (1941).
236. Schrader, H. (to The Firm of Th. Goldschmidt A.-G.), U. S. Patent 1,826,900 (Oct. 31, 1931).
237. Cahn, F. J., and Harris, B. R. (to The Emulsol Corp.), U. S. Patent 2,236,516 (April 1. 1941).
238. Th. Goldschmidt A.-G., French Patent 664,261 (Nov. 5, 1928).
239. Pfaff, K., *Riechstoff Ind. u. Kosmetik*, **9,** 2–5 (1934).
240. DeGroote, M. (to Tretolite Co.), U. S. Patent 2,052,284 (Aug. 25, 1936).
241. Jones, P. H. (to Union Oil Co. of California), U. S. Patent 2,271,696 (Feb. 3, 1942).
242. Holmes, R. L. (to Jasco, Inc.), U. S. Patent 2,414,740 (Jan. 21, 1947).
243. Brunstrum, L. C., and Liehe, H. J. (to Standard Oil Co.), U. S. Patent 2,398,173 (April 9, 1946).
244. Rinkenbach, W. H., *Ind. Eng. Chem.*, **18,** 1195 (1926).
245. Rinkenbach, W. H., *Ind. Eng. Chem.*, **19,** 925 (1927).

246. Rinkenbach, W. H., *Ind. Eng. Chem.*, **19**, 1291 (1927).
247. Rinkenbach, W. H., *Chem. & Met. Eng.*, **34**, 296 (1927).
248. Perrott, G. St. J., and Tiffany, J. E., U. S. Bureau of Mines, *Reports of Investigations No.* **2935**, 1929.
249. Coates, A. B., and Perrott, G. St. J., U. S. Bureau of Mines, *Reports of Investigations No.* **2923**, 1929.
250. Kekule, A., *Ber.*, **2**, 329 (1869).
251. Wieland, H., and Sakellarios, E., *Ber.*, **53B**, 203 (1920).
252. Henry, L., *Ber.*, **3**, 529 (1870); *Ann. chim. et phys.*, (4) **27**, 243 (1872).
253. Champion, P., *Z. Chem.*, **1871**, 469; *Compt. rend.*, **73**, 571–4 (1871).
254. Nef, J. U., *Ann.*, **309**, 126 (1899).
255. Claessen, C., German Patent 179,789 (Nov. 18, 1904).
256. Matthews, F. E., and Strange, E. H., British Patent 12,770 (May 30, 1912).
257. Jolicard, E., French Patent 456,456 (June 18, 1912).
258. Hibbert, H., U. S. Patents 1,213,367 (Jan. 23, 1917), 1,213,369 (Jan. 23, 1917), and 1,231,351 (June 26, 1917).
259. Oehme, H. (to The Chemical Foundation, Inc.), U. S. Patent 1,426,313 (Aug. 15, 1922).
260. Lewis, H. A., U. S. Patent 1,560,426 (Nov. 3, 1925).
261. Fichter, F., and Bloch, E., *Helv. Chim. Acta*, **22**, 1529–40 (1939).
262. Fichter, F., and Steinbuch, W., *Helv. Chim. Acta*, **26**, 695–704 (1943).
263. Fichter, F., Siegrist, W., and Buess, H., *Helv. Chim. Acta*, **18**, 18–25 (1935).
264. Nitroglycerin Aktiebolaget, French Patent 800,944 (July 22, 1936).
265. Naoum, P., translated by Symmes, E. M., "Nitroglycerine and Nitroglycerine Explosives," Baltimore, The Williams & Wilkins Co. 1928.
266. Demjanow, *Ann. Inst. Agron. Moscow*, **4**, 155 (1898); *Chem. Zentr.*, **1899**, 1064.
267. Perkin, W. H., *J. Chem. Soc. (London)*, **55**, 680 (1889).
268. Brandner, J. D., *Ind. Eng. Chem.*, **30**, 681–4 (1938); see also Marshall, A., *J. Soc. Chem. Ind. (London)*, **49**, 34T (1930).
269. Peterson, J. M., *J. Am. Chem. Soc.*, **52**, 3669 (1930).
270. Naoum, P., and Berthmann, A., *Z. ges. Schiess- u. Sprengstoffw.*, **26**, 188–90 (1931).
271. Bertoni, G., *Gazz. chim. ital.*, **15**, 353 (1885).
272. Henry, L., *Ann. chim. et phys.*, (4) **27**, 243 (1872).
273. Oppenheim, A., *Ber.*, **3**, 735 (1870).
274. Simpson, M., *Ann.*, **112**, 146 (1859).
275. Claesson, P., *J. prakt. Chem.*, (2) **20**, 2 (1879).
276. Purgotti, A., *Gazz. chim. ital.*, **22**, I, 419–21 (1892).
277. Majima, R., and Simanuki, H., *Proc. Imp. Acad. (Tokyo)*, **2**, 544–6 (1926).
278. Carlson, W. W., and Cretcher, L. H., *J. Am. Chem. Soc.*, **69**, 1952–6 (1947).
279. Carre, P., *Ann. chim. et phys.*, (8) **5**, 351 (1905).
280. Union chimique Belge, British Patent 493,813 (Oct. 14, 1938).
281. Bailly, O., and Gaumé, J., *Compt. rend.*, **178**, 1191–3 (1924).
282. Atherton, F. R., Openshaw, H. T., and Todd, A. R., *J. Chem. Soc.*, **1945**, 382–5.
283. Adams, C. E., and Shoemaker, B. H. (to Standard Oil Co.), U. S. Patent 2,372,244 (March 27, 1945).
284. Toy, A. D. F. (to Victor Chemical Works), U. S. Patent 2,382,622 (Aug. 14, 1945).
285. Councler, C., *J. prakt. Chem.*, (2) **18**, 392 (1878).
286. Meerwein, H., *Ber.*, **66**, 411 (1933).
287. Dupire, A., *Compt. rend.*, **202**, 2086–7 (1936).
288. Rippere, R. E., and LaMer, V. K., *J. Phys. Chem.*, **47**, 204 (1943).

289. Ruben, S. (to The Ruben Condenser Co.), Canadian Patent 330,058 (Feb. 7, 1933).
290. Thomas, L. H., *J. Chem. Soc.*, **1946**, 823–4.
291. Pascal, P., and Dupire, A., *Compt. rend.* **195**, 14–6 (1932).
292. Salmi, E. J., Merivuori, K., and Laaksonen, E., *Suomen Kemistilehti*, **19B**, 102–8 (1946); *Chem. Abstracts*, **41**, 5440 (1947).
293. Kienle, R. H., and Ferguson, C. S., *Ind. Eng. Chem.*, **21**, 399 (1929).
294. Kienle, R. H., and Schlingman, P. F., *Ind. Eng. Chem.*, **25**, 971 (1933).
295. Kienle, R. H., and Hovey, A. G., *J. Am. Chem. Soc.*, **52**, 3636 (1930).
296. Kienle, R. H., *Ind. Eng. Chem.*, **22**, 590 (1930).
297. Kienle, R. H., van der Meulen, P. A., and Petke, F. E., *J. Am. Chem. Soc.*, **61**, 2258 (1939).
298. Mark, H., and Whitby, G. S., Editors, "Collected Papers of Wallace H. Carothers on High Polymeric Substances," New York, Interscience Publishers, Inc., 1940.
299. Carothers, W. H., *Chem. Revs.*, **8**, 353 (1931) and *J. Am. Chem. Soc.*, **51**, 2548 (1929).
300. Carothers, W. H., and Van Natta, F. J., *J. Am. Chem. Soc.*, **52**, 314 (1930).
301. Carothers, W. H., Arvin, J. A., and Dorough, G. L., *J. Am. Chem. Soc.*, **52**, 3292 (1930).
302. Flory, P. J., *J. Am. Chem. Soc.*, **61**, 3334 (1939).
303. Carothers, W. H., and Arvin, J. A., *J. Am. Chem. Soc.*, **51**, 2560 (1929).
304. Flory, P. J., *Chem. Revs.*, **39**, 137 (1946); *J. Am. Chem. Soc.*, **58**, 1877 (1936); **62**, 1057 (1940); **62**, 1561 (1940); **62**, 2255 (1940); **62**, 2261 (1940); **63**, 3083 (1941); **63**, 3091 (1941); **63**, 3096 (1941); **64**, 2205 (1942); and *J. Chem. Phys.*, **12**, 425 (1944).
305. Hill, J. W., and Carothers, W. H., *J. Am. Chem. Soc.*, **55**, 5031 (1933).
306. Spanagel, E. W., and Carothers, W. H., *J. Am. Chem. Soc.*, **57**, 929, 935 (1935).
307. Carothers, W. H., and Hill, J. W., *J. Am. Chem. Soc.*, **54**, 1559, 1579 (1932).
308. Shorland, R. B., *J. Am. Chem. Soc.*, **57**, 115 (1935).
309. Fuller, C. S., *Ind. Eng. Chem.*, **30**, 472 (1938).
310. Bradley, T. F., Kropa, E. L., and Johnston, W. B., *Ind. Eng. Chem.*, **29**, 1270 (1937).
311. Overholt, J. L., and Elm, A. C., *Ind. Eng. Chem.*, **32**, 1348 (1940).
312. Kienle, R. H., and Hovey, A. G., *J. Am. Chem. Soc.*, **51**, 509 (1929).
313. Kienle, R. H., and Ferguson, C. S., *Chem. & Met. Eng.*, **39**, 599 (1932).
314. Ellis, C. (to Ellis-Foster Co.), U. S. Patent 2,007,965 (July 16, 1935).
315. Bradley, T. F., *Ind. Eng. Chem.*, **29**, 579 (1937).
316. Garvey, B. S., Jr., Alexander, C. H., Küng, F. E., and Henderson, D. E., *Ind. Eng. Chem.*, **33**, 1060 (1941).
317. Sager, T. P., *Ind. Eng. Chem., Anal. Ed.*, **4**, 388 (1932).
318. Vincent, H. L., *Ind. Eng. Chem.*, **29**, 1267 (1937).
319. Doscher, C. K., Kane, J. H., Cragwall, G. O., and Staebner, W. H., *Ind. Eng. Chem.*, **33**, 315 (1941).
320. Ellis, C. (to Ellis-Foster Co.), U. S. Patent 2,195,362 (March 26, 1940).
321. Kropa, E. L., and Bradley, T. F., *Ind. Eng. Chem.*, **31**, 1512 (1939).
322. Rust, J. B., *Ind. Eng. Chem.*, **32**, 64 (1940).
323. U. S. Tariff Commission, "Synthetic Organic Chemicals," Rept. No. 162, 2nd Series, Table 16B, 1947.
324. Wright, J. G. E., *Chem. & Met. Eng.*, **39**, 438 (1932).
325. *Modern Plastics*, **23** (10), 144 (1946); **23** (12), 146 (1946).
326. Fetter, E. C., *Chem. & Met. Eng.*, **53** (2), 154 (1946).

327. Kropa, E. L. (to American Cyanamid Co.), Canadian Patent 437,995 (Nov. 19, 1946).
328. Strain, F. (to Pittsburgh Plate Glass Co.), U. S. Patent 2,349,768 (May 23, 1944).
329. Muskat, I. E., and Strain, F. (to Pittsburgh Plate Glass Co.), U. S. Patents 2,370,565 (Feb. 27, 1945); 2,385,930; 2,385,933; 2,385,934 (Oct.2, 1945); 2,384,115; 2,384,124; 2,384,125; 2,384,126 (Sept. 4, 1945); 2,399,285; 2,399,286 (April 30, 1946); and 2,403,113 (July 2, 1946); and British Patent 592,172 (Sept. 10, 1947).
330. Crawford, J. W. C., and Mackereth, F. J. H. (to Imperial Chemical Industries), British Patent 581,251 (Oct. 7, 1946).
331. Patterson, D. G. (to American Cyanamid Co.), U. S. Patent 2,280,256 (April 21, 1942).
332. Kropa, E. L., and Bradley, T. F. (to American Cyanamid Co.), U. S. Patent 2,280,242 (April 21, 1942).
333. American Cyanamid Co., British Patent 548,137 (Sept. 28, 1942).
334. D'Alelio, G. F. (to General Electric Co.), U. S. Patent 2,407,479 (Sept. 10, 1946).
335. Kropa, E. L., and Nyquist, A. S. (to American Cyanamid Co.), U. S. Patent 2,491,409 (Dec. 13, 1949).
336. Shaffel, G. S. (to Westinghouse Electrical Corp.), U. S. Patent 2,470,651 (May 17, 1949).
337. Weith, G. S. (to Bakelite Corp.), U. S. Patent 2,475,731 (July 12, 1949).
338. Biggs, B. S., and Fuller, G. S., *Chem. Eng. News*, **21,** 962 (1943).
339. *Chem. Eng. News*, **21,** 306 (1943).
340. Cowan, J. C., and Ault, W. C. (to the United States of America), U. S. Patent 2,373,015 (April 3, 1945).
341. Cowan, J. C., and Ault, W. C., British Patent 593,788 (Oct. 27, 1947).
342. Cowan, J. C., Ault, W. C., and Teeter, H. M., *Ind. Eng. Chem.*, **38,** 1138 (1946).
343. Cowan, J. C., Wheeler, D. H., Teeter, H. M., Paschke, R. E., Scholfield, C. R., Schwab, A. W., Jackson, J. E., Bull, W. C., Earle, F. R., Foster, R. J., Bond, W. C., Beal, R. E., Skell, P. S., Wolff, I. A., and Mehltretter, C., *Ind. Eng. Chem.*, **41,** 1647–53 (1949).
344. Carson, C. M. (to Wingfoot Corp.), U. S. Patent 2,496,934 (Feb. 7, 1950).
345. Jayne, D. W., Jr., and Day, H. M. (to American Cyanamid Co.), U. S. Patent 2,489,711 (Nov. 29, 1949).
346. Jayne, D. W., Jr., Day, H. M., and Kropa, E. L. (to American Cyanamid Co.), U. S. Patents 2,490,001 and 2,490,005 (Nov. 29, 1949).
347. Pratt, B. C. (to E. I. du Pont de Nemours & Co.), U. S. Patent 2,456,314 (Dec. 14, 1948).
348. Brown, C. F. (to United States Rubber Co.), U. S. Patent 2,416,433 (Feb. 25, 1947).
349. Van Antwerpen, F. J., *Ind. Eng. Chem., News Ed.*, **19,** 1255 (1941).
350. Sen, H. K., *Indian Lac Research Inst. Ann. Rept.*, **1937–38,** 3–16.
351. Gidvani, B. S., *Chemistry & Industry*, **58,** 10 (1939).
352. Gidvani, B. S., *London Shellac Research Bur. Tech. Paper No. 17*, **1939**.
353. Caplan, S. (to Harvel Research Corp), U. S. Patent 2,301,253 (Nov. 10, 1942).
354. Gidvani, B. S., and Kamath, N. R., *Paint Manuf.*, **14,** 304 (1944).
355. Gidvani, B. S., and Kamath, N. R., *Paint Manuf.*, **15,** 93 (1945).
356. Rothrock, D. A., Jr., and Conyne, R. F. (to The Resinous Products & Chemical Co.), U. S. Patent 2,437,046 (March 2, 1948).
357. Opp, C. (to Interchemical Corp.), U. S. Patent 2,418,721 (April 8, 1947).
358. Whinfield, J. R., *Nature*, **158,** 930 (1946).

359. Whinfield, J. R., and Dickson, J. T., British Patents 578,079 (June 14, 1946); (to E. I. du Pont de Nemours & Co.), U. S. Patent 2,465,319 (March 22, 1949).
360. Dickson, J. T., British Patent 579,462 (Aug. 6, 1946).
361. Cady, W. H., *Am. Dyestuff Reptr.*, **37,** 699 (1948).
362. Dickson, J. T., Huggill, H. P. W., and Welch, J. C., British Patent 590,451 (July 17, 1947).
363. Cook, J. G. (to Imperial Chemical Industries, Ltd.), British Patent 590,417 (July 17, 1947).
364. Davidson, J. G. (to Carbide and Carbon Chemicals Corp.), U. S. Patent 1,791,301 (Feb. 3, 1931).
365. Rodman, E. A. (to E. I. du Pont de Nemours & Co.), U. S. Patent 2,404,313 (July 16, 1946).
366. Tuttle, F. J., and Kester, E. B., *Modern Plastics*, **24** (4), 163–6 (1946).
367. North, C. O. (to Herbert S. Kreighbaum), U. S. Patent 2,010,560 (Aug. 6, 1935).
368. Buckley, J. R. (to E. I. du Pont de Nemours & Co.), U. S. Patent 1,869,660 (Aug. 2, 1932).
369. Van Schaack, R. H., and Calvert, R. (to Van Schaack Bros. Chemical Works, Inc.), U. S. Patents 1,706,639 (March 26, 1929) and 1,733,639 (Oct. 29, 1929).
370. Steimmig, G. (to I. G. Farbenindustrie A.-G.), U. S. Patent 1,864,099 (June 21, 1932).
371. I. G. Farbenindustrie A.-G., British Patent 279,771 (April 26, 1926).
372. Frazier, R. B. (to Carbide and Carbon Chemicals Corp.), British Patent 410,797 (May 23, 1934).
373. Salo, M., and Vivian, H. F. (to Eastman Kodak Co.), U. S. Patent 2,410,685 (Nov. 5, 1946).
374. Cox, H. L., and Carruthers, T. F. (to Carbide and Carbon Chemicals Corp.), U. S. Patent 2,046,150 (June 30, 1936).
375. Carruthers, T. F. (to Carbide and Carbon Chemicals Corp.), U. S. Patent 2,310,395 (Feb. 9, 1943).
376. Hunter, M. J. (to The Dow Chemical Co.), U. S. Patent 2,390,027 (Nov. 27, 1945).
377. Morgan, J. D., and Lowe, R. E. (to Cities Service Oil Co.), U. S. Patent 2,423,844 (July 15, 1947).
378. H. T. Boehme A.-G., British Patent 351,456 (April 3, 1929).
379. Grether, E. F., and Du Vall, R. B. (to The Dow Chemical Co.), U. S. Patents 2,198,583 (April 23, 1940) and 2,234,374 (March 11, 1941).
380. Grether, E. F. (to The Dow Chemical Co.), U. S. Patent 2,142,126 (Jan. 3, 1939).
381. Izard, E. F. (to E. I. du Pont de Nemours & Co.), U. S. Patent 1,991,391 (Feb. 19, 1935).
382. Société Français Duco, French Patent 795,590 (March 17, 1936).
383. Bruson, H. A. (to American Cyanamid Co.), U. S. Patent 2,233,513 (March 4, 1941).
384. Staff, C. E. (to Carbide and Carbon Chemicals Corp.), U. S. Patent 2,311,260 (Feb. 16, 1943).
385. Bruson, H. A. (to The Resinous Products & Chemical Co.), U. S. Patent 2,374,327 (April 24, 1945).
386. Izard, E. F., and Salzberg, P. L. (to E. I. du Pont de Nemours & Co.), U. S. Patent 2,004,115 (June 11, 1935).
387. Loder, D. J. (to E. I. du Pont de Nemours & Co.), U. S. Patent 2,388,164 (Oct. 30, 1945).
388. Loder, D. J., and Teeters, W. O. (to E. I. du Pont de Nemours & Co.), U. S. Patent 2,350,964 (June 6, 1944).

389. Loder, D. J., and Teeters, W. O. (to E. I. du Pont de Nemours & Co.), U. S. Patent 2,357,594 (Sept. 5, 1944).
390. Zellhoefer, G. F., and Marvel, C. S. (to G. F. Zellhoeffer), U. S. Patent 2,226,599 (Dec. 31, 1940).
391. I. G. Farbenindustrie A.-G., British Patent 327,705 (Dec. 29, 1928).
392. Burger, C. A., and Maglio, M. M., *J. Am. Chem. Soc.*, **67**, 1424 (1945).
393. Fein, M. L., Ratchford, W. P., and Fisher, C. H., *J. Am. Chem. Soc.*, **66**, 1201–3 (1944).
394. Rehberg, C. E., and Fisher, C. H. (to the United States of America), U. S. Patent 2,396,434 (March 12, 1946).
395. Charlton, W., Evans, J. G., and Lawrie, L. G. (to Imperial Chemical Industries, Ltd.), British Patent 493,615 (Oct. 10, 1938).
396. Drake, N. L., and Carter, R. M., *J. Am. Chem. Soc.*, **52**, 3720–4 (1930).
397. Pollock, M. A. (to Pittsburgh Plate Glass Co.), U. S. Patent 2,407,446 (Sept. 10, 1946).
398. Muskat, I. E., and Strain, F. (to Pittsburgh Plate Glass Co.), U. S. Patent 2,384,115 (Sept. 4, 1945).
399. I. G. Farbenindustrie A.-G., German Patents 523,802 (April 9, 1929) and 529,808 (June 8, 1929).
400. Toy, A. D. F. (to Victor Chemical Works), U. S. Patent 2,400,577 (May 21, 1946).
401. Morris, R. E., Hollister, J. W., and Seegman, I. P., *Rubber Age*, **56**, 163–7 (1944).
402. Tipson, R. S., *J. Org. Chem.*, **9**, 235–41 (1944).
403. Butler, C. L., Nelson, W. L., Renfrew, A. G., and Cretcher, L. H., *J. Am. Chem. Soc.*, **57**, 575–8 (1935).
404. Butler, C. L., Renfrew, A. G., Cretcher, L. H., and Souther, B. L., *J. Am. Chem. Soc.*, **59**, 227–9 (1937).
405. Butler, C. L., and Renfrew, A. G., *J. Am. Chem. Soc.*, **60**, 1582–5 (1938).
406. Clapp, M. A., and Tipson, R. S., *J. Am. Chem. Soc.*, **68**, 1332–4 (1946).
407. Nair, C. N., and Peacock, D. H., *J. Indian Chem. Soc.*, **12**, 318–21 (1935).
408. Peacock, D. H., and Tha, P., *J. Chem. Soc.*, **1938**, 2303–5.
409. D'Alelio, C. F. (to General Electric Co.), U. S. Patent 2,403,791 (July 6, 1946).
410. Russell, W. F. (to R. T. Vanderbilt Co., Inc.), U. S. Patent 2,405,712 (Aug. 13, 1946).
411. Hill, W. H. (to American Cyanamid Co.), U. S. Patent 2,257,009 (Sept. 23, 1941).
412. Desseigne, G., *Bull. soc. chim. France*, **1946**, 98–9.
413. Scattergood, A., Miller, W. H., and Gammon, J., Jr., *J. Am. Chem. Soc.*, **67**, 2150–2 (1945).
414. Rippere, R. E., and LaMer, V. K., *J. Phys. Chem.*, **47**, 204–34 (1943).
415. Slinger, H. (to Imperial Chemical Industries, Ltd.), British Patent 571,663 (Sept. 4, 1945).

CHAPTER 7

ETHYLENE GLYCOL CONDENSATION POLYMERS

Condensation polymers of ethylene glycol have the general formula $HOCH_2CH_2(OCH_2CH_2)_nOH$. They are discussed here under the general headings diethylene glycol (where $n = 1$), triethylene glycol (where $n = 2$), and polyethylene glycols (where $n = 3,4,5, \ldots$).

DIETHYLENE GLYCOL

Diethylene glycol is similar in many respects to ethylene glycol, but is sufficiently individual to find special uses as a solvent, hygroscopic agent, plasticizer, lubricant, and conditioning agent. Also known as diglycol, 2,2'-oxydiethanol, 2,2-oxybisethanol, and bis(2-hydroxyethyl) ether, it has the structural formula $HOCH_2CH_2OCH_2CH_2OH$.

Diethylene glycol first attained industrial importance in 1928 when it was offered commercially by Carbide[1]. Dow entered the field in 1938, the Jefferson Chemical Company in 1949. Wyandotte Chemicals Corporation began offering it in mixtures with dipropylene glycol, also during 1949. In Germany, I. G. Farbenindustrie A.-G. sells diethylene glycol as "polyglycol," while in France it is sold by Kuhlmann-Francolor as "Brecolane NDG."

Preparation

The synthesis of diethylene glycol was first described in 1859 almost simultaneously by Lourenco[2,3] and by Wurtz[4,5]. Lourenco obtained it by reacting ethylene glycol with either ethylene dibromide or ethylene bromohydrin. Wurtz prepared it by reacting ethylene oxide with ethylene glycol and by the hydration of ethylene oxide.

Mohs[6] produced diethylene glycol by heating ethylene glycol monoacetate with the monosodium derivative of ethylene glycol. Cretcher and Pittenger[7] prepared it by the hydrolysis of ethylene glycol diacetate [from bis(2-chloroethyl) ether] in methanolic hydrochloric acid. Dimitriev and Dogadkina[8] obtained it in 10 per cent yield by heating ethylene glycol in a stream of carbon dioxide for 18 hours. These same investigators reported a 95 per cent yield when ethylene glycol was reacted with ethylene oxide in the presence of 0.05 per cent sulfuric acid in a sealed tube.

Diethylene glycol is obtained commercially for the most part as a co-product in the manufacture of ethylene glycol. The amount produced is dependent on the ratio of water to ethylene oxide, as shown in Table 7.1[9].

Courtesy of Edgar Fahs Smith Memorial Collection, University of Pennsylvania

FIGURE 7.1. Agostinho Vicente Lourenco (1822–1893), who first prepared the condensation polymers of ethylene glycol.

Details of a typical production method have been described by Morley[10]. It is also produced directly by the reaction of ethylene glycol with ethylene oxide[11].

TABLE 7.1.   YIELDS OF GLYCOLS AT 90 TO 95°C.

Mols of Water per Mol of Ethylene Oxide	% Yield from Ethylene Oxide Used		
	Ethylene Glycol	Diethylene Glycol	Triethylene Glycol
10.5	82.3	12.7	—
4.2	65.7	27.0	2.3
2.1	47.2	34.5	13.0

Properties

Diethylene glycol is a stable, high-boiling, slightly viscous, water-white liquid. It has a sharp taste, is practically odorless, and is extremely hygroscopic. Diethylene glycol combines most of the properties of ethylene glycol and of glycerol, with the added solvent power imparted by the ether group in the molecule. The compound is completely miscible with water, the lower alcohols, acetone, and ethylene glycol, and partially miscible with benzene, toluene, and carbon tetrachloride. It is also a solvent for nitrocellulose and for many dyes, resins, oils, and other organic compounds.

The physical properties of diethylene glycol are summarized in Table 7.2.* Additional values are given in the tables and charts that follow.

* See also: Romstatt, G., *Industrie chimique*, **23,** 567 (1936); Davidson, J. G., *Ind. Eng. Chem.*, **18,** 670 (1926); and Rinkenbach, W. H., *Ind. Eng. Chem.*, **19,** 474 (1927).

TABLE 7.2. PHYSICAL PROPERTIES OF DIETHYLENE GLYCOL

Azeotropes	see Table 7.3
Boiling point at 760 mm.	245.0°C.
at 50 mm.	164°C.
at 10 mm.	128°C.
Δb.p./Δp, 740 to 760 mm.	0.049°C./mm.
Coefficient of expansion at 20°C.	0.00064/°C.
Density (true) at 20°C.	1.1161 g./ml.
Dew points	see Fig. 7.2
Flash point (open cup)	290°F.
Freezing point	−8°C. (see Fig. 7.3)
Heat of combustion	567 kcal./mol (ref. 13)
Heat of vaporization at 760 mm.	150 Btu/lb.
at 10 mm.	279 Btu/lb.
Humectant values (relative)	see Table 7.4
Ignition temperature in air (apparent)	663°F.
Initial decomposition temperature	164°C. (ref. 14)
Liquid-vapor equilibria	see Figs. 7.4 and 7.5
Molecular weight	106.12
Refractive index, n_D at 20°C.	1.4472
$\Delta n_D/\Delta t$, 20 to 30°C.	0.00028/°C.
Solubility in water at 20°C.	Complete (see also Table 7.5)
Specific gravity (apparent) at 20/20°C.	1.1184 (see Figs. 7.6 and 7.7)
ΔSp. gr./Δt, 5 to 40°C.	0.00071/°C.
Specific heat at 20°C.	0.500 Btu/lb./°F. (see Fig. 7.8)
Surface tension at 25°C.	48.5 dynes/cm. (see Fig. 7.9)
Vapor pressure at 20°C.	<0.01 mm. (see Fig. 7.10)
Verdet constant at 5461 Ångstroms	0.01490 min./gauss cm. (ref. 15)
at 5893 Ångstroms	0.01264 min./gauss cm. (ref. 15)
Viscosity (absolute) at 20/C.	35.7 cps. (see Fig. 7.11)

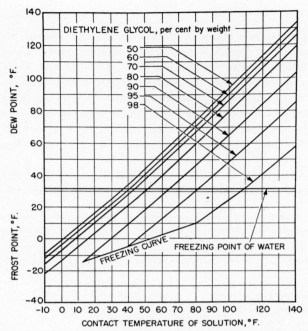

FIGURE 7.2. Effect of aqueous solutions of diethylene glycol on dew points at contact temperatures ranging from −10 to 140°F.

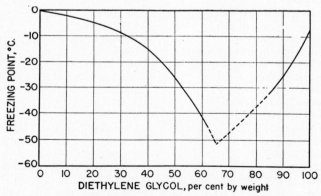

FIGURE 7.3. Freezing points of aqueous solutions of diethylene glycol.

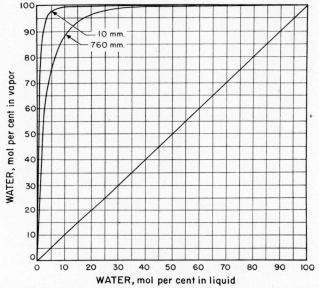

FIGURE 7.4. Liquid-vapor equilibria at atmospheric pressure and 10 mm. for the system diethylene glycol-water.

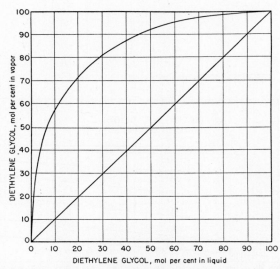

FIGURE 7.5. Liquid-vapor equilibria at 3 mm. pressure for the system diethylene glycol-triethylene glycol.

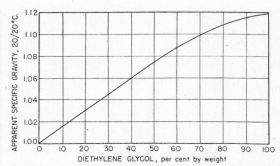

FIGURE 7.6. Apparent specific gravity at 20/20°C. of aqueous solutions of diethylene glycol.

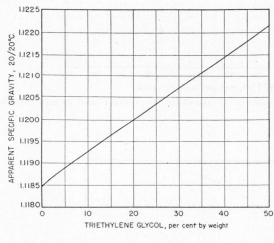

FIGURE 7.7. Apparent specific gravity at 20/20°C. of mixtures of diethylene glycol and triethylene glycol.

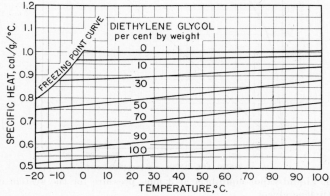

FIGURE 7.8. Specific heats of liquid aqueous solutions of diethylene glycol.

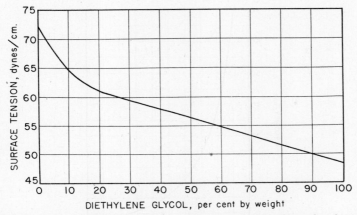

FIGURE 7.9. Surface tension of aqueous solutions of diethylene glycol at 25°C.

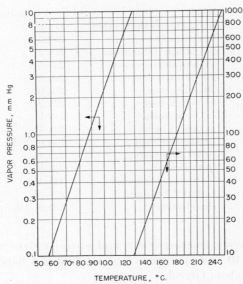

FIGURE 7.10. Vapor pressure of diethylene glycol.

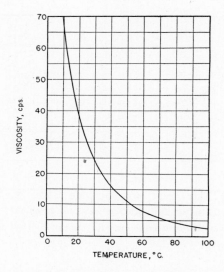

FIGURE 7.11. Absolute viscosity of diethylene glycol.

TABLE 7.3. AZEOTROPES OF DIETHYLENE GLYCOL[16, 17]

Second Component		Boiling Point of Azeotrope at 760 mm., °C.	Diethylene Glycol, % by wt.
Formula	Name		
H_2O	Water	no azeotrope	
$C_4H_8Cl_2O$	Bis(2-chloroethyl) ether	174.6	8
$C_6H_6O_2$	Pyracatechol	259.5	46
$C_6H_4ClNO_2$	*m*-Chloronitrobenzene	228.2	32
$C_6H_4ClNO_2$	*o*-Chloronitrobenzene	233.5	41
$C_6H_4ClNO_2$	*p*-Chloronitrobenzene	229.5	34
$C_6H_5NO_2$	Nitrobenzene	210.0	10
$C_7H_7NO_2$	*m*-Nitrotoluene	224.2	25
$C_7H_7NO_2$	*o*-Nitrotoluene	218.2	17.5
$C_7H_7NO_2$	*p*-Nitrotoluene	228.75	35
$C_8H_{18}O_4$	Ethoxytriglycol	135.0 (3 mm.)	83.4
$C_9H_{10}O_3$	Ethyl salicylate	225.15	30
C_9H_7N	Quinoline	233.6	29
$C_{11}H_{10}$	Methylnaphthalene	225.45	39
$C_{11}H_{14}O_2$	Isobutyl benzoate	228.65	37
$C_{12}H_{26}O$	Hexyl ether	129.9 (50 mm.)	15.5

Other specific gravity, freezing point, and viscosity data are presented in Tables 3.6 and 3.10 and in Figures 3.8 and 3.20 of Chapter 3, "Physical Properties of Ethylene Glycol."

TABLE 7.4. RELATIVE HUMECTANT VALUES OF DIETHYLENE GLYCOL[18]

Air temperature, °F.	Relative Humidity, %							
	20	30	40	50	60	70	80	90
	Diethylene Glycol, % by Wt. in Water							
0		81.3	73.5	65.0	53.0	45.0		
10	88.0	82.0	74.0	68.0	55.0	45.0	35.0	
20	89.0	82.5	76.0	70.0	58.0	46.0	35.0	
30	90.0	83.3	78.0	71.0	60.0	47.0	37.0	25.0
40	90.7	84.5	80.0	73.0	64.0	54.0	40.0	27.0
50	91.5	86.3	82.0	76.0	67.0	56.0	43.0	28.0
60	92.5	88.5	83.0	78.0	67.0	57.5	47.0	30.0
70	93.0	89.3	83.5	79.0	72.0	60.0	47.0	30.0
80	93.5	90.0	84.5	80.0	72.0	60.0	48.0	30.0
90	93.8	90.3	85.0	80.7	73.3	62.5	50.0	30.0
100	93.8	90.6	85.5	81.3	74.0	63.5	51.0	32.0
110	94.0	90.8	86.0	82.0	75.0	65.0	53.0	33.0
120	94.3	91.2	87.0	82.5	76.0	66.0	54.0	35.0

TABLE 7.5. SOLUBILITY OF VARIOUS MATERIALS IN DIETHYLENE GLYCOL[18]

Compound	Solubility, g./100 g. of diglycol
Benzene	45.5
Bis(2-chloroethyl) ether	miscible
Carbon tetrachloride	35.5
Chlorobenzene	112.0
Dibutyl phthalate	11.8
Diethanolamine	miscible
Ethyl ether	19.5
Ethylene glycol stearate	very slightly soluble
Methyl orange	4.2
Monoethanolamine	miscible
o-Dichlorobenzene	93.6
Phenol	miscible
Tetrachloroethylene	12.0
Toluene	20.7
Urea	24.0
Castor oil	0.1
Coconut oil	insoluble
Cottonseed oil	insoluble
Hydrous wool fat	slightly soluble
Lard oil	insoluble
Linseed oil	insoluble
Olive oil	insoluble

TABLE 7.5—*Continued*

Compound	Solubility, g./100 g. of diglycol
Paraffin oil	insoluble
Pine oil	miscible
Soya bean oil	insoluble
Sperm oil	insoluble
Tall oil	3.1
Tung oil	insoluble
Turkey Red oil	6.3
Animal glue (dry)	very slightly soluble
Dextrin	slightly soluble
Dextrin (10% in H_2O)	miscible
Gum damar	slightly soluble
Kauri gum	slightly soluble
Rosin	<2.0
Shellac	very slightly soluble
Sudan III	slightly soluble

Diethylene glycol exhibits the chemical properties of an ether and a primary alcohol. Wurtz[12] reported that treatment with concentrated hydriodic acid yielded ethylene iodide, while nitric acid oxidized the molecule to glycolic acid, oxalic acid, and diglycolic acid. In general, however, diethylene glycol resembles ethylene glycol in chemical behavior and enters into the reactions typical of all the glycols (see Chapter 1, "Glycols—An Introduction").

Derivatives

Diethylene glycol derivatives are prepared by methods analogous to those for the production of the corresponding ethylene glycol compounds. They are usually obtained as secondary products in the reaction of ethylene oxide with active hydrogen compounds. For details, see Chapter 5, "Ethylene Oxide," and Chapter 6, "Derivatives of Ethylene Glycol."

Ethers. The lower alkyl ethers of diethylene glycol are marketed under the trade-mark "Carbitol." Physical properties of the commercially important compounds of this type are listed in Table 7.6. They are excellent solvents for cellulose esters and are used in the formulation of lacquer thinners and quick drying varnishes, enamels, and printing inks. Containing the —CH_2CH_2OH group, they are also solvents for dyestuffs and wood stains. As mutual solvents, they are widely employed for coupling immiscible liquids used in the preparation of soluble oils, cutting oils, insecticides, dry-cleaning soaps, and leather compounds. They are components also of hydraulic fluids for braking systems, shock absorbers, aircraft landing gears, and many other types of recoil mechanisms and hydraulic control systems.

Esters. Ester-type derivatives of diethylene glycol are important as synthetic resins, plasticizers, emulsifiers, and explosives. Resins and plasticizers are covered on page 167, explosives on page 168. As emulsifiers, especially for the textile[19], cosmetic[20], and pharmaceutical[21] industries, the fatty acid esters of diethylene glycol have been extensively reviewed by Goldsmith[22].

Ether-Esters. The hydroxyl group in the monoethers of diethylene glycol forms esters when reacted with acids. These compounds are useful industrially as solvents and plasticizers. Physical properties of the important compounds of this type are listed in Table 7.6.

Miscellaneous. The hydroxyl groups of diethylene glycol can be replaced by chlorine atoms to form bis(2-chloroethyl) ether. This compound is a particularly good solvent for fats, waxes, and greases. Sold under the trade-name "Chlorex" solvent, bis(2-chloroethyl) ether is used by oil refineries for treating lubricating oils to improve their viscosity characteris-

TABLE 7.6. PHYSICAL PROPERTIES OF DIETHYLENE GLYCOL DERIVATIVES

	Diethylene Glycol Ethers					Diethylene Glycol Ether-Esters	
	Methyl	Ethyl	Butyl	Diethyl	Dibutyl	Ethyl Ether Acetate	Butyl Ether Acetate
Boiling point							
at 760 mm., °C.	194.2	201.9	230.4	188.9	254.6	217.7	246.4
at 50 mm., °C.	115	121	145	107	162	130	156
at 10 mm., °C.	82	87	109	73	122	92	120
Δb.p./Δp., 740 to 760 mm., °C./mm.	0.048	0.049	0.052	0.050	0.056	0.052	0.053
Density (true) at 20°C., g./ml.	1.0193	0.9881	0.9520	—	—	1.0096	0.9793
Flash point, Tag glass open cup, °F.	200	205	240	180	245	230	240
Freezing point, °C.	—	—	−68.1	−44.3	−60.2	−25	−32.2
Heat of vaporization at 1 atm., Btu/lb.	163	173	111	—	110 (calculated)	124	112
Molecular weight	120.15	134.17	162.22	166.22	218.33	176.21	204.26
Refractive index, n_D at 20°C.	1.4263	1.4273	1.4316	1.4115	1.4233	1.4213	1.4262
Solubility in water at 20°C., % by wt.	∞	∞	∞	∞	0.3	∞	6.5
Solubility of water in, at 20°C., % by wt.	∞	∞	∞	∞	1.4	∞	3.7
Specific gravity (apparent) at 20/20°C.	1.0211	0.9898	0.9536	0.9082	0.8853	1.0114	0.9810
ΔSp.gr./Δt, 5 to 40°C., /°C.	0.000883	0.000887	0.000839	0.000966	0.000844	0.001018	0.000954
Specific heat at 20°C., Btu/lb./°F.	0.514	0.552	0.546	—	0.43	0.538	0.480 (at 28°C.)
Vapor pressure at 20°C., mm.	0.2	0.1	0.02	0.4	0.02	0.15	0.04
Viscosity (absolute) at 20°C., cps.	3.87	4.5	6.49	1.40	2.39	2.79	3.56

tics[23]. It also is useful as an assistant in various textile operations, such as scouring, kier-boiling, and bleaching, as a solvent in the purification of butadiene, as a soil fumigant, and as a chemical intermediate, *i.e.*, for divinyl ether.

Applications

Diethylene glycol has a wide range of commercial uses, most of which developed as a result of its hygroscopic properties. It finds application as a humectant for tobacco, cork, printing ink, glue, and cellophane. It acts as a hygroscopic agent for lubricating textile fibers, for dehydrating natural gas, and for treating packing in gas mains. Diethylene glycol is a solvent for dyes and resins, a coupling agent for soluble oils, and an "inhibitor" in magnesium foundry sand mold mixes. It is widely used as a starting material in the production of explosives, resins, and plasticizers.

Textiles. Diethylene glycol softens certain natural and synthetic fibers and increases their stretching properties and flexibility. It acts as a hygroscopic conditioning agent and lubricant prior to warping and spinning for silk[24], worsted yarns[25], and acetate rayon[26]. Its use insures uniformity of twist setting and yarn conditioning[27].

Diethylene glycol finds extensive application as a coupling agent in the "soluble" or emulsifiable oils used so widely in the textile industry for lubrication, soaking, throwing, knitting, and finishing. The diethylene glycol serves to clarify and brighten such oils, producing mutual solubility of the ingredients and finer, more stable dispersions in water[28].

Because of its excellent solvent power for dyes of most types, diethylene glycol is widely employed as a textile dyeing and printing auxiliary[29, 30, 31].

Tobacco. In the processing of cigarette tobacco, it is standard practice to treat the tobacco with a casing or hygroscopic liquid in order that the product have improved moisture retention and hence reach the smoker in a fresh condition. Glycerol was the time-honored material for this purpose until 1933 when theoretical considerations involving the products of combustion suggested diethylene glycol might have certain advantages over the triol. Claims[32, 33, 34, 35, 36, 37] and counterclaims[38, 39, 40, 41, 42, 43] on the merits of diethylene glycol have ensued.

Anti-Leak. The widespread distribution of natural and other dry gases in cast iron mains which formerly carried "wet" manufactured gas created the problem of increased bell-and-spigot joint leakage resulting from the drying out and shrinkage of the jute or hemp packing. Prior to 1930, efforts were made to apply various liquids, such as gas oil and drip oil, to resaturate the packing without interrupting service. These measures provided only temporary relief, however, and were unsatisfactory in general.

In 1931, G. E. Hitz of Central Hudson Gas and Electric Company began to study the application of various fluids directly to the mains for this purpose. Extensive field tests in cooperation with Carbide were supplemented with a thorough laboratory investigation by the United Gas Improvement Company. A product based on diethylene glycol, sold as "Carboseal" antileak, was announced in 1935[44]. Patents were issued starting in 1937[45, 46, 47]. Jensen[48] has described the results of this treatment on gas mains.

"Carboseal" anti-leak is used primarily for four purposes: (1) correcting leakage in systems distributing dry gases; (2) controlling dust and rust in the mains; (3) treating dried out packing; and (4) as an anti-freeze in U-gauges. Methods for applying the anti-leak have been described[49].

Gas Dehydration. With the installation of high pressure transmission lines for natural gas, the problem of clogging in the lines due to the formation of hydrocarbon hydrates became quite serious. Calcium chloride brine was used to dehydrate the gas until 1938, when aqueous solutions of diethylene glycol were substituted[50]. The glycol has several advantages, including the fact that it is noncorrosive to the equipment employed. The natural gas is passed countercurrent to a concentrated aqueous solution of diethylene glycol, which absorbs the excess moisture. The absorbed water is removed from the solution by distillation, and the glycol is recycled through the absorber. The technical aspects, design, and operation of such natural gas dehydration systems have been thoroughly covered in the literature[51, 52, 53, 54, 55, 56, 57, 58].

Diethylene glycol is used in combination with an amine such as monoethanolamine for gas desulfurization along with dehydration[59, 60, 61]. A typical absorber solution consists of a mixture of 7 to 8 per cent monoethanolamine, 75 to 80 per cent diethylene glycol, and 12 to 16 per cent water (all by volume). Such a mixture will lower the dew point of the gas to a marked extent and reduce the hydrogen sulfide content to an insignificant concentration. Boiling the solution removes water and absorbed hydrogen sulfide, and the regenerated solution is ready for recycling through the system.

A dehydration-refrigeration plant employing diethylene glycol in combination with propane gas has also been described[62].

Cork. Another use where the marked hygroscopicity of diethylene glycol has proved of importance is in the plasticization of composition cork[63, 64, 65, 66, 67]. The glycol serves as a solvent for the glue or other protein and as a plasticizer for the cork. Its substitution for water eliminates shrinkage, curling, and brittleness in the product. One typical formulation consists of four pounds of diethylene glycol and one pound each of glue and latex for each three pounds of a resin binder, the whole to be mixed with 12 to 13 pounds of ground cork[68].

Courtesy of the Girdler Corporation

FIGURE 7.12. A "Girbotol" installation for gas dehydration with diethylene glycol and gas desulfurization with monoethanolamine.

Glues. Diethylene glycol is widely employed as a softening and moistening agent in bindery adhesives, especially for books[69]. Using the glycol for this purpose was principally the result of research conducted by the United States Government Printing Office in conjunction with the Employing Bookbinders Association of America and later with the Printing Industry of America. Its substitution for glycerol was advocated because of the diol's higher hygroscopicity and lower viscosity. Thinner glues result with correspondingly greater flexibility. Since less water is needed, warping of book covers in minimized. Adhesion of the paste to artificial leather covers is improved by the softening effect of the glycol on the pyroxylin coating.

Printing Inks. The broad solvent properties of diethylene glycol together with its marked hygroscopicity make it an ideal component of steam-set inks. Such inks contain essentially a pigment dispersed in a synthetic resin that is soluble in the glycol. The addition of steam precipitates a thin hard film of the resin, giving a fast setting ink that adheres to the surface of the paper.

Steam-set inks are used principally because they will not offset as do the types that require either oxidation or volatilization of a solvent to set them. In addition, they are odorless, rub-resistant, and brilliant in color.

The first steam-set inks were introduced by the Michigan Research Laboratories under the trade-name "Diene." They are now sold under a variety of names, such as "C. and C.," "Hydry," "Vaposet," "Misto," and "Quicko." For the most part the resin is of the modified maleic alkyd[70], zein[71], soybean[72], naphthol pitch[73], or phenolic[74] types.

Resins and Plasticizers. The most important of the ester-type derivatives of diethylene glycol are the various synthetic resins that involve diethylene glycol in their manufacture. Commercially available resins of diethylene glycol have been listed[75].

Like ethylene glycol, diethylene glycol can be condensed with maleic, fumaric, or similar acids to form polyesters that polymerize with vinyl monomers[76], such as vinyl acetate[77] and styrene[78], in the presence of a peroxide catalyst (see page 136). Copolymers of diethylene glycol maleate[79] and diethylene glycol fumarate[80] with styrene, vinyl acetate, or methyl methacrylate, for instance, are transparent resins which have good optical properties and which compare favorably in hardness with cast phenolic, vinyl, and acrylic resins. These materials are useful as laminating resins and adhesives. Resinous products suitable for coatings, inks, and cements are formed by reacting diethylene glycol, fumaric acid, and terpenes[81].

The esterification of diethylene glycol with rosin acids yields soft resins useful in nitrocellulose lacquers, enamels, and adhesives[82]. These resins are similar to those of the ester-gum types. Among those commercially available are "Flexalyn" (diethylene glycol diabietate), "Staybelite" Ester No. 2 (diethylene glycol ester of hydrogenated rosin), and "Poly-pale" Ester No. 2 (diethylene glycol ester of polymerized rosin)[83].

When used in the manufacture of alkyd resins as a partial replacement for glycerol, diethylene glycol serves to decrease the high degree of cross-linking that normally occurs in the curing of such resins. These modified alkyds possess a higher degree of alkali resistance than those prepared with glycerol alone[84].

Linear polyesters for use as plasticizers and in adhesives are prepared with diethylene glycol. One of these is obtained from the glycol, phthalic anhydride, and coconut oil[85]. Fatty acid esters of diethylene glycol have similar applications. For instance, the dipelargonate ester, sold commercially as "Plastolein" 9055, can be used with a wide variety of synthetic resins and rubbers[86]. Aromatic acid esters or mixed aromatic acid-fatty acid esters have also been suggested as plasticizers for polyvinyl chloride[87].

The reaction of phosgene with diethylene glycol and its monobutyl and monophenyl ethers yields a series of esters useful as resin intermediates[88], for example, diethylene glycol butyl carbonate and diethylene glycol phenyl carbonate. One resin, which is a copolymer of diethylene glycol allyl carbonate produced by the reaction of the glycol with allyl alcohol and phosgene, is sold as "Allymer" CR-39. It is used primarily as a clear glazing resin and can be cast into sheets, rods, and tubes. Diethylene glycol chloroformate and its amide, diethylene glycol dicarbamate, have been suggested as modifiers for phenol formaldehyde and urea and melamine resins. Modification of these diethylene glycol carbonate esters with acrylic and methacrylic acids produces polymerizable resins[89].

Explosives. Diethylene glycol dinitrate for explosive purposes was investigated and described by Rinkenbach in 1927[90]. Two patents for the manufacture of this compound were issued to Hough[91]. Although never as important in the United States as the corresponding ethylene glycol derivative, it found wide use in Germany during World War II, particularly as an ingredient of blasting explosives, rocket propellants, and low calorific gun powders[92, 93, 94].

For blasting purposes, diethylene glycol dinitrate is an excellent additive to nitroglycerin, 8 per cent giving an explosive composition of lower freezing point and greater power output. Although such a mixture is less sensitive to shock, its velocity of detonation, when exploded, exceeds that of nitroglycerin alone. In low-calorific gun powders, such as those containing nitroguanidine, incorporation of diethylene glycol dinitrate decreases gun-barrel erosion and the resulting flash.

Sand Mold Mixes. Diethylene glycol as an inhibitor in magnesium, aluminum, and other foundry sand mold mixes[95, 96] keeps the molten metal from reacting with either the moisture in the sand or the sand itself. It also prevents drying out of the sand, decreases the amount of water required, and lowers the local temperature.

The inhibitory action of diethylene glycol in this application is attributed to its reaction with the boric acid of the sand mix. The borate ester formed has good high-temperature protection properties. It forms an enveloping protective atmosphere around the molten alloy and gives a surface on the casting which is resistant to oxidation from "burning".

Miscellaneous. Diethylene glycol is used as a reaction medium because of its good heat stability and broad solvent powers. The decarboxylation of quinolinic acid to nicotinic acid at 135 to 140°C. can be carried out

FIGURE 7.13. Assembling cores in a magnesium sand-casting mold. Diethylene glycol is added to the sand mix to keep the molten metal from reacting with either the moisture in the sand or the sand itself.

in diethylene glycol[97]. It can be used as a solvent for the preparation of divinyl ether by dehydrohalogenation of bis(2-chloroethyl) ether with potassium hydroxide[98]. Diethylene glycol has been employed as a solvent for cresylic acid mixtures in the measurement of critical temperatures[99]. In the saponification of esters prior to identification of the individual components, diethylene glycol acts as a solvent for both the esters and the potassium hydroxide[100].

Diethylene glycol as a coupling agent for soluble oils is not limited to the textile industry. The added solubility imparted by the ether group in the molecule has resulted in its use in oils employed in metal cutting, agricultural sprays, and polishes[101, 102].

Diethylene glycol has been used in the compounding of GR-S with fine particle silica[103]. The glycol produces fast cures and improves the physical properties of the synthetic rubber.

Diethylene glycol finds many other minor applications. Although relatively unimportant as an anti-freeze for automobile cooling systems because of its solvent action on car finishes, diethylene glycol was incorporated during World War II into a military anti-freeze formulation as an extender for ethylene glycol[104]. It has been employed as a diluent in brake fluids[105, 106], as a solvent for boric acid and sodium tetraborate in electrolytic condensers[107], and as the circulating medium in boxcar automatic heating systems[108]. It has been suggested as a sterilizing medium for dental and surgical instruments[109].

TRIETHYLENE GLYCOL

Triethylene glycol is similar to diethylene glycol in many of its properties and uses. Also known as triglycol, ethylene glycol dihydroxydiethyl ether, and di-β-hydroxyethoxyethane, it has the structural formula $HOCH_2CH_2OCH_2CH_2OCH_2CH_2OH$.

Triethylene glycol was first prepared by Lourenco[2, 3] and by Wurtz[4, 5], who produced it as by-products in their diethylene glycol syntheses. It is obtained commercially as a co-product in the manufacture of ethylene glycol from ethylene oxide. As in the case of diethylene glycol, the amount produced is dependent on the ratio of water to ethylene oxide, being favored by higher ratios of the oxide[10]. Triethylene glycol has been offered in commercial quantities by Carbide since 1928 and by Dow since 1940.

TABLE 7.7. PHYSICAL PROPERTIES OF TRIETHYLENE GLYCOL

Boiling point at 760 mm.	287.4°C.
at 50 mm.	198°C.
at 10 mm.	162°C.
$\Delta b.p./\Delta p$, 740 to 760 mm.	0.054°C./mm.
Coefficient of expansion at 20°C.	0.00069/°C.
Dew points	see Fig. 7.14
Fire point	345°F.
Flash point (open cup)	330°F.
Freezing point	−7.2°C.
Heat of vaporization at 1 atm.	179 Btu/lb.
Humectant values (relative)	see Table 7.8
Initial decomposition temperature	206°C. (ref. 14)
Molecular weight	150.17
Refractive index, n_D at 20°C.	1.4559
$\Delta n_D/\Delta t$, 20 to 30°C.	0.00031/°C.
Specific gravity (apparent) at 20/20°C.	1.1254
$\Delta sp. gr./\Delta t$, 5 to 40°C.	0.00078/°C.
Specific heat at 20°C.	0.525 Btu/lb./°F. (see Fig. 7.15)
Surface tension at 20°C.	45.2 dynes/cm.
Vapor pressure at 20°C.	<0.01 mm. (see Fig. 7.16)
Viscosity (absolute) at 20°C.	47.8 cps. (see Fig. 7.17)

Triethylene glycol is a water-white, odorless liquid with a boiling point approximately 44°C. above that of diethylene glycol. It is completely miscible with water and is a good solvent for nitrocellulose and various gums and resins. The important physical properties of triethylene glycol are listed in Table 7.7.* Other information is presented graphically in the figures that follow. Liquid-vapor equilibrium and specific gravity data for mixtures of triethylene glycol and diethylene glycol are plotted in Figures 7.4 and 7.6, respectively. Kinematic viscosities of mixtures of triethylene glycol and ethylene glycol are shown in Figure 3.20, Chapter 3, "Physical Properties of Ethylene Glycol."

Applications

Triethylene glycol is useful as an air disinfectant and as an intermediate in the production of resins and plasticizers. Because its fields of usefulness overlap those of the other glycols, it is utilized primarily when a compound of lower volatility is required.

Air Disinfection. Triethylene glycol is used as an air disinfectant in hospital wards, theaters, offices, and homes. Germ-free air conditioning[110] at reduced cost[111] has been reported[112, 113].

The use of the glycols for air disinfection was first reported in 1940 by English investigators[114, 115] who used propylene glycol as a carrier for hexylresorcinol aerosols. The discovery that the glycols themselves formed effective aerosols for aerial disinfection was made by Robertson and his associates[116]. As sterilization of the test chambers was accomplished within a few seconds, calculations indicated that the bactericidal activity could not be due to contact between the aerosol and the droplets carrying the bacteria[117]. It was later found that aerial disinfection resulting from the use of various glycols is due to the presence of glycol vapor in the air[118].

While propylene glycol and dipropylene glycol have been used occasionally for air sanitation, triethylene glycol is generally preferred because of the extremely small amounts required. A glycol vapor concentration in the air of 50 to 100 per cent of saturation should be maintained at all times. Air at 70°F. and 40 per cent humidity saturated with triethylene glycol vapor will carry 0.18 pounds per million cubic feet[119], or approximately one-half part per million on a volume basis. Experience indicates that to allow for condensation and absorption the rate of vaporization should be approximately twice the amount theoretically required.

Humidity should be maintained between 20 and 50 per cent for most effective anti-bacterial action, although good results have been obtained between 15 and 55 per cent. As a general rule, the dry bulb temperature should be held between 60 and 85°F.

---

* See also Davidson, J. G., *Ind. Eng. Chem.*, **18,** 669 (1926).

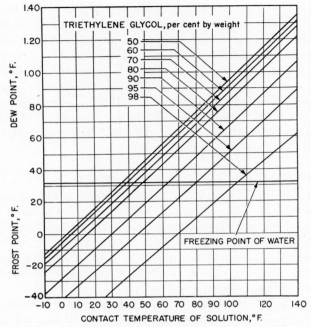

FIGURE 7.14. Effect of aqueous solutions of triethylene glycol on dew points at contact temperatures from −10 to 140°F.

TABLE 7.8. RELATIVE HUMECTANT VALUES OF TRIETHYLENE GLYCOL[18]

Air Temperature, °F.	Relative Humidity, %							
	20	30	40	50	60	70	80	90
	Triethylene Glycol, % by Wt. in Water							
0	91.0	84.5	80.0	62.0				
10	91.5	86.5	81.0	63.5				
20	92.0	87.0	82.0	65.0	50.0	42.0	32.0	
30	93.0	88.5	83.0	67.0	57.0	45.0	35.0	20.0
40	94.0	90.0	85.0	75.0	63.0	48.0	40.0	30.0
50	>95	91.2	87.0	80.0	70.0	54.0	43.0	30.0
60	>95	92.0	88.5	82.0	70.0	57.0	45.0	30.0
70	>95	93.0	89.3	83.0	75.0	61.0	46.0	30.0
80	>95	93.5	90.5	85.0	77.0	63.0	47.0	35.0
90	>95	94.3	90.9	86.0	80.0	64.0	50.0	37.0
100	>95	94.8	91.2	86.5	81.0	65.0	52.0	40.0
110	>95	95.2	92.0	87.5	82.0	68.5	54.0	42.0
120	>95	96.0	92.3	88.0	82.5	70.0	57.0	43.0

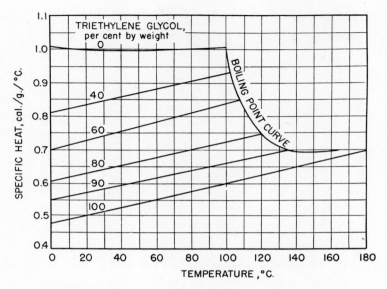

FIGURE 7.15. Specific heats of aqueous solutions of triethylene glycol.

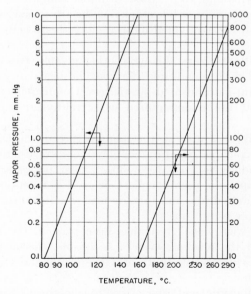

FIGURE 7.16. Vapor pressure of triethylene glycol.

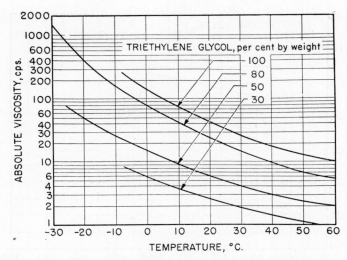

FIGURE 7.17. Absolute viscosities of aqueous solutions of triethylene glycol.

The rate at which bacteria and viruses are destroyed in laboratory tests is very rapid. Laboratory tests on *beta*-hemolytic streptococcus indicate that about 85 per cent of the bacteria are killed as they are sprayed into the air and the remaining 15 per cent within two minutes[120]. Pneumococcus is killed even more rapidly, while staphylococci are somewhat less sensitive. Viruses appear to be inactivated more rapidly than bacteria[121, 122, 123, 124, 125].

Resins and Plasticizers. Like the other glycols, triethylene glycol is readily esterified with mono- and dicarboxylic acids to yield derivatives that are important as resins and plasticizers. Commercially produced synthetic resins that are manufactured with triethylene glycol have been listed[75].

Triethylene glycol is used in the manufacture of various resins of the alkyd type. Convertible unsaturated polyesters are useful as laminating agents and in adhesives (see page 136). Linear polyesters, formed with acids such as adipic, are useful as plasticizers. The reaction product of the glycol, phthalic anhydride, and tartaric acid, for instance, acts as a plasticizer for cellulose ester films[126].

In Germany, triethylene glycol has been used in the manufacture of various resins of the phenolic type[127]. A flexible, thermosetting phenolic resin (Beckonit 540) involves both ethylene glycol and triethylene glycol in its preparation.

The di-2-ethylbutyric acid ester of triethylene glycol[128], sold as "Flexol" plasticizer 3GH, is an excellent plasticizer for the polyvinyl butyral resins used in the manufacture of high quality safety glass. This product can also be used as a plasticizer for nitrocellulose lacquers and for polyvinyl acetate.

A less volatile plasticizer, produced by esterifying triethylene glycol with 2-ethylhexanoic acid[128], is sold as "Flexol" plasticizer 3GO. It also can be employed in vinyl chloride resin compositions, in synthetic rubber compounds, and in polyvinyl butyral cloth coating formulations.

The diacetate of triethylene glycol is a partially water-soluble plasticizer for vinyl resins employed in fusing cloth[129]. A mixed acetate-butyrate ester serves as a plasticizer for cellulose acetate[130]. The esterification product of triethylene glycol and a C_6–C_{10} coconut oil fatty acid fraction (predominantly caprylic acid), sold as "S.C." Plasticizer, is used with vinyl resins[131]. Aromatic esters have been evaluated as plasticizers for polyvinyl chloride[87].

The Germans manufactured several such esters for plasticizing nitrocellulose and polyvinyl chloride resins[132]. For the most part they were reaction products of the glycol and fatty acid mixtures ("Plastomel" KF, "Mollit" KF, "Plasticizer J. 1203," "Weich" SCHKO, and "Geloton").

Resins useful in coatings and plastic compositions are obtained by reacting triethylene glycol with allyl chloroformate[133].

Miscellaneous. Because it is less volatile than diethylene glycol and almost as hygroscopic, triethylene glycol is sometimes employed in the formulation of composition cork and in various gas dehydration processes

Courtesy of Libbey-Owens-Ford Glass Company

FIGURE 7.18. Safety glass fractured by the weight of the dropped bowling ball is held together by the plastic interlayer, a polyvinyl butyral resin plasticized with the di-2-ethylbutyric acid ester of triethylene glycol.

where vapor losses are quite important. The trend in gas dehydration is toward the use of triethylene glycol since the solutions can be concentrated at higher temperatures[134, 135]. It has been suggested for the dehydration of air in blast furnaces[136]. At least one natural gas dehydration plant has been so designed that it can be converted to the use of triethylene glycol in place of diethylene glycol[137]. A process for the manufacture of maleic anhydride by a vapor-phase catalytic oxidation of hydrocarbons involves dehydrating the influent air with triethylene glycol[138].

Triethylene glycol dinitrate is of some commercial importance. Because of its relatively low volatility, good stability, and excellent gelatinization characteristics, the Germans selected this compound as an ingredient of gun powders for use in the tropics during World War II[93]. Used with gun cotton, it is particularly suitable for low calorific double-based powders. The Germans also employed the dinitrate as a propellant for their "Nebel Werfer" rockets[94]. In addition, triethylene glycol dinitrate is useful for increasing the cetane number of Diesel fuels[139].

Besides being important as plasticizers, the fatty acid derivatives of triethylene glycol are used as emulsifiers, demulsifiers, and lubricants[22]. For example, an emulsion of mineral oil and water with an ester of triethylene glycol and coconut oil fatty acids as the emulsifying agent is an antiparasitic spray for plants[140].

In Germany, triethylene glycol has been used as a liquid contact carrier for the high-pressure carbon monoxide synthesis of butyl acrylate[141]. This process—involving butyl alcohol, carbon monoxide, and acetylene, with a nickel bromide catalyst—could be operated continuously for the manufacture of the acrylate ester.

Triethylene glycol acts as a plasticizer for nitrocellulose lacquers used as the electrophoretic coatings in electron-tube parts[142]. Triethylene glycol can be used as a solvent extractor to separate resin-forming aromatic hydrocarbons, such as styrene or p-methyl styrene, from mixtures of light oil fractions[143]. It has also been suggested as a monostat fluid in electronic relay-type pressure-control mechanisms. A drop of sulfuric acid is added to increase the conductivity of the glycol[144].

POLYETHYLENE GLYCOLS

The polyethylene glycols above triethylene glycol range from water-white liquids to wax-like solids. Also known as polyglycols or polyoxyethylene glycols, these compounds are water-soluble, nonvolatile, unctuous materials. They are used as lubricants, vehicles, solvents, binders, and intermediates in the rubber, food, pharmaceutical, cosmetic, agricultural, textile, paper, petroleum, and many other industries.

Four liquid polyethylene glycols and five solid polyethylene glycols are produced by Carbide. Its solid polyethylene glycols are sold under the registered trade-mark "Carbowax." Each product represents a band of molecular weights, the average of which (except in the case of "Carbowax" compound 1500) is employed in characterizing the particular member of the series. The liquid compounds are thus known as polyethylene glycols 200, 300, 400, and 600, while the solids are sold as "Carbowax" compounds 1000, 1500, 1540, 4000, and 6000. Another series of polyethylene glycols (Polyglycol E400, E600, E1200, and E4000) are produced by Dow.

A series of polyethylene glycols manufactured in Germany are known as Polyglycol P's. A numerical suffix, used to designate each product, refers to the units of ethylene oxide involved in its manufacture. Polyglycol P-6, P-8, P-9, and P-12 are yellow, viscous liquids; P-18 a semi-solid brown wax and P-60 and P-80 yellow waxes. Another product, known as "Oxydwachs," with a molecular weight of approximately 4000 is also offered commercially[132].

Preparation

Polyethylene glycols were first prepared in 1859 by Lourenco[2], who heated a mixture of ethylene glycol and ethylene dibromide in a sealed tube at 115 to 120°C. He isolated materials of molecular weight as high as that of hexaethylene glycol[3].

At about the same time, Wurtz[4, 12] reported isolating polyethylene glycol fractions after heating ethylene oxide with ethylene glycol, and ethylene oxide with water, for several weeks. He also obtained a series of polyethylene glycol acetates from the polymerization of ethylene oxide in the presence of acetic acid. However, as in the case of the glycols themselves, the individual acetates could not be isolated in a pure state.

Mohs[6] obtained a polymeric product from the reaction of 2-hydroxyethyl acetate and the sodium alcoholate of ethylene glycol. Wurtz[145] observed the formation of a solid polymer when ethylene oxide stood in contact with a trace of alkali or zinc chloride. This polyoxide melted at 56°C. and was soluble in water and alcohol but insoluble in ether. Roithner[146] found that the polymerization catalyzed by alkali proceeded more rapidly at 50 to 60°C.

Staudinger and Schweitzer[147] investigated the polymerization of ethylene oxide under the influence of various catalysts and succeeded in separating a mixture of the polyethylene glycols into their individual components. They isolated the pure hexamer, $HOCH_2CH_2(OCH_2CH_2)_5OH$, and characterized it as a heavy viscous liquid, boiling at 325°C. at a pressure of 0.025 mm. Of the catalysts examined, these investigators reported anhydrous stannic chloride, metallic sodium or potassium, and trimethylamine to be the best, with stannic chloride being particularly effective even at temperatures as low as $-80°C$. The product with stannic chloride was divided into several fractions by solution in benzene and fractional precipitation with ether. This procedure yielded five distinct fractions ranging in molecular weight from 430–440 to 4650–4900.

The rate of polymerization of ethylene oxide with various catalysts at 20°C. was studied by Staudinger and Lohmann[148]. Their results are summarized in Table 7.9.

Matignon, Moureu, and Dodé[9] hydrated ethylene oxide in aqueous solutions containing 0.5 per cent sulfuric acid as a catalyst to find that the proportion of polyethylene glycols prepared depended on the ratio of oxide to water. Coleman and Moore[149] reported that when ethylene glycol is heated at temperatures below 210°F. with less than 10 per cent of its weight of sulfuric acid, polyethylene glycols are formed.

The first direct method for synthesizing a single polyethylene glycol was devised by Perry and Hibbert[150], who reacted the dichloride of a pure lower molecular weight polyglycol with two mols of the monosodium alcoholate of another pure polyglycol. This reaction may be written as follows:

$$\begin{bmatrix} CH_2 \\ | \\ O \\ | \\ CH_2 \end{bmatrix}_x \begin{matrix} -CH_2Cl \\ \\ \\ \\ -CH_2Cl \end{matrix} + 2 \begin{bmatrix} CH_2 \\ | \\ O \\ | \\ CH_2 \end{bmatrix}_y \begin{matrix} -CH_2ONa \\ \\ \\ \\ -CH_2OH \end{matrix} \rightarrow \begin{bmatrix} CH_2 \\ | \\ O \\ | \\ CH_2 \end{bmatrix}_{(x+2y+2)} \begin{matrix} -CH_2OH \\ \\ \\ \\ -CH_2OH \end{matrix} + 2NaCl$$

The two most suitable methods for forming the monosodium alcoholate entail the use of sodium methoxide and metallic sodium, respectively. Primarily, the dichloride derivative used in the synthesis was bis(2-chloroethyl) ether. However, they found that any polyethylene glycol could be converted into the corresponding dichloride by thionyl chloride in pyridine solution. Using this general procedure, Hibbert et al.[150, 151, 152] were able to prepare pure tetra-, hexa-, octa-, and decaethylene glycols and the 42-membered, 90-membered, and 186-membered polyethylene glycols, as well as several of the corresponding dichlorides.

TABLE 7.9. RATE OF POLYMERIZATION OF ETHYLENE OXIDE AT 200°C .

Catalyst	Yield of Polymer, %	Molecular Weight	Time of Reaction
Trimethylamine ⎫ Sodium or potassium ⎬ Stannic chloride ⎭	5	2000	1–2 weeks
Sodamide	1–2	10,000	2–3 months
Zinc oxide	10–20	60,000	3–4 months
Strontium oxide	10–20	100,000	2–3 months
Calcium oxide	50	120,000	about 2 years

Commercially the polyethylene glycols are produced batchwise in steel reaction tanks fitted with circulating pumps and external heat exchangers. To either water, ethylene glycol, or diethylene glycol containing a catalytic proportion of sodium hydroxide, ethylene oxide is added at a rate to maintain the temperature of the liquid contents between 120 and 135°C. The total pressure on the system at this temperature is about 60 pounds per square inch gauge. Since the reaction liberates heat, it is necessary to apply cooling water to the heat exchanger to maintain this temperature and pressure. After all the ethylene oxide has been added, the system is maintained at substantially constant temperature for an additional two to five hours to permit completion of the reaction. When the pressure on this system at constant temperature remains unchanged for at least an hour, the reaction is considered finished. The reaction mass is then neutralized and filtered.*

Structure. Roithner[146] assigned a cyclic structure to the polyethylene oxides; however, this structure cannot be supported for the products obtained by the usual methods. Although cyclic propylene oxide polymers have been prepared (see page 277), a similar procedure with ethylene oxide yields only a small amount of a higher cyclic product, which is probably the tetramer, because dioxane is formed much more readily.

Staudinger[155] proposed two mechanisms for the polymerization of ethylene oxide. He suggested that the formation of all short chains takes place by a stepwise process. The outside limit of chain growth by this method is set at 10 or 12 repeating units. The second mechanism involving free radicals explains the formation of high polymers. Staudinger believed that as a consequence of the free radical mechanism, the reaction mixture contains at all times only the monomer and the completely inert polymerized product.

Perry and Hibbert[156], however, accounted for the formation of both high and low polymers of ethylene oxide by a stepwise addition mechanism only. Their scheme of reactions is outlined as follows:

$$CH_2 \!-\! CH_2 \diagdown \diagup O + HOH \rightarrow \begin{array}{c} CH_2OH \\ | \\ CH_2OH \end{array}$$

$$\begin{array}{c} CH_2OH \\ | \\ CH_2OH \end{array} + CH_2 \!-\! CH_2 \diagdown \diagup O \rightarrow \begin{array}{c} CH_2OH \\ | \\ CH_2\!-\!O\!-\!CH_2\!-\!CH_2OH \end{array}$$

The reactions involved are those taking place when ethylene oxide reacts

---

* Ellis[153] has briefly reviewed a few of the important manufacturing methods that have been described in the literature for carrying out the polymerization of ethylene oxide. The German operations at Ludwigshafen have been described[154].

with substances containing active hydrogen. The "reactive intermediates" are polyethylene glycols. These authors showed that the members of this polymeric series are identical with products formed in the polymerization of ethylene oxide. To substantiate the theory, Perry and Hibbert proved that polyethylene glycols from diethylene glycol up through the 18-membered compound (hypothetical intermediates of the stepwise polymerization of ethylene oxide) were capable of reacting with ethylene oxide in the presence of potassium hydroxide as a catalyst to form higher polymers.

Further evidence for the presence of two free hydroxyl groups at either end of the polyethylene oxide chain, and therefore a linear structure for the molecule, is provided by the mode of synthesis and by the fact that the compounds give the expected reactions for hydroxyl groups, *e.g.*, replacement with chlorine, evolution of hydrogen upon reaction with metallic potassium, and the Zerewitinoff test[152].

In agreement with Perry and Hibbert, Flory[157] represented the formation of polyethylene glycols as

$$M_1 + M \rightarrow M_2$$

$$M_2 + M \rightarrow M_3$$

where M_1 is the initial substance bearing the propagating functional group (hydroxyl) and M represents ethylene oxide. He demonstrated that in a polymer formed exclusively by the addition of monomer to a fixed number of polymer molecules, the number of species of various sizes is represented by Poisson's distribution law. He derived equations representing weight fraction distributions and depicted graphically the calculated weight per cents of various species in several polymers having average size of 6 to 500 units of polyethylene oxide. Figure 7.19 shows the theoretical polymer distribution of polyethylene glycols as calculated by the method of Flory. It can be seen that as the molecular weight increases, the base of the curve broadens out to include a wider range of individual components.

Viscosity measurements indicate that the polyethylene oxides exist in two forms[155, 158]. The lower polymers possess the ordinary "zig-zag" configuration

while the higher polymers exist in what is termed the "meandering" form.

$$
\begin{array}{ccc}
\overset{\displaystyle O}{\diagup\!\diagdown} & \overset{\displaystyle O}{\diagup\!\diagdown} & \overset{\displaystyle O}{\diagup\!\diagdown} \\
CH_2 \quad CH_2 & CH_2 \quad CH_2 & CH_2 \\
| \qquad\; | & | \qquad\; | & | \\
CH_2 \quad CH_2 & CH_2 \quad CH_2 & CH_2 \\
\diagdown\!\diagup & \diagdown\!\diagup & \\
O & O &
\end{array}
$$

These configurations were substantiated by the x-ray studies of Sauter[159] and of Barnes and Ross[160], who showed in addition the structural similarity of Staudinger's polymerized ethylene oxides and the pure polyethylene glycols of Perry and Hibbert. Hibbert and Lovell[161] advanced additional evidence for these configurations by calculating that the long chains are highly convoluted in solution.

Properties

The physical properties of the polyethylene glycols vary with molecular weight in a characteristic fashion. The freezing or melting range, specific gravity, flash point, and viscosity increase as the molecular weight increases. Vapor pressure, hygroscopicity, and solubility in organic compounds decrease as the molecular weight increases. The polyethylene glycols are completely water-soluble and are miscible with many waxes, gums, oils, starches, and organic solvents.

Physical properties of the pure polyethylene glycols prepared by

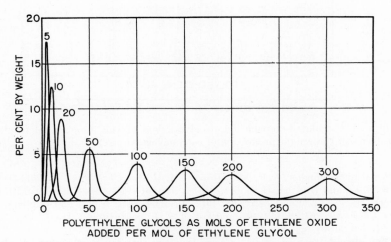

FIGURE 7.19. Theoretical polymer distribution of polyethylene glycols. The numbers on the curves indicate the mol ratio of ethylene oxide to ethylene glycol.

Hibbert, Perry, Fordyce, and Lovell (see page 178) are shown in Table 7.10.* Physical properties of the commercially available polyethylene glycols, which are actually mixtures of several condensation polymers (see Figure 7.20), are summarized in Table 7.11.** Additional physical property data are given in the figures that follow and in Figure 3.20 of Chapter 3, "Physical Properties of Ethylene Glycol."

Chemically, the polyethylene glycols resemble ethylene glycol and diethylene glycol. The two terminal hydroxyl groups of the molecule are typical primary alcohol groups in that they form ethers and esters. In addition, evidence exists that the long chains of multiple ether groups will form definite association complexes with compounds such as silicotungstic acid[162].

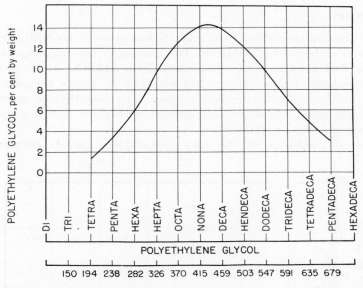

FIGURE 7.20. Calculated distribution of polyethylene glycols in polyethylene glycol 400 in terms of the weight proportion of each molecular size.

* See also: Gallaugher, A. F., and Hibbert, H., *J. Am. Chem. Soc.*, **59**, 2514 (1937); Lovell, E. L., and Hibbert, H., *J. Am. Chem. Soc.*, **61**, 1916 (1939); Fordyce, R., and Hibbert, H., *J. Am. Chem. Soc.*, **61**, 1912 (1939); Lovell, E. L., and Hibbert, H., *J. Am. Chem. Soc.*, **62**, 2141 (1940); and Lovell, E. L., and Hibbert, H., *J. Am. Chem. Soc.*, **62**, 230 (1940).

** See also: Livengood, S. M., *Chem. Inds.*, **63**, 948 (1948); Weissler, A., Fitzgerald, J. W., and Resnick, I., *J. Applied Phys.*, **18**, 434 (1947); Svirbley, W. J., and Lander, J. J., *J. Am. Chem. Soc.*, **67**, 2189 (1945); and Couper, A., and Eley, D. D., *J. Polymer Sci.*, **3**, 345 (1948).

TABLE 7. 10. PHYSICAL PROPERTIES OF PURE POLYETHYLENE GLYCOLS

Compound	Appearance	Refractive Index, n_D at 60°C.	Density, g./ml. at 60°C.	Freezing Point °C.	Boiling Point, °C.	Molecular Weight		Molar Refraction	
						Calcd.	Obsd.	Calcd.[a]	Obsd.
Tetraethylene glycol	Colorless liquid	1.4593[b]			144.0–145.5 (at 0.10 mm.); 160 (at 2–3 mm.)	194.1	206.0		
Hexaethylene glycol	Colorless liquid	1.4500	1.0948	2.1	185–185.7 (at 0.015 mm.)	282	289	68.881	69.22
Octaethylene glycol	Colorless liquid				206–9 (at 0.015–0.018 mm.)				
Decaethylene glycol	Colorless oil				220–3 (at 0.010 mm.)				
Octadecaethylene glycol	White crystal-solid	1.4550	1.0949	23.8		810	803	199.431	200.7
42-Membered polyethylene glycol	White crystalline solid	1.4563		33.8		1866	1748	460.526	463.7
90-Membered polyethylene glycol	White crystalline solid	1.4570		40.6		3978			
186-Membered polyethylene glycol	White crystalline solid	1.4572		44.1		8192			

[a] Calculations are based on the atomic value suggested by Auwers and Eisenlohr, *Ber.*, **43,** 806 (1910).
[b] Refractive index, n_D at 20°C.

TABLE 7.11. PHYSICAL PROPERTIES OF COMMERCIALLY AVAILABLE POLYETHYLENE GLYCOLS

Average Molecular Weight	Freezing Range, °C. (see Figures 7.21 and 7.22)	Specific Gravity, 20/20°C.	Flash Point, °F.	Saybolt Viscosity at 210 °F. sec. (see Figures 7.23, 7.24, and 7.25)	Solubility in Water at 20°C., % by wt. (see Figure 7.26)	Comparative Hygroscopicity (glycerol = 100)	pH of 5% Aqueous Solution at 25°C.
			Liquid Polyethylene Glycols				
200	190–210	Super-cools 1.12	340	38–42	Complete	70	4–7
300	285–315	−15–8	1.13	385	42–48	Complete 60	4–7
400	380–420	4–10	1.13	435	45–55	Complete 55	4–7
600	570–630	20–25	1.13	475	56–66	Complete 40	4–7
			Solid Polyethylene Glycols ("Carbowax" Compounds)				
1000	950–1050	38–41	530	85–100	Approx. 70	35	4–7
1500[a]	500–600	38–41	1.151[b]	430	70–90	73	35	4–7
1540	1300–1600	43–46	1.15	460	120–150	70	30	4–7
4000	3000–3700	53–56	1.204[b]	535	350–400	62		4.5–7.5
6000	6000–7500	60–63[c]	480	3200–4200	Approx. 50		4.5–7.5

[a] A mixture of approximately equal parts by weight of polyethylene glycol 300 and "Carbowax" compound 1540. [b] Density, g./cc. at 20°C. [c] Melting point range.

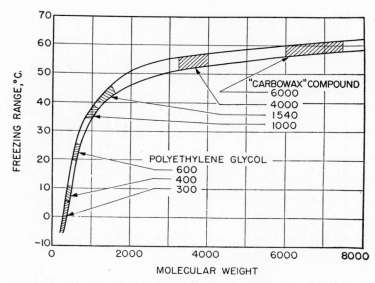

FIGURE 7.21. Freezing ranges of polyethylene glycols and "Carbowax" compounds.

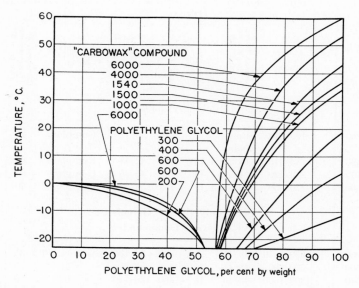

FIGURE 7.22. Phase diagrams of aqueous solutions of polyethylene glycols and "Carbowax" compounds. Below −23°C. all mixtures supercool and have no definite freezing points.

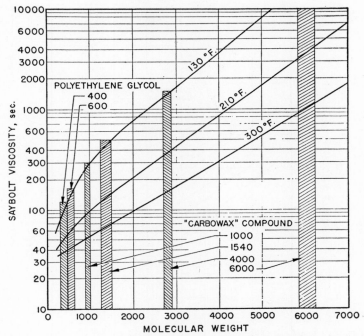

FIGURE 7.23. Saybolt universal viscosities of polyethylene glycols and "Carbowax" compounds.

Derivatives

Polyethylene glycol ethers (alkyl, aryl, and alkaryl) are prepared commercially by reacting the corresponding hydroxy compound with ethylene oxide[163, 164]. Similarly, polyethylene glycol inorganic esters, such as the chlorides, are obtained by reacting the appropriate halohydrin with ethylene oxide[155]. Polyethylene glycol organic esters, however, are usually derived from the polyethylene glycols themselves[165], although they can be made by interaction of the acid with ethylene oxide[163, 166].

Polyethylene glycol esters, of which the fatty acid derivatives are the most important, may be prepared simply by esterifying the polyglycol with a stoichiometric quantity of acid in the presence of an acid catalyst, such as sulfuric acid. The fatty acid esters, which comprise an important class of nonionic surface-active agents, are widely used as emulsifying agents, detergents, and dispersants, particularly in the agricultural, chemical, and textile industries[22, 167, 168, 169, 170, 171, 172]. Unlike conventional soaps, they are not precipitated by hard water or decomposed by mild acids. Their surface activity is a function of the balance that exists between the hy-

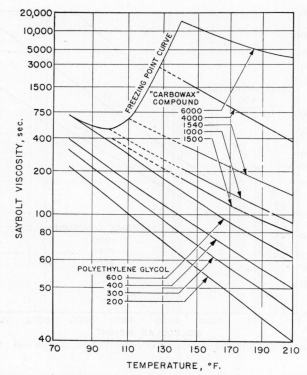

FIGURE 7.24. Saybolt viscosities of polyethylene glycols and "Carbowax" compounds at various temperatures.

drophobic long-chain acid portion and the hydrophilic polyoxyethylene chain.

Applications

The polyethylene glycols were made commercially available to fill an industrial need for water-soluble, nonvolatile, unctuous compounds. They are widely used alone or in blends as lubricants for rubber molds, textile fibers, and metal-forming operations. Certain of them are ingredients of pharmaceuticals, cosmetics, and miscellaneous products ranging from agricultural sprays to paper coatings to metal polishes.

Pharmaceuticals. In the pharmaceutical and related medical fields, certain polyethylene glycols are used as components of water-soluble ointment bases, as soluble dressings for open wounds, as carriers for penicillin, sulfa drugs, and peroxides, in shaped medical preparations, and as embedding mediums for microscopic study. They are utilized for such purposes

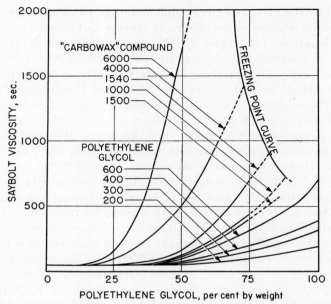

FIGURE 7.25. Saybolt viscosities of aqueous solutions of polyethylene glycols and "Carbowax" compounds at 25°C.

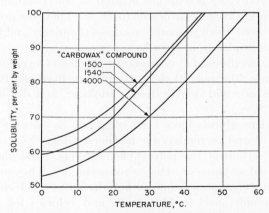

FIGURE 7.26. Solubility of "Carbowax" compounds in water.

primarily because of their water-solubility, low order of toxicity, and wide range of compatibilities[173].

The use of polyethylene glycols in many formulations where they are combined with other materials for skin application has been officially recognized by the Food and Drug Administration. Evidence exists that the medicament is released to the skin more quickly and effectively when it is dispersed in a base of the water-soluble (oil-in-water emulsion) type rather than in the standard grease (water-in-oil emulsion) type[174, 175, 176]. The "Carbowax" compound-type base has been found the most effective, being superior to Hydrophilic Ointment U. S. P. and Emulsifying Ointment B. P.[177]. The addition of various surface-active agents tends to inhibit crystal formation, which in turn improves the unctuousness of the ointments[178]. A comparable German product, known as "Postonal" ointment base[179], is identified as a polyethylene oxide containing 6 to 7 per cent water and an ethylene oxide-castor oil reaction product[180, 181].

Ointments based on the polyethylene glycols vary greatly as to composition and purpose[182]. A base composed of "Carbowax" compound 4000 and propylene glycol serves as an effective carrier for penicillin[183], penicillin and parachlorophenol[184], and bacitracin[185]. A propionate-propionic acid ointment and an undecylenate-undecylenic acid ointment in a propylene glycol-"Carbowax" compound base are effective in the treatment of dermatophytosis or athlete's foot[186]. An improved ammoniated mercury ointment is prepared using an emulsion base containing a "Carbowax" compound[187]. Other ointments[173] have been described, including formulations used in treating external otitis[188], burns[189], ringworm[190], and arsenic poisoning[191].

The solid polyethylene glycols are utilized as water-soluble suppository bases for carrying various medicaments[192, 193]. They do not dry or decompose when stored. Such preparations dissolve quickly and the medicines are rapidly and completely absorbed.

As embedding mediums for microscopic studies of eyes or muscle sections, for instance, the polyethylene glycols are particularly useful. The usual difficulties of rapid dehydration, shrinkage, and distortion are not encountered[194, 195].

The polyethylene glycols have been suggested as solvents for hormone preparations[196, 197] and as binders for hormone tablets[198].

Cosmetics. Certain of the polyethylene glycols, particularly the solid members, are used as bases or vehicles for cosmetics. They are ingredients of skin conditioner creams and aqueous hair dressings[199], solvents for "brom-acid" dye commonly used in lipsticks[200], and vehicles for nitrocellulose solvents used to remove nail polish[201, 202].

Rubber. Small amounts of "Carbowax" compounds 4000 or 6000 are useful as lubricants or release agents when applied to molds in which rubber parts, such as shoe soles or heels, are formed. Their use imparts an attractive finish to the molded rubber product. They are effective for both natural and synthetic rubbers. "Carbowax" 4000 is an excellent release

Courtesy of United States Rubber Company

FIGURE 7.27. Foam rubber cushion being stripped from a mold lubricated with "Carbowax" compound 4000.

agent for foamed rubber, while the 1500 compound is incorporated in rubber latices to act as a lubricant during calendering operations. "Carbowax" compound 4000 also acts as a dispersant for zinc oxide in the pigmenting of white stock made either from natural or GR-S rubber.

Textiles. The polyethylene glycols find wide application in the textile industry. They are utilized as assistants in spinning rayon, as ingredients of sizing compositions, and as dispersants of solvents in dyeing operations.

Because of their surface-active properties, the solid polyethylene glycols are used alone[203, 204] or in conjunction with anionic wetting agents[205] in rayon spinning baths to inhibit incrustation of the spinnerettes. Their addition to the cellulose pulp shredder box facilitates the shredding operation and improves the spinning qualities of viscose yarn formed from the

Courtesy of Industrial Rayon Corporation

FIGURE 7.28. Solid polyethylene glycols are added to rayon spinning baths to inhibit incrustation of the spinnerettes.

pulp[206]. In the cuprammonium method for producing rayon, "Carbowax" compound 4000 acts as an anticoagulent for the "blue" solution[207].

The solid polyethylene glycols are useful in sizing compositions because of their film-forming properties and their lubricating and plasticizing action. Such compositions are of several types, including: a polyvinyl alcohol-boric acid size for knitting nylon[208]; a polymethacrylic acid size for rayon[209]; and a polyvinyl acetate-boric acid size for "Dacron"[210]. "Carbowax" compound 1500 serves as a lubricant and ultimately as a knitting size for rayon yarn[211].

In dyeing operations, the polyethylene glycols have been used in the preparation of colored pigments and lakes[212] and as assistants in the dyeing of, and the stripping of dyestuffs from, textile fabrics[213].

Petroleum. The polyethylene glycols are of importance to the petroleum industry as intermediates in the production of demulsifiers for breaking crude-oil emulsions. The polyethylene glycol derivatives used for such operations include: the reaction product of polyethylene glycol 400 oxalate with ethyl ricinoleate[214]; the esterification products of various nitrogen-containing compounds with the diacid dimaleates of nonaethylene glycol or the solid polyethylene glycols[215]; the esterification product of nonaethylene glycol dihydrogen maleate and diethylene glycol monolaurate[216]; polyethylene glycol esters of boiled fatty acids or fatty oils[217]; and polyethylene glycol diesters of unsaturated fatty acids blown to a soft viscous consistency[218].

The polyethylene glycols are utilized as selective solvents for separating aromatic constituents present in petroleum[219]. Tetraethylene glycol is disclosed as a solvent in a continuous solvent extraction process for separating butadiene from C_4 hydrocarbon mixtures[220]. Tetraethylene glycol, among others, is also useful for removing methyl ethyl ketone from azeotropic distillates in the separation of hydrocarbons[221].

The solid polyethylene glycols are used in the production of lubricating greases of the sodium and lithium soap-based types[222]. Their incorporation promotes the reaction of the metals with the fatty acid components.

Metals. The polyethylene glycols, particularly the solid polymers, have several applications in the metals industry. Their addition to tin[223] and copper [224] plating baths produces deposits that are adherent, sponge-free, and bright in texture. They are additives to the phosphoric acid solutions used for electropolishing stainless steel[225] and aluminum and its alloys[226]. Their incorporation helps produce bright, specular surfaces. They are also employed as vehicles for metal polishes and tarnish removers[227]. One buffing compound, removable with hot water, is composed of an abrasive, a solid polyethylene glycol, and azelaic acid, which acts as an auxiliary binder[228].

Electronics. The polyethylene glycols are employed as lubricants in various electrical contact elements that are subjected to dry atmospheres and high altitudes[229]. One such element incorporates polyethylene glycols and polyesters to lubricate the porous blocks of bonded, finely divided carbon, graphite, or metal-graphite[230]. Similarly, carbon brushes impregnated with polyethylene glycols and aliphatic carboxylic acids reportedly show superior wear resistance at high altitudes[231]. Graphitized carbon commutator and slip ring brushes can be lubricated with the polyethylene glycols alone[232].

Polyethylene glycols find other applications in the field of electronics. For example, hexaethylene glycol is added to the nitrocellulose lacquers used for coating electron tube parts electrophoretically[233]. The use of "Carbowax" compound 4000 permits the formation of an even and uniform film of silver sulfide on the silver conductors that control high-frequency currents[234].

Resins and Plasticizers. Because of their two terminal hydroxyl groups and of the flexibility imparted to resinous intermediates by the introduction of the long polyoxyethylene chains, the polyethylene glycols are used in the production of various plastic compositions.

Resinous products are obtained by reacting vinyl esters with hexaethylene glycol[235] and by copolymerizing styrene with a polyethylene glycol maleate[236]. Such materials are useful as laminating resins. A polyethylene glycol maleate, modified with coumarin-indene resins or polyvinyl acetate, is useful as a thermoplastic adhesive composition for bottle labels[237]. Aqueous emulsified mixtures of polyesters, such as polyhexaethylene glycol maleate, and vinyl monomers can be polymerized with drying oil compounds, using a peroxide catalyst, to form tough, hard resins[238]. Such emulsion mixtures are claimed to be useful in the printing and impregnation of textiles, paper, and leather. The reaction product of "Carbowax" 1500 and shellac is a water-soluble resin that is not precipitated by acids[239].

Resin intermediates, such as polyethoxyethylol cyanamides and polyhaloformates, are formed by reacting the polyethylene glycols with calcium cyanamide[240] and with phosgene[241], respectively. Another intermediate, tetraethylene glycol bis(allyl carbonate), is prepared with tetraethylene glycol and allyl chloroformate[242]. Bis(2-cyanoethyl) ethers, which can be converted to polyamides, are obtained by the reaction of polyethylene glycols and acrylonitrile[243].

Polymerizable esters are formed by the reaction of polyethylene glycol 200 with methacrylic acid[244]. The diester is used in a thermosetting molding powder composition[245], and a mixture of the diester and methyl methacrylate is employed as a casting composition[246].

When condensed with fatty acids from corn oil, tung oil, and soybean oil, tetraethylene glycol forms polyesters that can be vulcanized with sulfur to rubber-like materials suitable for molding operations[247]. Similar products are obtained by reacting polyethylene glycols with partially esterified polyvinyl alcohol[248].

The polyethylene glycols have only limited application as resin plasticizers. Unsaturated long-chain fatty acid esters serve as plasticizers for cellulose esters and ethers[249]. Further reaction of the unsaturated esters with sulfur monochloride yields a plasticizer suitable for vinyl chloride-vinyl acetate and cellulose acetate resins. The di-2-ethylhexanoic ester of polyethylene glycol 200, sold under the trade-name "Flexol" plasticizer 4GO, is used with vinyl chloride-vinyl acetate films, synthetic rubber, and nitrocellulose lacquer. The polyethylene glycols themselves are plasticizers for starch adhesives[250], regenerated cellulosic articles[251], moisture-proof cellophane[252], urea-formaldehyde resins, glue, coated paper, and composition cork[253].

Incorporated into vinylidene chloride polymer and copolymer resins, tetraethylene glycol acts as a stabilizer against noncatalyzed heat deterioration[254].

Agriculture. The solid polyethylene glycols and their water soluble mono- and diesters are excellent spreading agents for agricultural sprays. They solubilize such substances as substituted phenoxyacetic and benzoic acids[255, 256, 257, 258, 259, 260, 261]. "Carbowax" compound 1500 has been investigated as a dispersant with 2,4-D to kill bindweed[262], destroy weed corn[263], and suppress ragweed pollen[264]. The solid polyethylene glycols have been studied as carriers for 2,4-D in the ripening of detached fruit[265, 266], retarding kidney-bean growth[267], and preventing a preharvest drop of fruit[268].

Miscellaneous. Among the miscellaneous applications for the polyethylene glycols may be mentioned their uses as: coatings, alone[269] or with soluble silicates[270], for soap granules to prevent dusting and clumping; binders for synthetic detergents in cake form[271]; vehicles for resins in steam set inks[272]; sensitizers, with lower alcohols or ethers, for photographic film to increase speed and improve contrast[273, 274]; constituents with gum arabic and alum of protective coatings for photographic films[275]; antistatic agents, in combination with an anionic wetting agent, for vinyl sheeting[276]; intermediates in the production of surface-active agents[277, 278] and anti-staling agents for bread[279]; reaction promoters in removing elements of hydrochloric acid from ethylene dichloride in the production of vinyl chloride[280]; selective solvents for extracting glycerides from sardine, tung, and other oils[281]; binding agents for holding glass tubes in bundles prior to cutting into beads[282]; ingredients, with cellulose acetate, of stopcock lubricant[283]; bases for the cakes of copper acetate and dyestuffs used as shark repellents[284]; binder, alone or in conjunction with water-insoluble waxes, for chemiluminescent substances that give visible light when dissolved in water[285]; mold lubricants for polystyrene molding compositions[286]; impregnating agents for the activated bauxite added to concrete to increase its workability and reduce the water ratio[287]; ingredients of a silicic acid solution used for impregnating paper, leather, and plastics[288, 289]; and as bases for water-soluble sticks suitable for removing various stains from fabrics[290].

Literature Cited

1. *Chem. & Met. Eng.*, **40,** 564 (1933).
2. Lourenco, A., *Compt. rend.*, **49,** 619 (1859).
3. Lourenco, A., *Ann. chim. et phys.* (*3*), **67,** 257 (1863).
4. Wurtz, A., *Compt. rend.*, **49,** 813 (1859).
5. Wurtz, A., *Ann. chim. et phys.* (*3*), **69,** 317 (1863).
6. Mohs, R., *Z. Chem.*, **1866,** 495; *Chem. Zentr.*, **1866,** 865; *Jahresber.*, **1866,** 505.
7. Cretcher, L. H., and Pittenger, W. H., *J. Am. Chem. Soc.*, **47,** 163 (1925).

8. Dimitriev, P., and Dogadkina, L., *J. Applied Chem. (U.S.S.R.)*, **14,** 110–9 (1941).
9. Matignon, C., Moureu, H., and Dodé, M., *Bull. soc. chim. France (5)*, **1,** 1308 (1934).
10. Morley, R. J., BIOS Final Report No. 776, Item 22, 1946.
11. Dennis, N., BIOS Final Report No. 1059, Items No. 22 and 30, 1947.
12. Wurtz, A., *Ann. chim. et phys. (3)*, **69,** 330 (1863).
13. International Critical Tables, Vol. **5,** page 164 (1929).
14. Gallaugher, A. F., and Hibbert, H., *J. Am. Chem. Soc.*, **59,** 2524 (1937).
15. Lagemann, R., *J. Polymer Sci.*, **3,** 663 (1948).
16. Horsley, L. H., *Anal. Chem.*, **19,** 508 (1947); **21,** 842 (1949).
17. "Glycols," New York, Carbide and Carbon Chemicals Corp., 1947.
18. "Dow Glycols," Midland, Michigan, The Dow Chemical Co., 1947.
19. Dollinger, J. H., *Rayon Textile Monthly*, **29** (4), 98 (1948).
20. Glickman, C. S., *Drug & Cosmetic Ind.*, **53,** 388 (1943).
21. Fiero, G. W., and Dutcher, M. W., *J. Am. Pharm. Assoc., Sci. Ed.*, **34,** 56 (1945).
22. Goldsmith, H. A., *Chem. Revs.*, **33,** 257–349 (1943).
23. Bennett, H. T. (to Mid-Continent Petroleum Corp.), U. S. Patents 2,003,233–9 (May 28, 1935).
24. Roberts, H. C., *Textile World*, **80,** 41 (1931).
25. Harvey, N. D., Jr., *Textile World*, **80,** 966 (1931).
26. Ordway, C. B., *Am. Dyestuff Reptr.*, **28,** 577 (1939).
27. Pearsall, G. M., and Harvey, N. D., Jr., *Textile World*, **84,** 2416 (1934).
28. Harvey, N. D., Jr., *Am. Dyestuff Reptr.*, **19,** 185, 242 (1930); **24,** 508 (1935).
29. Sala, C. J. (to E. I. du Pont de Nemours & Co.), U. S. Patent 2,047,650 (July 14, 1936).
30. Verity, B., *Am. Dyestuff Reptr.*, **27,** 290 (1938).
31. Saville, A. K., *Am. Dyestuff Reptr.*, **38,** 310 (1949).
32. Mulinos, M. G., and Osborne, R. L., *Proc. Soc. Exptl. Biol. Med.*, **32,** 241 (1934).
33. Cone, R. M., Hatcher, W. H., and Greenwald, W. F., *Chem. & Met. Eng.*, **43,** 128 (1936).
34. Mulinos, M. G., and Osborne, R. L., *N. Y. S. Med. J.*, **35,** 590 (1935).
35. Flinn, F. B., *Laryngoscope*, **45,** 149 (1935); **47,** 58 (1937).
36. Greenwald, W. F., *Med. Record*, **142,** 496 (1935); *Military Surgeon*, **78,** 366 (1936).
37. Wallace, G. B., Reinhard, J. F., and Osborne, R. L., *Arch. Otolaryngol.*, **23,** 306 (1936).
38. Haag, H. B., *J. Lab. Clin. Med.*, **22,** 341 (1937).
39. Holck, H. G. O., and Carlson, A. J., *Proc. Soc. Exptl. Biol. Med.*, **36,** 302 (1937).
40. Sharlit, H., *N. Y. S. Med. J.*, **35,** 1159 (1935).
41. Ballenger, H. C., *Arch. Otolaryngol.*, **29,** 115 (1939).
42. Finnegan, J. K., Fordham, D., Larson, P. S., and Haag, H. B., *J. Pharmacol. Exptl. Therap.*, **89,** 115 (1947).
43. Ballenger, H. C., and Johnson, V. H., *Arch. Otolaryngol.*, **25,** 75 (1937).
44. Hitz, G. E., "Experience in Leak Proofing Bell and Spigot Joints," Paper presented before the American Gas Assoc., Oct. 26, 1936.
45. Hitz, G. E., U. S. Patent 2,091,544 (Aug. 31, 1937).
46. Williams, D. B. (to The United Gas Improvement Co.), U. S. Patent 2,094,691 (Oct. 5, 1937).
47. Skeen, J. R., (to The United Gas Improvement Co.), U. S. Patents 2,141,959 (Dec. 27, 1938); 2,167,139 (July 25, 1939); and 2,315,550–5 (April 6, 1943).
48. Jensen, M. N., *Am. Gas J.*, **158** (1), 33 (1943).

49. "Correcting Leakage in Gas Distribution Systems with 'Carboseal' Anti-Leak," New York, Carbide and Carbon Chemicals Corp., 1945.
50. Carson, H. J., *Gas Age*, **82** (3), 17 (1938).
51. Brockschmidt, C. L., *Gas*, **18** (4), 28 (1942).
52. Senatoroff, N. K., *Gas*, **21** (6), 25, 28, 30, 33, 37 (1945); *Oil Gas J.*, **44** (32), 98 (1945).
53. Carter, R. A., *Gas*, **17** (12), 26 (1941).
54. *Petroleum Refiner*, **19** (2), 49 (1940); **25** (2), 115 (1946); **26** (4), 132 (1947).
55. Bacon, T. S., *Gas Age*, **89** (11), 17 (1942).
56. Russell, G. F., Reid, L. S., and Huntington, R. L., *Trans. Am. Inst. Chem. Engrs.*, **41,** 315 (1945).
57. Wade, H. N., *Petroleum Eng.*, **14** (6), 184 (1943); **14** (7), 100 (1943).
58. Parker, R. W., *Petroleum Eng.*, **14** (4), 110 (1943).
59. Headlee, A. J. W., and Hall, J. L., *Ind. Eng. Chem.*, **36,** 299 (1944).
60. Bacon, T. S., *Am. Gas J.*, **148** (6), 25 (1938); *Gas Age*, **81** (11), 30 (1938); and *Oil Gas J.*, **37** (1), 113, 116 (1938).
61. Ames, C. B., *Mines Mag.*, **32,** 508 (1942).
62. Flood, H. L., *Petroleum Eng.*, **11** (8), 113 (1940).
63. McManus, C. E. (to Crown Cork & Seal Co., Inc.), U. S. Patent 2,121,810 (June 28, 1938).
64. Tennant, W. J. (to Crown Cork & Seal Co., Inc.), British Patent 514,541 (Nov. 10, 1939).
65. Frink, N. S. (to Crown Cork & Seal Co., Inc.), U. S. Patent 2,121,791 (June 28, 1938).
66. Ehrlich, J. (to Erko Corp.), U. S. Patent 2,455,921 (Dec. 14, 1948).
67. Irey, K. M., and Debing, L. M. (to Resinox Corp.), U. S. Patent 2,128,880 (Aug. 30, 1938).
68. McManus, C. E. (to Crown Cork & Seal Co., Inc.), U. S. Patent 2,158,469 (May 16, 1939).
69. Kantrowitz, M. S., and Blaylock, F. R., G.P.O.-P.I.A. Joint Research Bulletin, Binding Series No. 2, "Bookbinding Pastes" (1947), Binding Series No. 3, "Bindery Glues" (1947), and Bindery Series No. 8, Series No. 3, "Bindery Glues" (1948).
70. Erickson, R. E., and Thoma, P. J. (to Michigan Research Laboratories), U. S. Patents 2,244,103 (June 3, 1941); 2,289,638 (July 14, 1942); 2,299,135 (Oct. 20, 1942); 2,300,880-1 (Nov. 3, 1942); 2,309,580 (Jan. 26, 1943); 2,313,328 (March 9, 1943); 2,323,710 (July 6, 1943); 2,327,594-7 (Aug. 24, 1943); 2,332,066 (Oct. 19, 1943); and 2,336,983-4 (Dec. 14, 1943).
71. Coleman, R. E. (to The Zein Corp. of America), U. S. Patents 2,188,895 (Feb. 6, 1940) and 2,185,112-26 (Jan. 26, 1939); Bernardi, D. J. (to Interchemical Corp.), U. S. Patent 2,285,183 (June 2, 1942); Denton, R. A. (to Sun Chemical Corp.), U. S. Patent 2,436,954 (March 2, 1948); Kroeger, J. W., and O'Connor, H. F. (to Frederick H. Levey Company), U. S. Patent 2,366,970 (Jan. 9, 1945).
72. Schmutzler, A. F., and Othmer, D. F., *Ind. Eng. Chem.*, **35,** 1196 (1943).
73. Lee, E. D. (to Interchemical Corp.), U. S. Patent 2,415,827 (Feb. 18, 1947).
74. Rietz, C. A., and Lecture, R. F. (to Interchemical Corp.), U. S. Patent 2,468,779 (May 3, 1949).
75. "Synthetic Organic Chemicals," U. S. Tariff Commission Report No. 162, p. 116, Table 16B, 1947.
76. Bradley, T. F., Kropa, E. L., and Johnston, W. B., *Ind. Eng. Chem.*, **29,** 1270 (1937).

77. Ellis, C. (to Ellis-Foster Co.), U. S. Patent 2,255,313 (Sept. 9, 1941).
78. Kropa, E. L., and Bradley, T. F., *Ind. Eng. Chem.*, **31**, 1512 (1939).
79. Rust, J. B., *Ind. Eng. Chem.*, **32**, 64 (1940).
80. Doscher, C. K., Kane, J. H., Cragwall, G. O., and Staebner, W. H., *Ind. Eng. Chem.*, **33**, 315 (1941).
81. Bradley, T. F., and Johnston, W. B. (to American Cyanamid Co.), U. S. Patents 2,234,958 (March 18, 1941); 2,252,393 (Aug. 12, 1941); and 2,253,681 (Aug. 26, 1941).
82. Norman, G. M. (to Hercules Powder Co.), U. S. Patent 1,779,710 (Oct. 28, 1930).
83. Van Antwerpen, F. J., *Ind. Eng. Chem., News Ed.*, **19**, 1255 (1941).
84. Pieper, E. J. (to Armstrong Cork Co.), U. S. Patent 1,847,783 (March 1, 1932).
85. Bradley, T. F. (to Ellis-Foster Co.), U. S. Patent 1,923,715 (Aug. 22, 1933).
86. " 'Plastolein' Products," Cincinnati, Emery Industries, 1950.
87. Emerson, W. S., Longley, R. I., Jr., Darby., J. R., and Cowell, E. E., *Ind. Eng. Chem.*, **42**, 1431 (1950).
88. *Chem. Inds.*, **61**, 805 (1947).
89. Hammond, R. (to Imperial Chemical Industries, Ltd.), British Patents 606,716 and 606,717 (Aug. 19, 1948).
90. Rinkenbach, W. H., *Ind. Eng. Chem.*, **19**, 925 (1927).
91. Hough, A., U. S. Patents 1,868,388 (July 19, 1932) and 1,936,020 (Nov. 21, 1933).
92. Swanson, A. A., and Sager, D. D., P. B. Report No. 926, 1945.
93. Pratt, C. D., P. B. Report No. 12664, 1945.
94. Cooley, R. A., *Chem. Inds.*, **59**, 645 (1946).
95. Alico, J., "Introduction to Magnesium and Its Alloys," Chicago, Ziff-Davis Publishing Co., 1945.
96. Sanders, C., *Foundry*, **71** (6), 209 (1943).
97. Lee, J., and Heineman, S. D. (to Hoffmann-La Roche, Inc.), U. S. Patent 2,389,065 (Nov. 13, 1945).
98. Lott, W. A. (to E. R. Squibb & Sons), U. S. Patent 2,013,662 (Sept. 10, 1935).
99. Stevens, D. R., and Nickels, J. E., *Ind. Eng. Chem., Anal. Ed.*, **18**, 260 (1946).
100. Redemann, C. E., and Lucas, H. J., *Ind. Eng. Chem., Anal. Ed.*, **9**, 521 (1937).
101. Kapp, R. (to National Oil Products Company), U. S. Patent 2,207,256 (July 9, 1940).
102. " 'Petronate' and 'Petromix' for the Manufacture of Soluble Oils," Industrial Research Bulletin No. 10, Ser. G., New York, L. Sonneborn Sons, Inc.
103. Allen, E. M., Gage, F. W., and Wolf, R. F., *India Rubber World*, **120**, 577 (1949); **121**, 669 (1950).
104. U. S. Army Specification 4-1116, June 15, 1943.
105. Moses, D. V. (to E. I. du Pont de Nemours & Co.), U. S. Patent 2,090,263 (Aug. 17, 1937).
106. Tseng, A. T. K. (to Hydraulic Brake Co.), U. S. Patent 1,952,105 (March 27, 1934).
107. Lilienfeld, J. E. (to Ergon Research Laboratories, Inc.), U. S. Patent 1,986,779 (Jan. 1, 1935).
108. *Food Inds.*, **9**, 136 (1937).
109. Gurchot, C., and Mellars, N. D., *Science*, **92**, 516 (1940).
110. Coey, S. C., *Operating Eng.*, p. 42, July, 1948.
111. Engelbach, E. A., *Food Inds.*, **20** (6), 78 (1948).
112. Downs, C. R., and Spiselman, J. W. (to The Calorider Corp.), U. S. Patents 2,222,561 (Nov. 19, 1940) and 2,221,787 (Nov. 19, 1940).
113. Spiselman, J. W. (to Research Corp.), U. S. Patent 2,367,695 (Jan. 23, 1945).

114. Twort, C. C., Baker, A. H., Finn, S. R., and Powell, E. O., *J. Hyg.*, **40**, 253 (1940).
115. Andrews, C. H., and Lond, M. D., *Lancet*, **1940, II,** 770.
116. Robertson, O. H., Bigg, E., Miller, B. F., and Baker, Z., *Science*, **93**, 213 (1941).
117. Robertson, O. H., Bigg, E., Miller, B. F., Baker, Z., and Puck, T. T., *Trans. Assoc. Am. Physicians*, **56,** 353 (1941).
118. Puck, T. T., *J. Exptl. Med.*, **85,** 729 (1947).
119. Wise, H., and Puck, T. T., *Science*, **105,** 556-7 (1947).
120. Robertson, O. H., *Wisconsin Med. J.*, **46,** 311-7 (1947).
121. Harris, T. N., and Stokes, J., *Am. J. Med. Sci.*, **209,** 152 (1945).
122. Rosebury, T., Meiklejohn, G., Kingsland, L. C., and Boldt, M. H., *J. Exptl. Med.*, **85,** 65-76 (1947).
123. Krugman, S., and Swerdlow, B., *Proc. Soc. Exptl. Biol. Med.*, **71,** 680 (1949).
124. Robertson, O. H., Puck, T. T., Lemon, H. F., and Loosli, C. G., *Science*, **97,** 142 (1943).
125. Stokes, J., Jr., and Henle, W., *J. Am. Med. Assoc.*, **120,** 16 (1942).
126. Gardner, H. A., Knauss, C. A., and Van Heuckeroth, A. W., *Ind. Eng. Chem.*, **21,** 57 (1929).
127. Martin, S. R. W., P. B. Report No. 52858, 1946.
128. Reid, G. H. (to Carbide and Carbon Chemicals Corp.), U. S. Patent 2,229,222 (Jan. 21, 1941).
129. Carruthers, T. F., and Stoops, W. N. (to Carbide and Carbon Chemicals Corp.), U. S. Patent 2,318,670 (May 11, 1943).
130. Gloor, W. E. (to Hercules Powder Co.), U. S. Patent 2,198,665 (April 30, 1940).
131. *India Rubber World*, **118,** 360 (1947).
132. Blackmore, R. L., BIOS Final Report No. 1651, Item 22, 1946.
133. Muskat, I. E., and Strain, F. (to Pittsburgh Plate Glass Co.), U. S. Patents 2,370,565 (Feb. 27, 1945) and 2,238,933 (Oct. 2, 1945).
134. Peahl, L. H., *Oil Gas. J.*, **49** (10), 92 (1950).
135. Porter, J. A., and Reid, L. S., *Am. Inst. Mining Met. Engrs.*, **189,** 235-40 (1950).
136. *Chem. & Met. Eng.*, **47,** 312 (1940).
137. Reid, L. S., *Gas*, **22** (12), 35 (1946).
138. Downs, C. R. (to The Calorider Corp.), U. S. Patent 2,340,739 (Feb. 1, 1944).
139. Curme, G. O., Jr. (to Carbide and Carbon Chemicals Corp.), U. S. Patent 2,378,466 (June 19, 1945).
140. Orelup, J. W., U. S. Patent 2,190,673 (Feb. 20, 1940).
141. Merkel, P. B. Report No. 70326, Item 16, 1943.
142. Schneider, E. J. (to Sylvania Electric Products, Inc.), U. S. Patent 2,442,863 (June 8, 1948).
143. Soday, F. J. (to The United Gas Improvement Co.), U. S. Patent 2,295,612 (Sept. 15, 1942).
144. Runckel, W. J., and Oldroyd, D. M., *Ind. Eng. Chem.*, *Anal. Ed.*, **18,** 80 (1946).
145. Wurtz, A., *Ber.*, **10,** 90 (1877); *Bull. soc. chim. France (2)*, **29,** 530 (1878).
146. Roithner, E., *Monatsh.*, **15,** 665 (1894); *J. Chem. Soc.*, **68** (1), 319 (1895).
147. Staudinger, H., and Schweitzer, O., *Ber.*, **62,** 2395 (1929).
148. Staudinger, H., and Lohmann, H., *Ann.*, **505,** 41 (1933).
149. Coleman, G. H., and Moore, G. V. (to The Dow Chemical Co.), U. S. Patent 2,056,830 (Oct. 6, 1936).
150. Perry, S. Z., and Hibbett, H., *Can. J. Research*, **B14,** 77 (1936).
151. Fordyce, R., and Hibbett, H., *J. Am. Chem. Soc.*, **61,** 1910 (1939).
152. Fordyce, R., Lovell, E. L., and Hibbert, H., *J. Am. Chem. Soc.*, **61,** 1905 (1939).

153. Ellis, C., "The Chemistry of Synthetic Resins," Vol. II, p. 992, New York, Reinhold Publishing Corp., 1935.
154. Brandner, J. D., and Goepp, R. M., Jr., P. B. Report No. 85159.
155. Staudinger, H., "Die hochmolekularen organischen Verbindungen," Berlin, J. Springer, 1932.
156. Perry, S., and Hibbert, H., *J. Am. Chem. Soc.*, **62,** 2599 (1940).
157. Flory, P. J., *J. Am. Chem. Soc.*, **62,** 1561 (1940).
158. Ellis, C., "The Chemistry of Synthetic Resins," Vol. I, p. 74, New York, Chemical Catalog Co., Inc. (Reinhold Publishing Corp.), 1935.
159. Sauter, E., *Z. phys. Chem.*, **21,** 161, 186 (1933).
160. Barnes, W. H., and Ross, S., *J. Am. Chem. Soc.*, **58,** 1129 (1936).
161. Hibbert, H., and Lovell, E. L., *J. Am. Chem. Soc.*, **62,** 330 (1940).
162. Shaffer, C. B., and Critchfield, F. H., *Anal. Chem.*, **19,** 32 (1947).
163. Schoeller, C., and Wittwer, M. (to I. G. Farbenindustrie A.-G.), U. S. Patent 1,970,578 (Aug. 21, 1934).
164. Schlegel, F. (to The Procter and Gamble Co.), U. S. Patent 2,355,823 (Aug. 15, 1944).
165. Bennett, H., U. S. Patent 2,275,494 (March 10, 1942).
166. Loehr, O. (to I. G. Farbenindustrie A.-G.), U. S. Patent 1,710,424 (Apr. 23, 1929).
167. Schwartz, A. M., and Perry, J. W., "Surface Active Agents," New York, Interscience Publishers, Inc., 1949.
168. McCutcheon, J. W., *Soap Sanit. Chemicals*, **25** (8, 9, 10), 33, 42, 40 (1949).
169. Sisley, J. P., *Am. Dyestuff Reptr.*, **38,** 513 (1949).
170. "Esters by Glyco," Brooklyn, N. Y., Glyco Products Co., 1949.
171. "Polyethylene Glycol Esters," Philadelphia, Kessler Chemical Co., 1948.
172. Dollinger, J. H., *Soap Sanit. Chemicals*, **25** (1), 37 (1949); *Rayon Textile Monthly*, **29** (4), 98 (1948).
173. McClelland, C. P., and Bateman, R. L., *J. Am. Pharm. Assoc., Pract. Pharm. Ed.*, **10,** 30 (1949).
174. Bandelin, F. J., and Kemp, C. R., *J. Am. Pharm. Assoc., Sci. Ed.*, **35,** 65 (1946).
175. Zheutlin, H. E. C., and Fox, C. L., Jr., *J. Investigative Dermatol.*, **11,** 161 (1948).
176. Lockie, L. D., and Sprowls, J. B., *J. Am. Pharm. Assoc., Sci. Ed.*, **38,** 222 (1949).
177. Meyers, D. B., Nadkarni, M. V., and Zopf, L. C., *J. Am. Pharm. Assoc., Sci. Ed.*, **38,** 231 (1949).
178. Nadkarni, M. V., Meyers, D. B., and Zopf, L. C., *J. Am. Pharm. Assoc., Sci. Ed.*, **38,** 216 (1949).
179. Fleischmann, G., *Dermatol. Wochschr.*, **116,** 345–51 (1943).
180. Breinlich, J., *Deut. Apoth. Ztg.*, **55,** 397 (1940).
181. Osborne, R. M., P. B. Report No. 85149, 1947.
182. Meyers, D. B., Nadkarni, M. V., and Zopf, L. C., *J. Am. Pharm. Assoc., Pract. Pharm. Ed.*, **11,** 32 (1950).
183. Mohs, F. E., *Arch Surg.*, **52,** 466 (1946).
184. Meleney, F. L., Johnson, B. A., Pulaski, E. J., and Colonna, F., *J. Am. Med. Assoc.*, **130,** 121 (1946).
185. Meleney, F. L., and Johnson, B. A., *J. Am. Med. Assoc.*, **133,** 675 (1947).
186. Keeney, E. L., *Med. Clinics N. Am.*, **1945,** 323.
187. MacDonald, L. H., and Himelick, R. E., *J. Am. Pharm. Assoc., Sci. Ed.*, **37,** 368 (1948).

188. Senturia, B. H., and Doubly, J. A., *Laryngoscope,* **57,** 633 (1947).
189. Brush, B. E., Lam, C. R., and Ponka, J. L., *Surgery,* **21,** 662 (1947).
190. Maynard, M. T. R., *J. Investigative Dermatol.,* **8,** 223 (1947).
191. Rigby, G. W. (to the United States of America), U. S. Patent 2,445,366 (July 20, 1948).
192. Bockmühl, M., Middendorf, L., and Starck, W. (to Winthrop Chemical Co., Inc.), U. S. Patent 2,149,005 (Feb. 28, 1939).
193. Gillham, R. W., and Tomlinson, J. E., *Pharm. J.,* **162,** 472 (1949).
194. Carsten, M. E., *Arch. Path.,* **44,** 96 (1947).
195. Firminger, H. I., *Stain. Technol.,* **25,** 121 (1950).
196. Friedman, M. H. F., *J. Lab. Clin. Med.,* **29,** 530 (1944).
197. Miescher, K., and Meystre, C. (to Ciba Pharmaceutical Products, Inc.), U. S. Patent 2,411,631 (Nov. 26, 1946).
198. Henderson, E., *J. Clin. Endocrinol.,* **9,** 1324 (1949).
199. Wilkes, B. G., and Wassell, H. E., (to Carbide and Carbon Chemicals Corp.), U. S. Patent 2,309,722 (Feb. 2, 1943).
200. Continho, H., *Soap, Perfumery & Cosmetics,* **17,** 914 (1944).
201. Francisco, D. E. (to Carbide and Carbon Chemicals Corp), U. S. Patent 2,393,864 (Jan. 29, 1946).
202. Hauser, E., and Kovol, P., U. S. Patent 2,449,070 (Sept. 14, 1948).
203. Cresswell, A. (to North American Rayon Corp), U. S. Patent 2,442,331 (June 1, 1948).
204. Cowling, H. (to American Viscose Corp), U. S. Patent 2,397,338 (March 26, 1946).
205. Kline, H. B., Burkholder, A. H., and Israel, W. O. (to Industrial Rayon Corp.), U. S. Patent 2,422,021 (June 10, 1947).
206. Schlosser, P. H., and Gray, K. R. (to Rayonier, Inc.), U. S. Patent 2,393,817 (Jan. 29, 1946).
207. Brown, K. R. (to Atlas Powder Co.), U. S. Patent 2,350,985 (June 13, 1944).
208. Strain, D. E. (to E. I. du Pont de Nemours & Co.), U. S. Patent 2,300,074 (Oct. 27, 1942).
209. Seymour, G. W., and Miller, D. Y. (to Celanese Corp. of America), U. S. Patent 2,385,110 (Sept. 18, 1945).
210. Smith, R. J. (to Imperial Chemical Industries, Ltd.), U. S. Patent 2,459,052 (Jan. 11, 1949).
211. Mattinson, F. W., and Hoffman, R. (to Skenandoa Rayon Corp.), U. S. Patent 2,351,865 (June 20, 1944).
212. I. G. Farbenindustrie A.-G., French Patent 717,414 (May 21, 1931).
213. I. G. Farbenindustrie A.-G., British Patent 367,420 (Nov. 15, 1930).
214. DeGroote, M. (to Petrolite Corp., Ltd.), U. S. Patent 2,295,166 (Sept. 8, 1942).
215. DeGroote, M., and Keiser, B. (to Petrolite Corp., Ltd.), U. S. Patents 2,324,488 and 2,324,494 (July 20, 1943).
216. DeGroote, M., and Keiser, B. (to Petrolite Corp., Ltd.), U. S. Patent 2,328,062 (Aug. 31, 1943).
217. Salathiel, R. A. (to Standard Oil Development Co.), U. S. Patent 2,401,966 (June 11, 1946).
218. Kirkpatrick, W. H., and Wilson, D. L. (to Visco Products Co.), U. S. Patent 2,454,808 (Nov. 30, 1948).
219. Lyman, A. L. (to Standard Oil Co. of California), U. S. Patent 2,243,873 (June 3, 1941).

220. Coghlan, C. A. (to The Texas Co.), U. S. Patent 2,411,025 (Nov. 12, 1946).
221. Lake, G. R. (to Union Oil Co. of California), U. S. Patent 2,444,893 (July 6, 1948).
222. Bondi, A. A. (to Shell Development Co.), U. S. Patents 2,445,935 (July 27, 1948) and 2,475,589 (July 12, 1949).
223. Hoffman, R. A. (to E. I. du Pont de Nemours & Co.), U. S. Patent 2,457,152 (Dec. 28, 1948).
224. Avallone, S. C., Harris, A. W., and Whiting, E. J. (to The American Steel & Wire Co. of New Jersey), U. S. Patent 2,472,393 (June 7, 1949).
225. American Steel & Wire Co., Report No. 103A, Dec. 15, 1948.
226. Imperial Chemical Industries, Ltd., British Patent 592,442 (Sept. 18, 1947).
227. Wassell, H. E. (to Carbide and Carbon Chemicals Corp.), U. S. Patent 2,393,866 (Jan. 29, 1946).
228. Twyning, R. V., and Hakken, W. T., Jr. (to J. C. Miller Co.), U. S. Patent 2,436,128 (Feb. 17, 1948).
229. Savage, R. H. (to General Electric Co.), U. S. Patent 2,404,662 (July 23, 1946).
230. Savage, R. H. (to General Electric Co.), U. S. Patent 2,393,816 (Jan. 29, 1946).
231. Ramadanoff, D. (to National Carbon Co., Inc.), U. S. Patent 2,425,046 (Aug. 5, 1947).
232. Williford, E. A. (to National Carbon Co., Inc.), U. S. Patent 2,412,701 (Dec. 17, 1946).
233. Schneider, E. J. (to Sylvania Electric Products, Inc.), U. S. Patent 2,442,864 (June 8, 1948).
234. Mell, C. W. (to Radio Corp. of America), U. S. Patent 2,445,962 (July 27, 1948).
235. Croxall, W. J., and Neher, H. T. (to Rohm & Haas Co.), U. S. Patent 2,447,975 (Aug. 24, 1948).
236. Nye, L. E. (to U. S. Rubber Co.), U. S. Patent 2,461,761 (Feb. 15, 1949).
237. Gold, L. J., and Zweig, S. (to Milprint, Inc.), U. S. Patent 2,446,581 (Aug. 10, 1948).
238. Kropa, E. L. (to American Cyanamid Co.), U. S. Patent 2,473,801 (June 21, 1949).
239. Gardner, W. H., and Bassford, H. H., Jr. (to United States Shellac Importers Assoc., Inc.), U. S. Patent 2,387,388 (Oct. 23, 1945).
240. Ericks, W. P. (to American Cyanamid Co.), U. S. Patent 2,277,821 (March 31, 1942).
241. Pittsburgh Plate Glass Co., British Patent 587,933 (May 9, 1947).
242. Muskat, I. E., and Strain, F. (to Pittsburgh Plate Glass Co.), U. S. Patent 2,370,565 (Feb. 27, 1945).
243. Bruson, H. A. (to The Resinous Products & Chemical Co.), U. S. Patent 2,359,708 (Oct. 3, 1944).
244. White, J. O. (to E. I. du Pont de Nemours & Co.), U. S. Patent Application 671,918 (Published July 5, 1949).
245. Jepson, C. H. (to E. I. du Pont de Nemours & Co.), U. S. Patent Application 50,433 (Published Oct. 18, 1949).
246. Marks, B. M. (to E. I. du Pont de Nemours & Co.), U. S. Patent 2,468,094 (Apr. 26, 1949).
247. Cowan, J. C., and Wheeler, D. H. (to the United States of America), U. S. Patent 2,429,219 (Oct. 21, 1947).
248. Sonnichsen, H. M. (to E. I. du Pont de Nemours & Co.), U. S. Patent 2,351,301 (June 13, 1944).

249. Stamberger, P., U. S. Patent 2,459,298 (Jan. 18, 1949).
250. Kunze, W. G., and Evans, R. B. (to American Cyanamid Co.), Canadian Patent 452,626 (Nov. 16, 1948).
251. Rothrock, H. S. (to E. I. du Pont de Nemours & Co.), U. S. Patent 2,328,679 (Sept. 7, 1943).
252. Wolff & Company, K.g.a.A., Belgian Patent 448,609 (Feb., 1943).
253. McClelland, C. P., and Bateman, R. L., *Chem. Eng. News.*, **23,** 247 (1945).
254. Radcliffe, M. R. (to The Firestone Tire & Rubber Co.), U. S. Patent 2,459,746 (Jan. 18, 1949).
255. Jones, F. D. (to American Chemical Paint Co.), U. S. Patents 2,390,941 (Dec. 11, 1945) and 2,394,916 (Feb. 12, 1946).
256. Zimmerman, P. W., and Hitchcock, A. E., *Contribs. Boyce Thompson Inst.*, **12,** 321 (1942).
257. Mitchell, J. W., and Hamner, C. L., *Botan. Gaz.*, **105,** 474 (1944).
258. Beal, J. M., *Botan. Gaz.*, **106,** 165 (1944).
259. Marth, P. C., and Mitchell, J. W., *Botan. Gaz.*, **106,** 224 (1944).
260. Hamner, C. L., Moulton, J. E., and Tukey, H. B., *Botan. Gaz.*, **107,** 352 (1946).
261. Hamner, C. L., and Tukey, H. B., *Botan. Gaz.*, **107,** 379 (1946).
262. Hamner, C. L., and Tukey, H. B., *Science*, **100,** 154 (1944); *Botan. Gaz.*, **106,** 232 (1944).
263. Shafer, J., Jr., Hamner, C. L., and Carlson, R. F., *Proc. Am. Soc. Hort. Sci.*, **47,** 421 (1946).
264. Smith, F. G., *N. Y. Agr. Exptl. Sta., Farm Research*, **12** (3), 1, 2 (1946).
265. Mitchell, J. W., and Marth, P. G., *Botan. Gaz.*, **106,** 199 (1944).
266. Hansen, E., *Plant Physiol.*, **21,** 588 (1946).
267. Ennis, W. B., Jr., and Boyd, F. T., *Botan. Gaz.*, **107,** 552 (1946).
268. Tukey, H. B., and Hamner, C. L., *Science*, **101,** 253 (1945).
269. Bodman, J. W. (to Lever Brothers Co.), U. S. Patent 2,329,694 (Sept. 21, 1943).
270. Holuba, S. J. (to Colgate-Palmolive-Peet Co.), U. S. Patent 2,432,451 (July 8, 1947).
271. Katzman, M. (to The Emulsol Corp.), U. S. Patent 2,374,213 (April 24, 1945).
272. Erickson, D. R., and Thoma, P. J. (to Michigan Research Laboratories, Inc.), U. S. Patent 2,336,984 (Dec. 14, 1943).
273. Blake, R. K. (to E. I. du Pont de Nemours & Co.), U. S. Patent 2,441,389 (May 11, 1948).
274. Blake, R. K., Stanton, W. A., and Schulze, F. (to E. I. du Pont de Nemours & Co.), U. S. Patent 2,423,549 (July 8, 1947).
275. Potter, R. S., and Webster, L. (to Defender Photo Supply Co.), U. S. Patent 2,214,205 (Sept. 10, 1940).
275. Myers, C. S. (to Bakelite Corp.), U. S. Patent 2,393,863 (Jan. 29, 1946).
277. Geltner, D. (to Onyx Oil & Chemical Co.), U. S. Patent 2,405,784 (Aug. 13, 1946).
278. Geltner, D. (to The Richards Chemical Works, Inc.), U. S. Patent 2,379,703 (July 3, 1945).
279. Favor, H. H., and Johnston, N. F., *Cereal Chem.*, **24,** 346 (1947); **25,** 424 (1948).
280. Strosacker, C. J., and Amstutz, F. C. (to The Dow Chemical Co.), U. S. Patent 2,322,258 (June 22, 1943).
281. Batchelder, A. H. (to Standard Oil Co. of California), U. S. Patent 2,285,795 June 9, 1942).
282. Neidorf, S. W. (to Federal Telephone and Radio Corp.), U. S. Patent 2,436,819 (March 2, 1948).

283. Pearlson, W. H., *Ind. Eng. Chem., Anal. Ed.*, **16,** 415 (1944).
284. Tuve, R. L., Fogelberg, J. M., Brinnick, F. E., and Springer, H. S., U. S. Patent 2,458,540 (Jan. 11, 1949).
285. Lacey, H. T., Millson, H. E., and Heiss, F. H. (to American Cyanamid Co.), U. S. Patent 2,420,286 (May 6, 1947).
286. Ducca, F. W. (to Bakelite Corp.), U. S. Patent 2,353,228 (July 11, 1944).
287. Goldstein, H., and Liberthson, L. (to L. Sonnenborn Sons, Inc.), U. S. Patent 2,307,741 (Jan. 12, 1943).
288. Kirk, J. S. (to E. I. du Pont de Nemours & Co.), U. S. Patents 2,408,654 and 2,408,656 (Oct. 1, 1946).
289. Iler, R. K., and Kirk, J. S. (to E. I. du Pont de Nemours & Co.), U. S. Patent 2,408,655 (Oct. 1, 1946).
290. Wassell, H. E. (to Carbide and Carbon Chemicals Corp.), U. S. Patent 2,393,865 (Jan. 29, 1946).

CHAPTER 8

PROPYLENE GLYCOL PRODUCTION

P. R. RECTOR AND W. J. TOUSSAINT

COMMERCIAL HISTORY

Although Wurtz prepared propylene glycol (1,2-propanediol) by hydrolysis of propylene glycol diacetate as far back as 1859, it was first produced on a commercial scale in 1931 by Carbide at South Charleston, West Virginia. Propylene was converted to the chlorohydrin and the glycol, following a process similar to that for the production of ethylene glycol from ethylene.

During the early stages of its industrial growth, interest in propylene glycol centered on its use as a pharmaceutical vehicle to replace glycerol. By 1932 pharmacological studies[1, 2, 3] had clearly established the low order of toxicity of propylene glycol. Some five years later, Winthrop Chemical Company, Inc. (now Winthrop-Stearns, Inc.,) patented[4] its use as a water-soluble solvent for crystalline Vitamin D, and by 1943 propylene glycol was officially admitted to the National Formulary. Two years earlier Robertson[5] of the University of Chicago had reported the effectiveness of propylene glycol mists for the sterilization of air.

In 1935 Wagner Electric Corporation patented[6] a propylene glycol-castor oil base hydraulic fluid, later marketed as one of the Lockheed fluids. At about this time Du Pont was operating its fatty alcohol high-pressure process which yielded propylene glycol as a by-product. The Army Air Corps in 1941 standardized on a propylene glycol-butyl "Cellosolve" diluent for its castor oil hydraulic fluid[7].

The shortage of glycerol and the industrial glycols during World War II further stimulated interest in propylene glycol as an effective replacement for glycerol, particularly in pharmaceutical preparations and food flavors. Production increased in 1942 when Dow began its commercial manufacture at Midland, Michigan, partly to fill the increased demand for the glycol in hydraulic fluids. This was soon followed with a much larger production unit at Freeport, Texas. Largely as a result of the expanding market for glycols, particularly in nonvolatile-type anti-freeze, Wyandotte Chemicals Corporation in 1948 became a producer of a mixed ethylene glycol-propylene glycol. The most recent producer to enter the field was Celanese Corporation of America, which offered propylene glycol for the first time early in 1950.

As of November, 1951, propylene glycol was being produced in the United

States in five plants in three states—West Virginia, Texas, and Michigan. The two largest producers are Dow and Carbide, who manufacture it from propylene chlorohydrin. Wyandotte's production is likewise through the chlorohydrin. The Celanese process involves the hydration of propylene oxide recovered from the oxidation products of natural gas hydrocarbons. Prior to 1949, Du Pont produced a minor percentage of the domestic output as one of the products in the high-pressure catalytic hydrogenolysis process for making higher alcohols from coconut oil glycerides.

The domestic annual output of propylene glycol is somewhat less than one-fifth that of ethylene glycol. During World War II, its production is reported to have increased to over a million pounds per month[8]. By 1949, production had reached an annual level of almost 80 million pounds[9]. Industrial-grade propylene glycol was selling at a price of $0.175 per pound in tank-car quantities as of November, 1951.

METHODS OF PRODUCTION

Via Propylene Chlorohydrin

The production of propylene glycol by the chlorohydrin method is carried out under nearly the same conditions as for ethylene glycol. Patent literature describing the production of propylene chlorohydrin[10], propylene oxide[11], and propylene glycol[12] closely follows the chlorohydrin process described for the lower glycol (for details of the analogous method, see Chapter 2, "Ethylene Glycol Production"). Yields and efficiencies are also comparable.

In the preparation of propylene chlorohydrin, a mixture of two isomers results that is 90 per cent 1-chloro-2-propanol[13]. This is to be expected from the indicated mechanism

$$CH_3CH{=}CH_2 \;+\; Cl^+ \;\rightarrow\; CH_3CH{-}CH_2$$
$$\underset{Cl^+}{\diagdown\diagup}$$

$$CH_3CH{-}CH_2 \;\rightarrow\; [CH_3\overset{+}{C}HCH_2Cl]$$
$$\underset{Cl^+}{\diagdown\diagup}$$

$$[CH_3\overset{+}{C}HCH_2Cl] \;+\; OH^- \;\rightarrow\; CH_3CHOHCH_2Cl$$

because of the greater stability of the secondary carbonium ion $[CH_3\overset{+}{C}HCH_2Cl]$.

Commercial propylene chlorohydrin boils at 127.4°C. It forms a homogeneous constant boiling mixture with water, distilling at 95.4°C. and containing 54.2 per cent of propylene chlorohydrin. 1-Chloro-2-propanol boils at 126.7°C. and 2-chloro-1-propanol at 133-134°C.

By Direct Oxidation of Hydrocarbon Gases

The vapor phase, partial oxidation of aliphatic hydrocarbons such as propane and butane results in the formation of, among other products, propylene oxide[14, 15]. After separation from the other compounds in the reaction mixture, this is hydrolyzed to propylene glycol in the usual manner.

Hydrogenolysis of Glycerides

Higher alcohols are generally produced commercially on a large scale by the high-pressure catalytic hydrogenolysis of coconut oil glycerides[16]. The principal disadvantage of the use of glycerides, as compared with other fatty acid esters, is that the glycerol produced as a by-product of the process is not stable under the conditions of the reaction and cannot be recovered. Presumably it is reduced to a large extent to propylene glycol in view of the fact that the latter can be obtained in good yields directly from glycerol under similar conditions of hydrogenation[17].

Miscellaneous

Most of the other procedures for preparing propylene glycol are adaptations of methods known to be satisfactory for obtaining ethylene glycol. Methods include: hydrolysis of propylene glycol diacetate with barium hydroxide[18]; reduction of glycerol α-monochlorohydrin in water with sodium amalgam[19]; destructive distillation of monosodium glycerate obtained by reacting 95 per cent glycerol with powdered sodium hydroxide[20, 21, 22]; hydration of allyl alcohol by heating to 100°C. with 10 per cent hydrochloric acid[23]; reduction of acetol with sodium amalgam in alkaline solution[24]; hydrogenation of glycidol in the presence of palladium-charcoal in ether[25]; hydrogenation of butyl lactate in the presence of copper chromite catalyst at 250°C. and 150 to 200 atmospheres pressure[26]; and hydroxylation of propylene with hydrogen peroxide in tertiary butanol in the presence of osmium tetroxide[27].

Propylene glycol is obtained directly from propylene dichloride or propylene dibromide by prolonged heating with water[28]. It is also prepared by heating aqueous solutions of the dihalides with lead oxide[29], potassium carbonate[30], and sodium bicarbonate and copper[31]. Yields of 48 per cent from the dichloride have been obtained by heating with aqueous sodium carbonate at 209°C. and 48 atmospheres pressure[32]. Using sodium bicarbonate at a temperature of 210°C. and 182 atmospheres pressure increased the yields to 60 to 65 per cent.

In the early stages of the slow combustion of propylene at high pressures, a mixture of propylene oxide, propionaldehyde, and allyl alcohol is formed. Under appropriate conditions, the oxide is hydrolyzed to the glycol. At 269°C. and 17.6 atmospheres pressure, and using a 4:1:38 propylene-oxygen-steam mixture, 19.7 per cent of the starting oxygen appears in the condensable products as propylene oxide and propylene glycol[33].

Because of their ready availability and low cost, sugars have received considerable attention since 1912 as starting materials for the preparation of lower polyhydric alcohols, such as glycerol and propylene glycol[34, 35, 36, 37, 38, 39, 40]. Satisfactory starting materials include glucose, sorbitol, sucrose, and molasses[41, 42, 43, 44, 45, 46, 47, 48, 49, 50, 51].

During 1944, the I. G. Farbenindustrie plant at Hoechst am Main in Germany actually produced 1530 metric tons of polyhydric alcohol mixtures by hydrogenolysis of sugars. The mixture, sold as a glycerol substitute under the trade name "Glycerogen," had the following composition: glycerol, 40 per cent; propylene glycol, 40 per cent; and hexahydric alcohol, 20 per cent. Details of the methods of production are discussed in P.B. Reports Numbers 218 and 1832.

TRIMETHYLENE GLYCOL

Trimethylene glycol or 1,3-propanediol ($HOCH_2CH_2CH_2OH$) is a less familiarly known isomer of ordinary propylene glycol or 1,2-propanediol. At the present time it is of relatively little commercial importance.

The following account of its occurrence and properties is taken from a paper by Rayner[52]. Trimethylene glycol was first mentioned as occurring in certain glycerols by Noyes and Watkins as long ago as 1895. For many years it was not much in evidence in glycerol technology, largely because it was not necessary to produce glycerol of a higher specific gravity than 1.260 at 15.5°C. either for the manufacture of nitroglycerin or for other uses. In 1914, the specific gravity demanded by nitroglycerin manufacturers was raised to 1.262, and the difficulty experienced by certain distillers in obtaining the bulk of their distillate at this specific gravity was found to be due largely to the presence of trimethylene glycol in varying amounts in the crude glycerol distilled. Due to its relative volatility, the bulk of the glycol passes away to the sweet-water condensers, but the seriousness of the presence of very small amounts in the glycerol will be evident when it is realized that the presence of a little over 1 per cent will reduce the specific gravity of a distillate that would otherwise be 1.263 to 1.260.

According to Rayner, trimethylene glycol is formed by the fermentation of the glycerol produced by the saponification of fats (with lye). Normally, crude glycerol contains less than 1 per cent of trimethylene glycol, occasionally 2 to 3 per cent, and sometimes even as much as 10 per cent. The small amount of glycol present mainly passes away to the sweet water and is found in the sweet-water glycerol to the extent of 5 to 10 per cent.

Pure trimethylene glycol is a colorless, odorless liquid with a specific gravity of 1.0554 at 20/20°C. and a boiling point of 210 to 211°C., which is about 80°C. lower than that of glycerol. Except that it is considerably less viscous than glycerol, its physical properties are very similar, and the characteristic properties of glycerol are retained; it is quite as hygroscopic, and in aqueous solutions it effectively lowers the freezing point of water. Its solutions are practically identical in freezing point with equivalent glycerol solutions. Its presence in small amounts is not objectionable in glycerol intended for nitration, as its nitration product is stated to be as stable as nitroglycerin; early statements to the contrary were probably due to the presence of unstable nitrogen compounds which are likely to be found in association with it.

It is possible to obtain large quantities of comparatively pure trimethylene glycol from sweet-water glycerol. The glycol can be effectively separated by a simple fractional distillation in an ordinary glycerol still. After treatment with charcoal and redistillation, the glycol is obtained as a pale yellow product with a fairly good odor and taste. In this form it is capable of replacing glycerol for many industrial purposes.

Trimethylene glycol is normally recovered commercially in glycerol plants only when there is sufficient demand for the product. It has been prepared synthetically[53] by heating γ,γ'-dihydroxydipropyl ether with hydrobromic acid and hydrolysis of the reaction product with sodium hydroxide. The glycol also is formed, along with acrolein, by heating 2-(β-hydroxyethyl)-1,3-dioxane with dilute sulfuric acid[54].

Trimethylene glycol is a useful starting material in the synthesis of the local anesthetic "Metycaine," the preparation of which involves trimethylene chlorohydrin[55].

Literature Cited

1. Seidenfeld, M. A., and Hanzlik, P. J., *J. Pharm.*, **44,** 109 (1932).
2. Hanzlik, P. J., *Ind. Eng. Chem.*, **24,** 836 (1932).
3. Hunt, R., *Ind. Eng. Chem.*, **24,** 361, 836–7 (1932).
4. Hooper, C. W. (to Winthrop Chemical Co., Inc.), U. S. Patent, 2,030,792 (Feb. 11, 1936).
5. Robertson, O. H., *Science*, **93,** 213–4 (1941).
6. Doelling, G. L. (to Wagner Electric Corp.), U. S. Patent 1,997,998 (April 16, 1935).
7. Air Corps Specification No. 3586-A, Feb. 17, 1941.
8. Roehm, L. S., *Am. Perfumer Essent. Oil Rev.*, **46** (10), 35 (1944).
9. U. S. Tariff Commission Report, "Synthetic Organic Chemicals," 1950.
10. Ferreo, P., and Valendries, C. (to Société Carbochimique), U. S. Patent 2,103,813 (Dec. 28, 1937).
11. Burdick, J. N. (to Carbide and Carbon Chemicals Corp.), U. S. Patent 1,589,359 (June 22, 1926).
12. Youtz, M. A. (to Standard Oil Co.), U. S. Patent 1,875,312 (Aug. 30, 1932).
13. Smith, L., *Z. physik. Chem.*, **93,** 59 (1918); *Chem. Abstracts*, **13,** 1461 (1919).
14. Robertson, N. C. (to Celanese Corp. of America), U. S. Patent 2,477,087 (July 26, 1949).

15. Michael, V. F., and Phinney, J. A. (to Stanolind Oil and Gas Co.), U. S. Patent 2,482,284 (Sept. 20, 1949).
16. Lazier, W. A. (to E. I. du Pont de Nemours & Co.), U. S. Patent 2,109,844 (March 1, 1938).
17. Larchar, A. W. (to E. I. du Pont de Nemours & Co.), U. S. Patent 1,963,997 (June 26, 1934).
18. Wurtz, A., *Ann. chim. et phys.*, (3) **55,** 438 (1859).
19. Lourenco, A., *Ann.*, **120,** 91 (1861).
20. Belohoubek, A., *Ber.*, **12,** 1873 (1879).
21. Morley, H. F., and Green, A. G., *J. Chem. Soc.*, **47,** 132 (1885).
22. Raschig, F., and Prahl, W., *Ber.*, **61,** 185 (1928).
23. Solonina, *J. Russ. Phys. Chem. Soc.*, **19,** 311 (1887).
24. Kling, A., *Compt. rend.*, **135,** 970 (1902).
25. Kötz, A., and Richter, K., *J. prakt. Chem.*, (2) **111,** 397 (1925).
26. Bowden, E., and Adkins, H., *J. Am. Chem. Soc.*, **56,** 689 (1934).
27. Milas, N. A., and Sussman, S., *J. Am. Chem. Soc.*, **59,** 2345 (1937).
28. Niederist, G., *Ann.*, **196,** 359 (1879).
29. Eltekow, A., *J. Russ. Phys. Chem. Soc.*, **10,** 210 (1878).
30. Hartmann, O., *J. prakt. Chem.*, (2) **16,** 383 (1877).
31. Matter, O., German Patent 369,502 (Feb. 20, 1923).
32. Klebanskii, A. L., and Dolgopol'skii, I. M., *J. Applied Chem. (U.S.S.R.)*, **7,** 1181 (1934).
33. Newitt, D. M., and Mene, P. S., *J. Chem. Soc.*, **1946,** 97–100.
34. Ipatieff, V., *Ber.*, **45,** 3224 (1912).
35. Zartman, W. H., and Adkins, H., *J. Am. Chem. Soc.*, **55,** 4559 (1933).
36. Tanno, T., *J. Chem. Soc. Japan*, **59,** 709–18 (1938); *Chem. Abstracts*, **32,** 9047 (1938).
37. Yosikawa, K., and Hanai, S., *Bull. Inst. Phys. Chem. Research (Tokyo)*, **17,** 1262 (1938).
38. Hass, H. B., and Patterson, J. A., *Ind. Eng. Chem.*, **33,** 615 (1941).
39. Natta, G., Rigamonti, R., and Beati, E., *Ber.*, **76B,** 641–56 (1943).
40. Lenth, C. W., and Du Puis, R. N., *Ind. Eng. Chem.*, **37,** 152–7 (1945).
41. I. G. Farbenindustrie A.-G., British Patent 299,373 (Oct. 24, 1927).
42. Lautenschläger, K. L., Bockmühl, M., Ehrhart, G., and Krohs, W. (to I. G. Farbenindustrie A.-G.), U. S. Patent 1,915,341 (June 27, 1933).
43. Rothrock, H. S. (to E. I. du Pont de Nemours & Co.), U. S. Patent 2,004,135 (June 11, 1935); British Patent 430,576 (July 18, 1935).
44. Henkel & Cie G.m.b.H., French Patent 844,415 (July 25, 1939).
45. Bombrini Parodi-Delfino, Swiss Patent 213,251 (May 1, 1941).
46. Lenth, C. W., and Du Puis, R. N. (to Association of American Soap and Glycerine Producers, Inc.), U. S. Patents 2,201,235 (May 21, 1940) and 2,290,439 (July 21, 1942); British Patents 490,211 (Aug. 5, 1938) and 499,417 (Jan. 24, 1939); and French Patent 816,952 (Aug. 21, 1937).
47. Du Puis, R. N. (to Association of American Soap and Glycerine Producers, Inc.), U. S. Patent 2,282,603 (May 12, 1942).
48. Stengel, L. A. (to Commercial Solvents Corp.), U. S. Patent 2,325,206 (July 27, 1943).
49. Stengel, L. A., and O'Loughlin, W. K. (to Commercial Solvents Corp.), U. S. Patent 2,325,207 (July 27, 1943).
50. Bottoms, R. R., U. S. Patent 2,335,731 (Nov. 30, 1943).
51. Stengel, L. A., and Maple, F. E. (to Commercial Solvents Corp.), U. S. Patent 2,381,316 (Aug. 7, 1945).

52. Rayner, A., *J. Soc. Chem. Ind.*, **45,** 265-6, 287-8T (1926).
53. Rojahn, C. A., *Ber.*, **54,** 3120 (1921).
54. Neuberg, C., Hirsch, J., and Reinfurth, E., *Biochem. Z.*, **105,** 336 (1920).
55. Furnas, C. C., Editor, "Rogers' Manual of Industrial Chemistry," 6th Ed., Vol. **2,** p. 1309, New York, D. Van Nostrand Co., Inc., 1942.

CHAPTER 9

PHYSICAL PROPERTIES OF PROPYLENE GLYCOL

W. S. JONES AND W. S. TAMPLIN

Propylene glycol (1,2-propanediol) is a colorless, odorless liquid with a sweetish taste, and is completely miscible with water and most organic solvents. Although somewhat more volatile than ethylene glycol, propylene glycol is about three times as viscous at room temperature.

This chapter contains most of the available physical data on the pure compound (summarized in Table 9.1) and some of the more important physical properties of its aqueous and nonaqueous solutions. Propylene glycol contains an asymmetric carbon atom and therefore occurs in two optically active forms (dextro- and levorotatory isomers). Except as noted, all of the data were determined on the optically inactive (racemic) mixture of the two isomers, which is the product obtained by most methods of synthesis. In general, the properties are arranged alphabetically.

Absorption Spectra

Weniger[1] published an infrared absorption spectra of propylene glycol in 1910. However, as in the case of ethylene glycol (see page 27), it is apparent that his sample was contaminated with moisture. A curve submitted by Dow[2] in 1949 is shown in Figure 9.1. The data were obtained on a sample of pure propylene glycol using a 0.0155-mm. cell.

The following shifts (lines) observed in the Raman spectrum of propylene glycol have been tabulated by Hibben[3]: $\Delta \bar{\nu}$ 830, 919, 1050, and 2918.

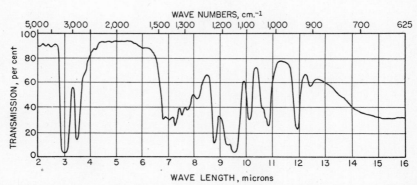

FIGURE 9.1. Infrared absorption spectrum of propylene glycol at 26°C. (cell length, 0.0155 mm.).

TABLE 9.1. PHYSICAL PROPERTIES OF PROPYLENE GLYCOL
$CH_2OHCHOHCH_3$

Absorption spectra		see page 210
Azeotropes		see page 211
Boiling point at 760 mm.	187.4°C.	see page 235
at 50 mm.	116°C.	
at 10 mm.	85°C.	
Δb.p./Δp, 740 to 760 mm.	0.042°C./mm.	
Coefficient of expansion at 20°C.	0.00073/°C.	
Density (true) at 20°C.	1.0363 g./ml.	see page 213
Dew points		see page 219
Dielectric constant at 20°C.	32.0 esu	see page 216
Fire point	225°F.	see page 216
Flash point	225°F.	see page 216
Freezing point		see page 217
Heat of combustion at constant volume and 20°C.	435.9 kcal./mol	see page 218
Heat of formation at 20°C.	119.5 kcal./mol	ref. 4
Heat of vaporization at 760 mm.	170 cal./g.	see page 218
Hygroscopicity		see page 219
Molecular weight, 1951	76.09	
Pressure-volume-temperature data		see page 219
Refractive index, n_D at 20°C.	1.4326	see page 221
$\Delta n_D/\Delta t$, 20 to 30°C.	0.00030/°C.	
Solubility		see page 222
Specific gravity (apparent) at 20/20°C.	1.0381	see page 214
ΔSp.gr./Δt, 0 to 40°C.	0.00073/°C.	
Specific heat at 20°C.	0.593 cal./g./°C.	see page 227
Spontaneous ignition temperature	835°F.	ref. 5
Surface tension at 25°C.	72.0 dynes/cm.	see page 229
Thermal conductivity	0.00145 cal.-cm./sec./ cm.²/°C.	see page 229
Vapor-liquid equilibrium data		see page 232
Vapor pressure		see page 232
Verdet constant at 25°C. and 5461 Å	0.01540 min./gauss cm.	ref. 6
5893 Å	0.01291 min./gauss cm.	
Viscosity (absolute) at 20°C.	56.0 cp.	see page 237

The shift $\Delta\bar{\nu}$ 830 is relatively strong; intensities of the other shifts are not given. While a shift equivalent to $\Delta\bar{\nu}$ 3400 in ethylene glycol (see page 29) has not been reported for propylene glycol, it is undoubtedly present.

Azeotropes

Propylene glycol forms azeotropic mixtures with dodecane (67 per cent glycol by weight), tetradecane (76 per cent glycol by weight), and aniline (43 per cent glycol by weight). The azeotropes boil at 175, 179, and 179.5°C., respectively, at 760 mm.[7] Other azeotropes have been listed by Horsley[7]. There is no azeotrope of propylene glycol and water.

TABLE 9.2. DENSITY AND SPECIFIC GRAVITY OF PROPYLENE GLYCOL

Temperature,°C.	True Density, g./ml.	Apparent Specific Gravity			
		$t/4$°C.	$t/15$°C.	$t/20$°C.	$t/25$°C.
0	1.0508	1.0509	1.0519	1.0528	1.0540
1	01	01	11	20	32
2	1.0493	1.0494	04	13	25
3	86	87	1.0497	06	18
4	79	79	89	1.0498	10
5	1.0472	1.0472	1.0482	1.0491	1.0503
6	64	65	75	84	96
7	57	57	67	76	88
8	50	50	60	69	81
9	43	43	53	62	74
10	1.0435	1.0436	1.0445	1.0454	1.0466
11	28	29	38	47	59
12	21	22	31	40	52
13	13	14	23	32	44
14	06	07	16	25	37
15	1.0399	1.0400	1.0409	1.0418	1.0430
16	92	1.0393	02	11	23
17	84	85	1.0394	03	15
18	77	78	87	1.0396	08
19	70	71	80	89	01
20	1.0363	1.0363	1.0372	1.0381	1.0393
21	55	56	65	74	86
22	48	49	58	67	79
23	41	41	50	59	71
24	33	34	43	52	64
25	1.0326	1.0327	1.0336	1.0345	1.0357
26	19	19	28	37	49
27	12	12	21	30	42
28	04	05	14	23	35
29	1.0297	1.0298	07	16	28
30	1.0290	1.0290	1.0299	1.0308	1.0320
31	82	83	92	01	13
32	75	76	85	1.0294	06
33	68	68	77	86	1.0298
34	61	61	70	79	91
35	1.0253	1.0254	1.0263	1.0272	1.0284
36	46	46	55	64	76
37	39	39	48	57	69
38	32	32	41	50	62
39	24	24	33	42	54
40	1.0217	1.0217	1.0226	1.0235	1.0247

Density

When Wurtz[8] first prepared propylene glycol in 1859, he reported densities of 1.051 and 1.038 at 0 and 23°C., respectively, which are in surprisingly good agreement with more recent determinations. Numerous subsequent investigators[9, 10, 11, 12, 13, 14, 15, 16] have reported density values.

Density values for purified propylene glycol over the temperature range 0 to 40°C. are given in Table 9.2. The change of density with temperature is practically constant, being 0.0007 at 0°C. and 0.0008 at 50°C.

Table 9.2 also gives commonly used values for the apparent specific gravity over the temperature range 0 to 40°C. These data were derived from the density values by means of the equations on page 31.

The densities of aqueous propylene glycol solutions over the entire composition range have been determined by Carbide and Dow. A large-scale plot of the data was made and smooth curves drawn through the points (Figure 9.2). The values in Table 9.3 were taken from these curves.

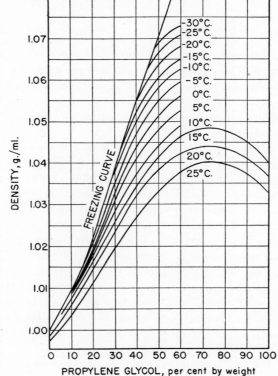

FIGURE 9.2. Densities of aqueous solutions of propylene glycol.

TABLE 9.3. DENSITY OF AQUEOUS SOLUTIONS OF PROPYLENE GLYCOL

Temper-ature, °C.	Propylene Glycol, per cent by weight										
	0	10	20	30	40	50	60	70	80	90	100
	True Density, g./ml.										
25	0.9971	1.0037	1.0115	1.0195	1.0271	1.0332	1.0375	1.0397	1.0395	1.0373	1.0326
20	0.9982	1.0058	1.0146	1.0234	1.0319	1.0382	1.0423	1.0439	1.0435	1.0410	1.0363
15	0.9991	1.0078	1.0165	1.0255	1.0344	1.0416	1.0464	1.0485	1.0481	1.0453	1.0399
10	0.9997	1.0082	1.0178	1.0282	1.0376	1.0445	1.0490	—	—	—	1.0435
5	0.9999	1.0089	1.0189	1.0305	1.0410	1.0483	1.0526	—	—	—	1.0472
0	0.9999	1.0092	1.0196	1.0327	1.0442	1.0520	1.0559	—	—	—	1.0508
−5	—	—	1.0203	1.0354	1.0469	1.0547	1.0593	—	—	—	1.0544
−10	—	—	1.0216	1.0374	1.0498	1.0582	1.0624	—	—	—	1.0589
−15	—	—	—	—	1.0517	1.0606	1.0650	—	—	—	1.0616
−20	—	—	—	—	—	—	—	—	—	—	1.0652
−25	—	—	—	—	—	—	—	—	—	—	1.0688
−30	—	—	—	—	—	—	—	—	—	—	1.0727

A density maximum occurs in this system at approximately 70 per cent glycol. This corresponds to 36 mol per cent or a ratio of two mols of water to one of propylene glycol. It is probable that one molecule of water is hydrogen-bonded to each hydroxyl group of the glycol to form a complex having a density greater than that of either of the pure propylene glycol or water.

Table 9.4 gives the variation in composition of propylene glycol-water mixtures for each 0.001 change in specific gravity. This table may be used to determine the approximate composition of such a mixture by measuring the specific gravity of the solution at 20/20°C. However, it is important to note that every specific gravity value above that of the pure glycol (except the maximum point) corresponds to two compositions. To determine which is correct, a small amount of water may be added to the sample and the increase or decrease in specific gravity noted.

The only available data on the specific gravities of propylene glycol-dipropylene glycol solutions cover the range of 0 to 10 per cent dipropylene glycol. A sample of dipropylene glycol (sp. gr. 1.0252 at 20/20°C.), purified by molecular distillation and having a boiling range of 1.0°C. at 50 mm., was used for the determinations. The values in Table 9.5 were taken from a plot of the original data.

For the densities of ethylene glycol-propylene glycol solutions see Chapter 3, "Physical Properties of Ethylene Glycol," page 34.

TABLE 9.4. APPARENT SPECIFIC GRAVITY OF AQUEOUS SOLUTIONS
OF PROPYLENE GLYCOL

Apparent Sp. Gr., 20/20°C.	Propylene Glycol, % by wt.	Apparent Sp. Gr., 20/20°C.	Propylene Glycol, % by wt.	Apparent Sp. Gr., 20/20°C.	Propylene Glycol, % by wt.
1.0000	0.00	1.0200	24.16	1.0400	50.3
1.0010	1.42	1.0210	25.28	1.0410	52.3
1.0020	2.83	1.0220	26.40	1.0420	54.4
1.0030	4.17	1.0230	27.52	1.0430	56.9
1.0040	5.48	1.0240	28.63	1.0440	59.7
1.0050	6.78	1.0250	29.74	1.0450	63.5
1.0060	8.05	1.0260	30.90	1.0455	66.3
1.0070	9.28	1.0270	32.05		
1.0080	10.48	1.0280	33.21	1.04595[a]	72.95
1.0090	11.65	1.0290	34.38	1.0455	79.9
1.0100	12.83	1.0300	35.58	1.0450	82.8
1.0110	14.00	1.0310	36.78	1.0440	86.6
1.0120	15.14	1.0320	38.04	1.0430	89.5
1.0130	16.28	1.0330	39.32	1.0420	92.0
1.0140	17.41	1.0340	40.65	1.0410	94.3
1.0150	18.55	1.0350	42.01	1.0400	96.4
1.0160	19.68	1.0360	43.43	1.0390	98.4
1.0170	20.80	1.0370	44.95	1.03813	100.0
1.0180	21.92	1.0380	46.58		
1.0190	23.04	1.0390	48.37		

[a] Note: Beyond this point the specific gravity decreases with increasing propylene glycol content.

TABLE 9.5. APPARENT SPECIFIC GRAVITY OF MIXTURES OF PROPYLENE GLYCOL
AND 0 TO 10 PER CENT DIPROPYLENE GLYCOL

Apparent Sp. Gr., 20/20°C.	Dipropylene Glycol, % by wt.	Apparent Sp. Gr., 20/20°C.	Dipropylene Glycol, % by wt.	Apparent Sp. Gr., 20/20°C.	Dipropylene Glycol, % by wt.
1.03809	0.00	1.03760	3.80	1.03710	7.67
1.03805	0.31	1.03755	4.19	1.03705	8.06
1.03800	0.70	1.03750	4.57	1.03700	8.45
1.03795	1.09	1.03745	4.96	1.03695	8.84
1.03790	1.47	1.03740	5.35	1.03690	9.22
1.03785	1.86	1.03735	5.74	1.03685	9.61
1.03780	2.25	1.03730	6.12	1.03680	10.00
1.03775	2.64	1.03725	6.51		
1.03770	3.02	1.03720	6.90		
1.03765	3.41	1.03715	7.29		

Dielectric Constant

White and Morgan[17] have determined the dielectric constant and power factor of propylene glycol in the range of −90 to −40°C. for several frequencies between 1 and 100 kilocycles. A plot of the experimental data, which were obtained by means of a direct-reading capacitance bridge, is shown in Figure 9.3. Over most of this temperature range propylene glycol, in common with other viscous liquids, exhibits anomalous dispersion, *i.e.*, change of dielectric constant and dielectric absorption with frequency. Above −45°C. the dielectric constant is independent of frequency in the range below 100 kilocycles.

Data at 20°C. are as follows: dielectric constant (static or low-frequency value), 32.0 esu; temperature coefficient $\left(\frac{1}{\epsilon}\cdot\frac{d\epsilon}{dt}\right)$, 0.0063 per °C.[18]

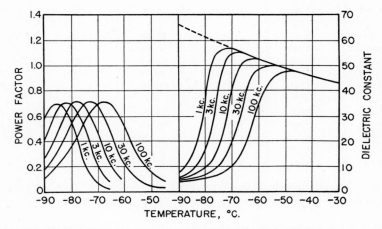

FIGURE 9.3. Dielectric constants and power factors of propylene glycol at various temperatures for frequencies from 1 to 100 kilocycles.

Flammability

Carbide data, determined with a Cleveland open-cup tester, show that the addition of 10 per cent by weight of water to propylene glycol raises the flash point from 225 to 245°F. and the fire point from 225 to 260°F. A solution containing 15 per cent water does not flash. Other values reported for propylene glycol include: flash points, 210°F.[19] and 230°F.[5]; fire points, 216°F.[19] and 235°F.[5]

Sullivan, Wolfe and Zisman[5] also reported a value of 38 per cent oxygen for the spray flammability limit. This is defined as the minimum amount of oxygen required in an oxygen-nitrogen stream to cause the ignition of a fine spray of the glycol by means of an electric arc. Because of the empirical nature of this test, the original paper should be consulted for the experimental procedure and interpretation of the results.

Bigg, Jennings, and Fried[20] have made several more specialized tests of the flammability characteristics of propylene glycol. Their work was undertaken because of the interest in this compound as an "air-treatment" agent, and their tests were designed to cover possible hazardous conditions occurring in this application.

Freezing Point

All attempts to freeze pure propylene glycol apparently have been unsatisfactory. This may be due in part to its high viscosity at low temperatures as well as to the fact that the usual material is a racemic mixture.

In lieu of the freezing point, the pour point has been used to characterize the behavior of propylene glycol at low temperatures. Values of $-60°$C. and $-77°$C. have been reported by Carbide and Dow, respectively. The poor agreement between the two values is not surprising in view of the nature of the test.

Carbide and Dow have obtained freezing points of aqueous solutions of propylene glycol from 0 to 60 per cent glycol, and the two sets of values are in good agreement. Their results are plotted in Figure 9.4. The values in Table 9.6 were taken from this curve. The solid phase separating is ice. Solutions containing more than 60 per cent propylene glycol cannot be made to solidify; their pour points are below $-70°$C.

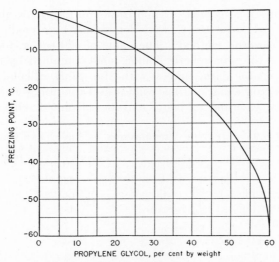

FIGURE 9.4. Freezing point of aqueous solutions of propylene glycol. Solutions containing more than 60 per cent propylene glycol set to a glass below $-60°$C.

TABLE 9.6. Freezing Points of Aqueous Solutions of Propylene Glycol

Propylene Glycol, % by wt.	Freezing Point, °C.	Propylene Glycol, % by wt.	Freezing Point, °C.
0	0	30	−13.0
5	−1.6	35	−16.5
10	−3.2	40	−20.8
15	−5.2	45	−25.8
20	−7.5	50	−31.7
25	−10.0	55	−40
		60	−57

Heat of Combustion

Two sets of values have been reported for the heat of combustion of propylene glycol at constant volume: 436.2 kcal./mol or 1731 Btu/mol[21] and 435.9 kcal./mol or 1730 Btu/mol[4]. A value at constant pressure was given as 436.5 kcal./mol or 1732 Btu/mol[4]. Considering that these determinations were made more than 50 years apart, the agreement is excellent. These values are based on the oxidation of the liquid glycol to liquid water and gaseous carbon dioxide.

Heat of Vaporization

Carbide values for the heat of vaporization of propylene glycol over the temperature range 85 to 150°C. were determined by a modification of the Coolidge condensation method[22]. The value of 170 cal./g. for the heat of vaporization at the atmospheric boiling point, obtained by extrapolation of the experimental data, agrees with the value calculated from the Clausius-Clapeyron equation. The values in Table 9.7 were taken from a line through the experimental points and the calculated value of 170 cal./g.

TABLE 9.7. Heat of Vaporization of Propylene Glycol

Temperature, °C.	Heat of Vaporization, cal./g.	Temperature, °C.	Heat of Vaporization, cal./g.
40	208	120	190
60	204	140	186
80	200	160	180
100	195	180	173
		187	170

Hygroscopicity

Hygroscopicity, loosely understood to be the affinity of a substance for water vapor, is actually a complex phenomenon based on the rate of diffusion of water across the vapor-liquid interface. This rate is controlled by many factors, including concentration, temperature, surface area, liquid depth, and liquid and vapor film coefficients. Inasmuch as it is impractical to measure the effect of all these variables, simplified empirical tests have been developed to determine the relative hygroscopicity of various substances. Obviously, determinations made under different conditions such as those shown in Table 9.8 are not directly comparable[23]. Both sets of data show that the amount of water absorbed per unit time by propylene glycol is about the same as that absorbed by glycerol; moreover, in similar tests both propylene glycol and glycerol absorbed water vapor at a slower rate than ethylene glycol (see Chapter 3, page 44).

In connection with studies on natural-gas absorption, Carbide determined the effect of aqueous solutions of propylene glycol on dew points at various contact temperatures. See Figure 9.5.

The Dow Chemical Company[19] has published relative humectant values for propylene glycol over the temperature range of 0 to 120°F. (Table 9.9). This property is somewhat related to hygroscopicity in that it is the limiting concentration of water that will be taken up when the solution is in contact with air at a given relative humidity and temperature.

Pressure-Volume-Temperature Data

The volumetric behavior of liquid propylene glycol under pressure has been investigated by P. W. Bridgman[24] from 0 to 12,000 kg./cm.^{2} at 0, 50,

TABLE 9.8. HYGROSCOPICITY OF PROPYLENE GLYCOL

Water Absorbed, % of original weight		Time, days	Reference
Propylene Glycol	Glycerol		
13.9	10.5	1[a]	23
25.3	22.0	3	
37.7	38.5	7	
57.7	59.7	14	
45	38	2[b]	Carbide
58	48	3	
83	84	7	

[a] 5 g. of sample with 17.9 sq. in. of surface area exposed at room temperature to an atmosphere of 100 per cent relative humidity.

[b] 100 per cent relative humidity at 100°F.

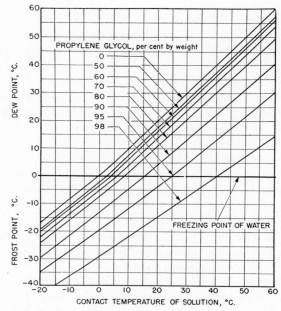

FIGURE 9.5. Effect of aqueous solutions of propylene glycol on dew points at contact temperatures ranging from −20 to 60°C.

TABLE 9.9. RELATIVE HUMECTANT VALUES OF PROPYLENE GLYCOL

Air Temperature, °F.	Relative Humidity, %							
	20	30	40	50	60	70	80	90
	Propylene Glycol, % by wt. in water							
0	93.0	88.0	78.0	73.7	70.0	62.5	45.0	—
10	93.5	87.5	78.0	73.7	70.5	63.0	46.0	30.0
20	93.0	87.5	78.5	73.7	71.0	63.0	47.0	30.0
30	92.7	88.0	79.5	74.0	71.0	62.0	48.0	30.0
40	93.0	89.5	81.0	76.0	71.5	64.0	50.0	30.0
50	93.5	90.5	83.0	77.5	72.0	66.0	51.0	31.0
60	93.7	90.8	84.0	78.0	72.0	66.0	52.0	32.0
70	94.0	91.0	85.0	78.5	73.0	66.5	52.5	33.0
80	94.3	91.2	85.0	79.0	73.0	66.0	52.5	34.0
90	94.4	91.2	85.5	79.5	73.5	67.0	53.0	35.0
100	94.4	91.25	85.0	80.5	74.0	67.0	53.0	35.0
110	94.4	91.26	86.0	81.0	75.0	67.5	53.0	33.0
120	94.4	91.27	86.5	81.3	75.0	68.0	54.0	33.0

and 95°C. Taking the volume of the liquid at zero pressure and 0°C. as unity, the volumes occupied by the same mass at other temperatures and pressures are shown in Table 9.10 (Figure 9.6). The average deviation from smooth curves of a single one of the 73 experimental points was 0.13 per cent of the maximum effect.

Commercial material having a density of 1.0340 at 20°C. was used for these determinations. By means of a volume-temperature coefficient obtained from differential readings at 0 and 50°C., Bridgman obtained a value of 1.0486 for the density at 0°C. These values are not in very close agreement with the best density data (see Table 9.2), indicating an uncertain amount of impurity in the sample. For most purposes, however, the values in Table 9.10 should prove sufficiently accurate.

A resumé of the several derived functions which can be obtained from experimental data of this kind will be found in Chapter 3, Table 3.13 on page 46.

TABLE 9.10. PRESSURE-VOLUME-TEMPERATURE DATA
FOR LIQUID PROPYLENE GLYCOL

Pressure, kg./cm.²	Relative Volume at		
	0°C.	50°C.	95°C.
0	1.0000	—	—
500	0.9819	1.0129	—
1000	0.9664	0.9947	1.0201
1500	0.9540	0.9794	1.0027
2000	0.9432	0.9659	0.9877
3000	0.9237	0.9454	0.9637
4000	0.9070	0.9266	0.9430
5000	0.8935	0.9120	0.9257
6000	0.8809	0.8989	0.9110
7000	0.8679	0.8864	0.8985
8000	0.8569	0.8750	0.8867
9000	0.8472	0.8652	0.8763
10000	0.8380	0.8563	0.8672
11000	0.8294	0.8477	0.8589
12000	0.8219	0.8400	0.8514

Refractive Index

The refractive index of pure propylene glycol varies linearly at the rate of 0.00030 per °C., the index at 20°C. being 1.4326 for sodium D light. Other values reported in the literature[4, 13, 14, 19] are in fair agreement.

Refractive index measurements provide an excellent means of determining the composition of propylene glycol-water mixtures. Table 9.11, covering the entire range of compositions at 25°C., is based on Carbide

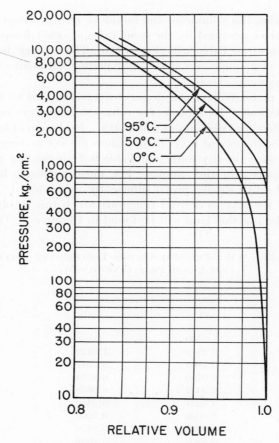

FIGURE 9.6. Pressure-volume-temperature relationship for liquid propylene glycol.

data determined by means of a Zeiss Pulfrich refractometer using a sodium vapor lamp as a light source.

The refractive index of mixtures of propylene glycol and ethylene glycol varies linearly with composition.

Solubility

The solvent properties of propylene glycol are similar to those of ethylene glycol. It is completely soluble in water. Most of the lower molecular weight aliphatic compounds containing oxygen or nitrogen are miscible in all proportions with propylene glycol; in general, aromatic and halogenated compounds are only partially miscible.

TABLE 9.11.   REFRACTIVE INDICES OF AQUEOUS SOLUTIONS OF PROPYLENE GLYCOL

Refractive Index, n_D at 25°C.	Propylene Glycol, % by wt.	Refractive Index, n_D at 25°C.	Propylene Glycol, % by wt.	Refractive Index, n_D at 25°C.	Propylene Glycol, % by wt.	Refractive Index, n_D at 25°C.	Propylene Glycol, % by wt.
1.3325	0.0	1.3550	20.3	1.3800	43.0	1.4050	67.4
30	0.4	60	21.2	10	43.9	60	68.5
40	1.3	70	22.2	20	44.8	70	69.5
		80	23.1	30	45.7	80	70.6
		90	24.0	40	46.6	90	71.7
1.3350	2.3	1.3600	24.9	1.3850	47.5	1.4100	72.8
60	3.2	10	25.8	60	48.5	10	74.0
70	4.1	20	26.7	70	49.4	20	75.2
80	5.0	30	27.6	80	50.3	30	76.3
90	5.9	40	28.6	90	51.3	40	77.5
1.3400	6.8	1.3650	29.5	1.3900	52.3	1.4150	78.7
10	7.7	60	30.4	10	53.3	60	79.9
20	8.6	70	31.3	20	54.3	70	81.1
30	9.5	80	32.2	30	55.2	80	82.3
40	10.4	90	33.1	40	56.2	90	83.6
1.3450	11.3	1.3700	34.0	1.3950	57.2	1.4200	84.9
60	12.2	10	34.9	60	58.2	10	86.2
70	13.1	20	35.8	70	59.2	20	87.5
80	14.0	30	36.7	80	60.2	30	88.8
90	14.9	40	37.6	90	61.2	40	90.1
1.3500	15.8	1.3750	38.5	1.4000	62.2	1.4250	91.4
10	16.7	60	39.4	10	63.2	60	92.7
20	17.6	70	40.3	20	64.2	70	94.0
30	18.5	80	41.2	30	65.2	80	95.4
40	19.4	90	42.1	40	66.3	90	96.8
						1.4300	98.3
						10	99.7
						12	100.0

Solubility data for substantially pure compounds including a number of important pharmaceuticals are given in Table 9.12[19, 25]. Table 9.13[19, 25, 26] contains similar data for commercial products of general interest. Solubilities of flavoring materials in aqueous solutions of propylene glycol, taken from a compilation[25] by B. L. Lemke and Company, are given in Tables 9.14 and 9.15.

TABLE 9.12. Solubility of Some Substantially Pure Compounds
in Propylene Glycol

Compound	Solubility at 25°C., g./100 g. of propylene glycol
Amyl acetate	∞
Antipyrine	25
Benzaldehyde	∞ (0–40°C.)
Benzene	23.8
Benzocaine	very soluble in dilute aqueous solutions
Benzyl alcohol	25
Bis(2-chloroethyl) ether	144
Bismuth hydroxide	soluble
Bismuth thioglycolate	10.4
Camphor	10.8
Carbon tetrachloride	30.5
Chlorobenzene	29.0
Chlorothymol	soluble
Citral	∞
Coumarin	5.2 (50°F.)
	9.7 (68°F.)
	16.8 (86°F.)
	36.6 (104°F.)
Desoxycorticosterone acetate	soluble
Dibutyl phthalate	8.8
o-Dichlorobenzene	24.1
Diethanolamine	∞
Diothane	5
Ethyl acetate	∞
Ethyl ether	∞
Ethyl formate	∞
Ethyl vanillin	8.7 (32°F.)
	29.9 (77°F.)
Eucalyptol	24.8
Glycol stearate	very slightly soluble
Hexylresorcinol	soluble
α-Ionone	∞
Isoamyl formate	∞
Menthol	>50
Methyl anthranilate	∞
Methyl salicylate	24.7
Monoethanolamine	∞
Paraldehyde	very soluble
Perchloroethylene	11.7
Phenethyl alcohol	∞
Phenobarbital	soluble
Phenol	∞
Phenothiazine	soluble
Salicyl alcohol	4.2

TABLE 9.12—*Continued*

Compound	Solubility at 25°C., g./100 g. of propylene glycol
Sodium bismuth thioglycolate	10.4
Sodium iodobismuthite	6.4
Sulfadiazine	0.3
Sulfanilamide	11.1
Sulfapyridine	3.1
Sulfathiazole	3.1
Thymol	soluble
Toluene	14.0
Trichloro-*tert*-butanol	>60
Vanillin	11.5 (32°F.)
	20.1 (50°F.)
	38.9 (68°F.)
	48.1 (77°F.)
	88.2 (86°F.)
	402 (104°F.)
Vitamin A	soluble
Vitamin D	soluble

TABLE 9.13. Solubility of Miscellaneous Commercial Materials in Propylene Glycol

Material	Solubility at Room Temperature, g./100 g. of propylene glycol
Animal glue	very slightly soluble
Cassia oil	∞
Castor oil	0.8
Cellulose acetate	insoluble
Clove oil	∞
Coconut oil	insoluble
Cottonseed oil	insoluble
Dextrin	slightly soluble
Dextrin (10% in water)	∞
Glycol distearate	very slightly soluble
Gum damar	slightly soluble
Hydrous wool fat	slightly soluble
Kauri gum	slightly soluble
Lard oil	insoluble
Lemon oil	0.81
Linseed oil	slightly soluble
Methyl orange	0.6
Nitrocellulose	insoluble
Nutmeg oil	1.53
Olive oil	insoluble

TABLE 9.13—*Continued*

Material	Solubility at Room Temperature, g./100 g. of propylene glycol
Orange oil	0.26
Paraffin oil	insoluble
Pine oil	∞
Rosin	slightly soluble
Rubber	insoluble
Sassafras oil	2.02
Shellac	very slightly soluble
Soya bean oil	insoluble
Sperm oil	insoluble
Sudan III	slightly soluble
Tall oil	9.9
Tung oil	insoluble
Turkey Red oil	3.7
Urea	26.0
"Vinylite" resin AYAF	insoluble
"Vinylite" resin VYHH	insoluble

TABLE 9.14. SOLUBILITY OF FLAVORING MATERIALS IN AQUEOUS PROPYLENE GLYCOL SOLUTIONS

Material	Propylene glycol, % by volume				
	100	80	60	40	20
	Solubility, at 25°C., % by weight solute in final mixture				
Amyl acetate	∞	∞	∞	1.48	1.34
Benzaldehyde	∞	18.97	4.62	1.80	0.82
Cassia oil	∞	3.13	0.85	0.69	0.21
Citral	∞	0.35	0.17	0.10	0.04
Clove oil	∞	1.19	0.26	0.24	0.12
Coumarin	7.70	5.05	2.30	0.50	0.32
Ethyl acetate	∞	∞	∞	11.65	8.09
Ethyl formate	∞	∞	∞	—	17.45
Ethyl vanillin	14.20	10.80	5.20	1.84	0.79
Eucalyptol	19.90	4.75	1.73	0.35	0.25
Isoamyl formate	∞	5.22	4.51	1.68	1.53
Lemon oil	0.81	0.52	0.32	0.13	0.03
Methyl anthranilate	∞	∞	∞	—	—
Nutmeg oil	1.53	0.34	0.17	0.14	0.11
Orange oil	0.26	0.13	0.08	0.06	0.03
Phenyl ethyl alcohol	∞	∞	∞	18.95	3.11
Sassafras oil	2.02	1.21	0.20	0.12	0.08
Vanillin	20.20	20.10	12.60	5.85	2.09

TABLE 9.15. SOLUBILITY OF COUMARIN, ETHYL VANILLIN, AND VANILLIN
IN AQUEOUS PROPYLENE GLYCOL SOLUTIONS AT VARIOUS TEMPERATURES

Propylene Glycol, per cent by volume	Temperature, °F.					
	32	50	68	77	86	104
	Solubility, oz. solute per gal. of final mixture					
Coumarin						
0	0.12	0.17	0.22	0.27	0.34	0.52
20	—	0.18	0.33	—	0.53	0.87
40	—	0.33	0.53	—	1.20	2.40
60	—	1.60	2.68	—	3.74	6.67
80	—	3.34	5.34	—	9.35	17.4
100	—	4.94	8.80	—	14.4	26.7
Ethyl Vanillin						
0	0.20	0.27	0.37	0.45	0.55	0.85
20	0.33	—	—	1.07	—	—
40	0.61	—	—	2.54	—	—
60	2.40	—	—	7.48	—	—
80	6.41	—	—	16.6	—	—
100	8.00	—	—	23.0	—	—
Vanillin						
0	0.47	0.68	1.07	1.40	1.80	3.10
20	0.67	1.33	1.60	2.87	4.00	8.42
40	1.66	2.66	4.00	8.41	11.7	41.7
60	5.10	8.01	13.4	19.8	33.4	88.0
80	10.6	16.7	26.7	32.0	46.7	93.5
100	10.3	16.7	28.0	32.7	46.7	80.1

Specific Heat

Substantially complete data on the specific heat of propylene glycol and
its aqueous solutions from 0°C. to the atmospheric boiling points of the
respective mixtures have been reported by Dow and Carbide. In addition,
Gucker and Marsh[27] investigated compositions from 20 to 50 weight per
cent glycol over the temperature range of −32 to +1.7°C., and Parks
and Huffman[11] obtained data on pure propylene glycol from −182 to +4°C.

All four sets of data were plotted and smooth curves drawn through the
points (Figure 9.7). The values in Table 9.16 were read from the curves.
It is interesting to note that the minimum appearing in the specific heat-
temperature curve for water at approximately 35°C. also appears in mixtures containing as high as 20 per cent propylene glycol.

The data of Parks and Huffman on the specific heat of propylene glycol
at low temperatures are shown in Table 9.17 and plotted in Figure 9.8.

TABLE 9.16. SPECIFIC HEAT OF AQUEOUS SOLUTIONS OF PROPYLENE GLYCOL

Temper- ature, °C.	Propylene Glycol, % by wt.										
	0	10	20	30	40	50	60	70	80	90	100
	Specific Heat, cal./g./°C.										
−60	—	—	—	—	—	—	0.760	0.695	0.615	0.545	0.482
−50	—	—	—	—	—	—	0.762	0.698	0.626	0.557	0.496
−40	—	—	—	—	—	—	0.766	0.705	0.636	0.570	0.509
−30	—	—	—	—	—	0.823	0.772	0.711	0.647	0.583	0.523
−20	—	—	—	—	0.887	0.828	0.778	0.718	0.657	0.597	0.537
−10	—	—	—	0.934	0.887	0.833	0.785	0.727	0.668	0.610	0.552
0	1.009	0.994	0.968	0.934	0.890	0.838	0.792	0.735	0.680	0.623	0.565
10	1.002	0.990	0.965	0.934	0.893	0.845	0.799	0.745	0.692	0.636	0.579
20	0.999	0.989	0.963	0.935	0.897	0.852	0.807	0.754	0.703	0.648	0.593
30	0.997	0.989	0.963	0.937	0.902	0.860	0.817	0.765	0.716	0.662	0.607
40	0.998	0.989	0.965	0.940	0.907	0.868	0.827	0.777	0.728	0.675	0.622
50	0.998	0.990	0.968	0.944	0.912	0.877	0.837	0.788	0.741	0.688	0.635
60	0.999	0.992	0.973	0.949	0.918	0.885	0.847	0.801	0.753	0.702	0.649
70	1.001	0.994	0.977	0.955	0.926	0.894	0.857	0.813	0.766	0.715	0.663
80	1.002	0.997	0.981	0.961	0.934	0.903	0.867	0.825	0.779	0.728	0.678
90	1.004	0.998	0.985	0.968	0.942	0.913	0.878	0.837	0.793	0.741	0.692
100	1.006	1.002	0.990	0.975	0.951	0.923	0.888	0.851	0.806	0.754	0.705
110	—	—	—	—	—	—	—	0.863	0.818	0.767	0.719
120	—	—	—	—	—	—	—	—	—	0.781	0.733
130	—	—	—	—	—	—	—	—	—	—	0.747
140	—	—	—	—	—	—	—	—	—	—	0.761
150	—	—	—	—	—	—	—	—	—	—	0.775
160	—	—	—	—	—	—	—	—	—	—	0.788
170	—	—	—	—	—	—	—	—	—	—	0.803
180	—	—	—	—	—	—	—	—	—	—	0.817
187.4	—	—	—	—	—	—	—	—	—	—	0.827

An examination of these values reveals a striking behavior in the temperature range of −90 to −120°C. where a discontinuity in the specific heat curve occurs. These investigators believe that in this range the compound changes from the liquid to a "solid" state. Apparently the molecules are not arranged in a regular pattern as in the case of a true crystalline solid, but rather in a random manner which is characteristic of glass-like materials. The transition temperature range varies somewhat with the rate of cooling.

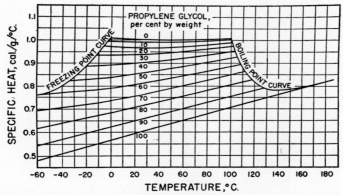

FIGURE 9.7. Specific heats of liquid aqueous solutions of propylene glycol at atmospheric pressure.

TABLE 9.17.   SPECIFIC HEAT OF PROPYLENE GLYCOL AT LOW TEMPERATURES

Temperature, °C.	Specific Heat, cal./g./°C.	Temperature, °C.	Specific Heat, cal./g./°C.
0	0.57	−100[a]	0.46
−10	0.55	−100[a]	0.48
−20	0.54	−120[a]	0.29
−30	0.52	−130	0.23
−40	0.51	−140	0.21
−50	0.50	−150	0.20
−60	0.48	−160	0.19
−70	0.47	−170	0.18
−80	0.46	−180	0.16
−90[a]	0.46		

[a] Transition range from liquid to glass.

Surface Tension

The only data available on the surface tension of propylene glycol were determined by Dow and Carbide (Table 9.18). These investigations show the surface tension of pure propylene glycol and its aqueous solutions over the entire range of composition at 25°C. (Figure 9.9). The Carbide data were determined by means of a DuNoüy interfacial tensiometer used in a constant-temperature room held at 25.0 ± 0.5°C.

Thermal Conductivity

Bates and Hazzard[28] carefully determined the thermal conductivity of

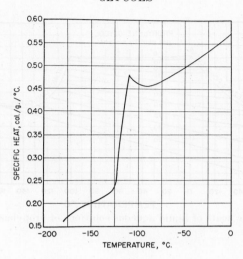

FIGURE 9.8. Specific heat of propylene glycol at low temperatures.

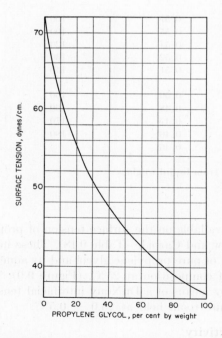

FIGURE 9.9. Surface tension of aqueous solutions of propylene glycol at 25°C.

TABLE 9.18. SURFACE TENSION OF PROPYLENE GLYCOLAND ITS AQUEOUS SOLUTIONS AT 25°C.

Propylene Glycol, % by wt.	Surface Tension, dynes/cm.	Propylene Glycol, % by wt.	Surface Tension, dynes/cm.
0	72.0	60	42.5
5	65.7	65	41.6
10	61.2	70	40.6
15	57.8	75	39.8
20	55.0	80	39.1
25	52.7	85	38.4
30	50.8	90	37.7
35	49.0	95	37.1
40	47.4	100	36.51
45	46.0		
50	44.7		
55	43.6		

TABLE 9.19. THERMAL CONDUCTIVITY OF PROPYLENE GLYCOL AND ITS AQUEOUS SOLUTIONS

Temperature, °C.	Propylene Glycol, % by wt.					
	0	20	40	60	80	100
	Thermal Conductivity, cal.-cm./sec./cm.^{2}/°C.					
0	0.00139	0.00117	0.00100	0.00083	0.00068	0.00054
10	142	119	100	82	67	53
20	145	121	100	82	66	52
30	148	123	101	81	65	51
40	0.00151	0.00125	0.00101	0.00080	0.00064	0.00050
50	154	127	101	80	63	49
60	157	129	102	79	62	48
70	160	131	102	78	61	47
80	0.00163	0.00133	0.00102	0.00078	0.00060	0.00045
90	165	135	102	77	59	44
100	169	137	103	77	58	43
110	172	139	103	76	57	42
120	175	141	104	75	56	41

propylene glycol and its aqueous solutions over the entire range of composition from 20 to 120°C. Table 9.19 is based on these data. Inasmuch as the experimental points fell on a series of straight lines, it was considered justifiable to extrapolate the data to 0°C. (Figure 9.10).

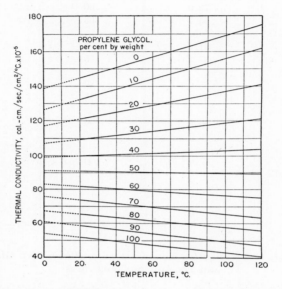

FIGURE 9.10. Thermal conductivities of aqueous solutions of propylene glycol from 0 to 120°C.

Vapor-Liquid Equilibrium Data

Vapor-liquid equilibrium data for the system propylene glycol-water were determined at atmospheric pressure by Dow and at 140 millimeters by Carbide. The data in Table 9.20 indicate that except for low concentrations of water, pressure has little effect on the system. Dow's boiling point diagram for the system is shown in Figure 9.11. These curves were plotted from the data in Table 9.21.

Vapor-liquid equilibrium data for the system propylene glycol-dipropylene glycol at 10 mm. are given in Table 9.22 (Figure 9.12).

Vapor Pressure

A number of investigators[4, 11, 12, 13, 14, 15, 16, 29, 30, 31, 32, 33, 34, 35] have reported the vapor pressure of propylene glycol at one or more temperatures. The first of these was Wurtz[8] whose value of 188–189°C. for the atmospheric boiling point, reported in 1859, is found to be correct within the limits

TABLE 9.20. VAPOR-LIQUID EQUILIBRIA FOR THE SYSTEM
PROPYLENE GLYCOL-WATER

	Water, mol per cent in	
	Vapor	
Liquid	Atmospheric pressure	140 mm.
0	0.0	0.0
10	58.5	72.6
20	83.8	87.1
30	91.7	93.8
40	95.7	96.4
50	97.6	97.7
60	98.3	98.5
70	98.8	98.8
80	99.3	99.3
90	99.7	99.7
100	100.0	100.0

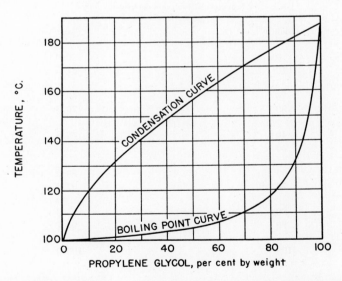

FIGURE 9.11. Boiling point diagram at atmospheric pressure for the system propylene glycol-water.

TABLE 9.21. BOILING POINT DIAGRAM FOR THE SYSTEM
PROPYLENE GLYCOL-WATER AT 760 MM.

Temperature, °C.	Propylene Glycol, % by wt. in	
	Boiling liquid	Condensing vapor
100	0.0	0.0
110	58.5	3.8
120	82.7	10.0
130	89.5	18.3
140	93.0	29.0
150	95.2	41.2
160	96.7	55.0
170	98.0	70.4
180	99.0	87.0
187.4	100.0	100.0

TABLE 9.22. VAPOR-LIQUID EQUILIBRIA AT 10 MM. FOR THE SYSTEM
PROPYLENE GLYCOL-DIPROPYLENE GLYCOL

Propylene Glycol, mol per cent in	
Liquid	Vapor
0	0.0
10	37.5
20	57.4
30	70.3
40	78.8
50	85.0
60	89.2
70	92.6
80	95.3
90	97.7
100	100.0

of precision which he claimed. With few exceptions, subsequent data are
in reasonably good agreement.

Gallaugher and Hibbert[36] have shown that ethylene glycol decomposes

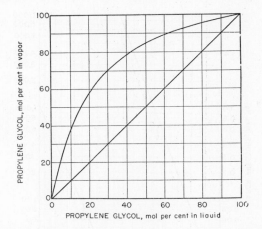

FIGURE 9.12. Vapor-liquid equilibria at 10 mm. pressure for the system propylene glycol-dipropylene glycol.

TABLE 9.23. VAPOR PRESSURE OF PROPYLENE GLYCOL

Temperature, °C.	Vapor Pressure, mm.	Temperature, °C.	Vapor Pressure, mm.	Temperature, °C.	Vapor Pressure, mm.	Temperature, °C.	Vapor Pressure, mm.
0	0.01	50	0.99	100	23.1	150	205
5	0.02	55	1.42	105	30.3	155	245
10	0.03	60	2.03	110	39.3	160	299
15	0.05	65	2.87	115	49	165	353
20	0.08	70	3.98	120	62	170	420
25	0.13	75	5.46	125	76	175	505
30	0.20	80	7.40	130	93	180	590
35	0.31	85	9.95	135	114	185	695
40	0.46	90	13.4	140	140	187.4	760
45	0.67	95	17.8	145	170	190	825
						195	960
						200	1110

slowly at its atmospheric boiling point, and it is very probable that propylene glycol behaves similarly. This, together with the possible presence of impurities in the materials used for the determinations, probably accounts for much of the divergence of the values reported for the boiling point at atmospheric pressure. A consideration of all the available data indicates that the most probable value is 187.4°C. The boiling points at other pressures shown in Table 9.23 were read from the best line drawn through a large-scale plot of all the literature values drawn on log-pressure vs. reciprocal-temperature paper (Figure 9.13).

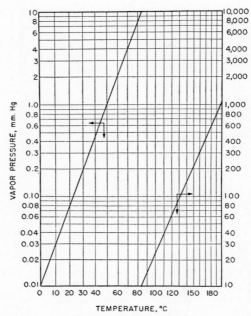

FIGURE 9.13. Vapor pressure of propylene glycol.

TABLE 9.24.   VAPOR PRESSURE OF AQUEOUS SOLUTIONS OF PROPYLENE GLYCOL

Tem-pera-ture, °C.	Propylene Glycol, % by volume							
	0	30	50	70	80	90	97	100
	Vapor Pressure, mm.							
20	17.5	17.0	13.6	11.5	10.2	5.6	—	0.08
30	31.8	30.3	24.8	21.0	18.2	10.2	—	0.20
40	55.3	51.5	42.7	36.3	31.3	18.0	5.4	0.46
50	92.5	85	72	61.0	51.0	30.1	9.4	0.99
60	149.4	137	117	98.0	84.0	49.0	16.0	2.03
70	233.7	212	185	155	131	76.0	26.2	3.98
80	355.1	322	285	236	202	118	42.2	7.40
90	546	475	425	353	298	177	63.0	13.4
100	760	690	615	520	433	257	95.0	23.1
110	—	980	890	740	615	373	143	39.3
120	—	—	—	—	855	525	207	62
130	—	—	—	—	—	720	295	93
140	—	—	—	—	—	985	408	140
150	—	—	—	—	—	—	560	205
160	—	—	—	—	—	—	755	299

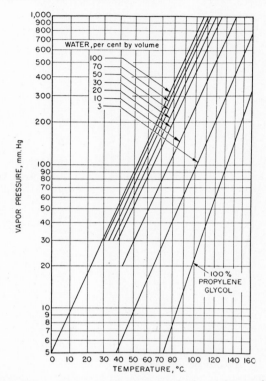

FIGURE 9.14. Vapor pressures of aqueous solutions of propylene glycol.

The pressures from 0 to 80°C. in Table 9.23 are based on data reported by Carbide and by Puck and Wise[34]. These determinations were made in connection with the interest which has developed in propylene glycol as an "air-treatment" agent and the resultant need for accurate vapor pressures at room temperatures.

Figure 9.14, showing vapor pressures of aqueous propylene glycol from 20 to 160°C. (Table 9.24), was prepared from Dow and Carbide data.

Viscosity

The viscosity of propylene glycol and its aqueous solutions has been determined by Carbide and Dow. Viscosity values for the pure compound are plotted in Figure 9.15. The curves in Figure 9.16 were drawn from the values in Table 9.25.

The effects of the addition of ethyl alcohol and isopropyl alcohol on the viscosity of aqueous solutions of propylene glycol are shown in Chapter 3, Figures 3.18 and 3.19. Kinematic viscosities of propylene glycol in mixtures with ethylene glycol are given also in Chapter 3, Figure 3.20.

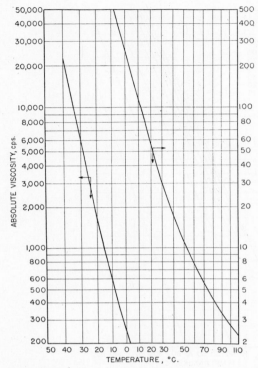

FIGURE 9.15. Absolute viscosity of propylene glycol.

TABLE 9.25. VISCOSITY OF AQUEOUS SOLUTIONS OF PROPYLENE GLYCOL

Temperature, °C.	Propylene Glycol, % by weight										
	0	10	20	30	40	50	60	70	80	90	100
	Absolute Viscosity, centipoises										
−40	—	—	—	—	—	—	1100	2100	4100	10000	22900
−30	—	—	—	—	—	200	340	580	1100	2300	6600
−20	—	—	—	—	46	78	140	230	400	790	1750
−10	—	—	—	12.0	20	35	59	96	160	305	585
0	1.79	2.6	4.2	7.1	12.5	18	29	47	72	135	243
10	1.31	1.8	2.9	4.0	7.2	9.3	16	22	34	59	111
20	1.01	1.35	2.1	3.0	4.4	6.4	9.3	14	20	33	56.0
30	0.80	1.10	1.6	2.0	2.9	4.0	5.6	7.8	12.5	19	30.3
40	0.65	0.88	1.20	1.6	2.2	2.9	3.9	5.4	7.4	12	18.0
50	0.55	0.73	0.98	1.30	1.7	2.5	2.9	3.9	5.3	7.9	11.3
60	0.47	0.61	0.79	1.00	1.3	1.7	2.2	2.8	3.9	5.4	7.7
70	0.41	0.53	0.68	0.84	1.10	1.3	1.7	2.2	2.9	3.9	5.5
80	0.36	0.46	0.58	0.69	0.88	1.1	1.3	1.7	2.0	2.9	4.2
90	0.32	0.39	0.49	0.59	0.73	0.91	1.1	1.3	1.8	2.4	3.3
100	0.28	0.32	0.43	0.48	0.58	0.64	0.83	1.0	1.4	1.6	2.7

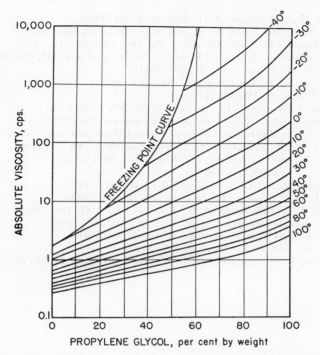

FIGURE 9.16. Absolute viscosities of aqueous solutions of propylene glycol, −40 to 100°C.

Literature Cited

1. Weniger, W., *Phys. Rev.*, **31,** 388 (1910).
2. Wright, N., and Young, C. W., Private Communication, 1949.
3. Hibben, J. H., "The Raman Effect and Its Chemical Applications," A. C. S. Monograph No. 80, New York, Reinhold Publishing Corp., 1939.
4. Moureu, H., and Dodé, M., *Bull. soc. chim. France*, (5) **4,** 637 (1937).
5. Sullivan, M. V., Wolfe, J. K., and Zisman, W. A., *Ind. Eng. Chem.*, **39,** 1607 (1947).
6. Lagemann, R., *J. Polymer Sci.*, **3,** 663 (1948).
7. Horsley, L. H., *Anal. Chem.*, **19,** 508 (1947); **21,** 842 (1949).
8. Wurtz, A., *Ann. chim. et phys.*, (3) **55,** 438 (1859).
9. Zander, A., *Ann.*, **214,** 178 (1882).
10. Tronov, B. V., Lukanin, A. A., and Pavlinov, A. A., *J. Russ. Phys. Chem. Soc.*, **59,** 1174 (1927).
11. Parks, G. S., and Huffman, H. M., *J. Phys. Chem.*, **31,** 1842 (1927).
12. Levene, P. A., and Walti, A., *Org. Syntheses*, **10,** 84 (1930).
13. Smyth, C. P., and Walls, W. S., *J. Am. Chem. Soc.*, **53,** 2115 (1931).
14. Schierholtz, O. J., and Staples, M. L., *J. Am. Chem. Soc.*, **57,** 2709 (1935).
15. Pukirev, A. G., *Trans. Inst. Pure Chem. Reagents (U.S.S.R.)*, **15,** 45 (1937).
16. Romstatt, G., *Industrie chimique*, **24,** 227 (1937).

17. White, A. H., and Morgan, S. O., *Physics*, **2**, 313 (1932).
18. Morgan, S. O., and Yager, W. A., *Ind. Eng. Chem.*, **32**, 1519 (1940).
19. "Dow Glycols," Midland, Michigan, The Dow Chemical Co., 1947.
20. Bigg, E., Jennings, B. H., and Fried, S., *Am. J. Med. Sci.*, **207**, 370 (1944).
21. Louguinine, W., *Compt. rend.*, **91**, 299 (1880).
22. Coolidge, A. S., *J. Am. Chem. Soc.*, **52**, 1874 (1930).
23. Rae, J., *Pharm. J.*, **155**, 151 (1945).
24. Bridgman, P. W., *Proc. Am. Acad. Arts Sci.*, **67**, 1 (1931–32).
25. "Propylene Glycol," New York, B. L. Lemke and Co., 1944.
26. "Glycols," New York, Carbide and Carbon Chemicals Corp., 1947.
27. Gucker, F. T., Jr., and Marsh, G. A., *Ind. Eng. Chem.*, **40**, 908 (1948).
28. Bates, O. K., and Hazzard, G., *Ind. Eng. Chem.*, **37**, 183 (1945).
29. Nef, J. U., *Ann.*, **335**, 203 (1904).
30. Abderhalden, E., and Eichwald, E., *Ber.*, **51**, 1312 (1918).
31. Färber, E., and Nord, F. F., *Biochem. Z.*, **112**, 314 (1920).
32. Boeseken, J., and Hermans, P. H., *Rec. trav. chim.*, **42**, 1104 (1923).
33. Kötz, A., and Richter, K., *J. prakt. Chem.*, (2) **111**, 397 (1925).
34. Puck, T. T., and Wise, H., *J. Phys. Chem.*, **50**, 329 (1946).
35. Stull, D. R., *Ind. Eng. Chem.*, **39**, 517 (1947).
36. Gallaugher, A. F., and Hibbert, H., *J. Am. Chem. Soc.*, **58**, 813 (1936).

CHAPTER 10

COMMERCIAL APPLICATIONS OF PROPYLENE GLYCOL

Propylene glycol is outstanding among the glycols in its application in products that are used or consumed daily by the average person. Prior to World War II, consumption was merely a few hundred thousand pounds a month, but when war requirements drained supplies of ethyl alcohol and glycerol, propylene glycol became tremendously important as a replacement for these vital chemicals in countless consumer items[1].

Like ethylene glycol, propylene glycol is primarily useful in automotive anti-freeze and industrial coolant solutions. It is also a component of hydraulic fluids and an intermediate for resins and plasticizers. Because propylene glycol may be used internally, it is incorporated into foodstuffs, pharmaceuticals, and cosmetics as a solvent, humectant, and preservative. An estimated 1950 end-use pattern for propylene glycol is shown in Table 10.1[2].

TABLE 10.1. ESTIMATED END-USE DISTRIBUTION FOR PROPYLENE GLYCOL, 1950

	Millions of Pounds
Anti-freezes and industrial coolants	30.0
Resins and plasticizers	16.6
Brake and hydraulic fluids	12.0
Tobacco	7.1
Foods	6.1
Pharmaceuticals	3.3
Cosmetics	2.5
Inks	1.0
Miscellaneous	6.4
Total	85.0

Anti-Freezes and Industrial Coolants

Propylene glycol has the property of lowering the freezing point of water, the degree depending on the concentration of the glycol (see page 217). The aqueous solutions are used as coolants, defrosting fluids, and anti-freezes.

Although ethylene glycol has been more widely accepted as a satisfactory anti-freeze, several million gallons of propylene glycol are also used annually in automobile cooling systems. The United States Army permits its use in anti-freeze solutions for military equipment in amounts up to 20 per cent by weight of the total glycols employed[3]. One product on the market contains 96 parts by volume of propylene glycol, two parts of inhibitors, and two parts of water[4].

Propylene glycol is the coolant in refrigerating systems for dairies, breweries, and food-packaging plants and on ships, trains, and planes. For such applications, the coolant's physiological action is of primary importance. Any propylene glycol solution escaping from the cooling coils is relatively innocuous and unobjectionable[5]. In addition, when used in such systems, usually in concentrations between 20 and 30 per cent by volume[6, 7], propylene glycol presents no corrosion difficulties. Gucker and Marsh[8] studied the cooling capacity of propylene glycol-water mixtures, showing with graphs and tables the most efficient mixture for any particular application.

Suitably inhibited propylene glycol solutions are satisfactorily replacing salt and calcium chloride brines in air cooling units[9] where corrosion is a factor. The National Board of Fire Underwriters sanctions their use in automatic, nonfreezing sprinkler systems[10]. Propylene glycol solutions are also effective as defrosting fluids for removing ice from airplane wings.

Resins and Plasticizers

Like ethylene glycol, propylene glycol[11] can be esterified with maleic, fumaric, or similar acids and the resulting esters converted with vinyl monomers and a peroxide catalyst into materials suitable as low pressure laminating resins and adhesives[12] (see page 136). Rubber-like substances derived from propylene glycol[13] are suitable for calendering onto cloth and for molding operations. Rosin esters[14] are useful as plasticizers and in adhesive compositions, lacquers, and enamels.

Linear polyesters of propylene glycol and phthalic anhydride are plasticizers for nitrocellulose and other resins[15]. Polypropylene glycol sebacate, sold as Paraplex G-25, acts as a plasticizer for polyvinyl chloride, polyvinyl acetate, and their copolymer resins[16]. These resinous compositions are used as impregnants and in adhesives, and can be molded by injection, compression, and extrusion[17]. One phthalate resin is a finishing composition for fabrics such as cotton[18]. A polyethylene glycol-propylene glycol sebacic acid derivative has been suggested for use in impregnating textile braid for covering rubber insulated wire[19].

Propylene glycol itself is an edible plasticizer useful in the manufacture of products that come in close contact with foodstuffs[20]. For instance, the phenolic resin binder in cork seals or cork crowns for various food product packages is plasticized with this glycol to keep the cork pliable and in proper condition to seal the container.[21] Propylene glycol is also the plasticizer used in the preparation of cellulose sausage casings. Any plasticizer that is not removed during washing is harmless in the final product.

Brake and Hydraulic Fluids

Propylene glycol is employed as a component of brake and hydraulic fluids that operate satisfactorily over a wide temperature range[22]. The glycol is formulated in fluids with bases of castor oil[23], modified castor oil[24], and glycerin[25].

Tobacco

Like diethylene glycol (see page 164), propylene glycol is used for treating tobacco during processing operations. It acts as a hygroscopic agent and preservative.

Foods

In the food manufacturing and processing field, propylene glycol is used as a solvent, humectant, and preservative. The possibility of toxic effects delayed its wider adoption by the industry until 1941 when Dr. H. O. Calvery of the Food and Drug Administration stated: "Propylene glycol in the amount normally used is permissible to replace glycerine and other solvents in food products without violating the requirements of the Food, Drug, and Cosmetic Act." As he pointed out at that time, "Many tons of propylene glycol have been used in foods, drugs, and cosmetics to replace glycerine and sugar solutions."[26]

Propylene glycol is widely used in flavor and extract preparations. The ideal solvent for flavor solutions should (1) be an active solvent for the common flavoring materials, (2) impart no odor or taste to the material to be flavored, and (3) be water-soluble, inexpensive, and nontoxic in the maximum concentration that could reasonably be used[27]. Propylene glycol is an ideal solvent for hundreds of flavoring materials for use in the baking and candy trades. (The wide variety of substances soluble in the glycol is indicated in Tables 9.12 through 9.15 in Chapter 9.) Its mutual solvent properties permit the dissolving of both aromatic chemicals and essential oils as well as dilution of these solutions with water. Propylene glycol is also useful for extracting flavors from natural flavoring materials, such as vanilla flavor from vanilla beans[28] and coffee flavor from ground roasted coffee[20], as well as fat from cocoa powder[29]. It is, in addition, a solvent for food colors and can be used to prevent foaming of liquid coffee extract during bottling[30].

Many substances used as flavoring materials are subject to mold growth. With table syrups and flavors packaged for home consumption, propylene glycol is an excellent preservative for preventing fermentation. Where it is necessary to use alcohol, propylene glycol may often be used to replace part of the alcohol at an appreciable saving in material cost. It is also useful as a solvent for butylated hydroxyanisole, an anti-oxidant for animal fats[31]. Hot liquid propylene glycol can be used to heat-sterilize canned foodstuffs[32].

Propylene glycol is used in small quantities as a humectant with many baked goods and packaged foods where some moisture must be present to offer a suitable consumer product as in the case of shredded coconut[33]. Various amounts of the glycol are employed (from 2 to 15 per cent), depending on the degree of preservation required and the amount of moisture present. Propylene glycol is also added to cereals to improve their firmness and friability[34] and to aqueous alcohol solutions for washing dates to prevent the fruit from sticking to processing machinery parts[35].

Pharmaceuticals

Propylene glycol is employed in pharmaceutical formulations of biological elixirs, antiseptics, salves, and ointments[36]. It is an excellent solvent for many organic chemicals used for medicinal purposes, as indicated in Table 9.12, Chapter 9. As in the case of the food industry, propylene glycol was slow in coming into general pharmaceutical use because of the time required to establish fully its freedom from harmful effects. However, the glycol was admitted to the National Formulary in 1943 and to the U. S. Pharmacopoeia in 1950.

Propylene glycol was first suggested as a vehicle for medicinal purposes in 1931 by Hanzlik, Seidenfeld, and Johnson[37]. At about the same time it was found to be useful for preparing stable solutions of barbiturates for injection[38]. In 1935 Brown[39] reported on the suitability of this glycol as a solvent for pharmaceutical use as follows:

(1) In assaying propylene glycol galenicals by extraction with ether or chloroform, the galenical should be diluted with at least one-fifth of its volume of water. (2) Solutions of certain alkaloids in propylene glycol can be freely diluted with water without precipitation. (3) Propylene glycol tends to mask the reactions of certain alkaloidal reagents, notably picric acid and tannic acid. (4) Phenolphthalein can be dispensed in propylene glycol solution in therapeutic doses. (5) The halogen salts of sodium and potassium are very soluble in propylene glycol. (6) Dyes are readily soluble; therefore the glycol would be a suitable preservative. (7) Propylene glycol would make a suitable preservative for syrups. (8) It is a solvent for most volatile oils. (9) It may be a suitable menstruum for tinctures (especially seneca) due to its nonvolatility, solvent powers, miscibility with water and alcohol, and preservative action. (10) Propylene glycol considerably retards the volatization of ethyl nitrite and may conveniently replace alcohol in "sweet spirit of nitre."

The pharmaceutical applications of propylene glycol are many. Jaros[40] reported the use of propylene glycol as a solvent for benzyl alcohol and diothane in a topical anesthetic for tonsillextirpy, and Douglas and Peyton[41] successfully used a solution of paraldehyde in the glycol as an anesthetic for the relief of pain in labor. Clark[42] claims that by replacing 25 per cent of the water in National Formulary VI antiseptic solution with propylene glycol, a product of more pleasant odor and taste results. Others have reported that it has been used as a component of a base for phenolic ointments[43] and employed to administer steroid hormones[44], isolate the lactogenic hormone[45], inject quinidine[46] and conjugates of adrenaline with sterols[47], and extract active constituents from materials containing tannins, saponins, and anthraquinone derivatives[48]. It is also a component of sulfathiazole paste[49] and ointment[50], sulfanilamide-sulfathiazole gauze dressings[51], undecylenic acid ointments for treating fungus infections[52], and of digitalis[53], riboflavin[54, 55], iodine[56], aerolin compound[57], and tolyl dihydroxypropyl ether[58] solutions.

Propylene glycol has been used as a solvent for some of the water-soluble vitamins. As early as 1936 an advertisement appeared in one of the pharmaceutical journals for a vitamin product described as a solution of pure crystallized Vitamin D in propylene glycol. Data on the treatment of rickets in children with such a preparation were reported[59] in 1937.

Propylene glycol as a drug vehicle has been found to exert anti-oxidant and stabilizing activity[60]. Solutions of epinephrine in pure propylene glycol and in 60 to 70 per cent aqueous solutions of propylene glycol were protected from oxidation. Propylene glycol also protected epinephrine solutions in the presence of liver slices and inhibited the decomposition of other drugs such as apomorphine, physostigmine, "Chlorarsen," and arsphenamine.

The treatment of mixed infections with penicillin using propylene glycol as a vehicle has been studied, but further research on the stability of such solutions is indicated[61, 62, 63, 64]. Chloromycetin,[65] which is only slightly soluble in water, and aureomycin hydrochloride[66] can be administered in propylene glycol. An ointment base composed of white petrolatum, white wax, stearic acid, propylene glycol, and distilled water is used in administering streptomycin[67].

Cosmetics

One of the many advantages of emulsified cosmetic preparations is that grease-like materials can be presented in an attractive form. The cosmetic industry uses propylene glycol as a component of these emulsified preparations in products ranging from skin lotions[68] to tooth pastes[69]. Cessna, Ohlmann, and Roehm[70] reported that propylene glycol favors the formation of water-in-oil type emulsions and that cosmetic formulations should be prepared with this in mind to prevent separation and inversion. The propylene glycol acts as a softening agent, preservative, humectant, spreader, and emollient. Since it is an excellent solvent for dyes and most perfumes, it allows rapid and complete dispersion of these ingredients throughout the preparation, whether it is shampoo or lipstick. In lipsticks it is also the solvent for the "brom acid" employed[71]. It is added to vanishing creams to help overcome the flaking or "rolling" effect common to such formulations. In cold creams and cleansing creams it assists in coupling the oil, lanolin, and soap into the water. Its presence in hand lotions helps assure their complete and rapid absorption by the skin. In brushless shaving creams it is essential to maintaining moisture in the cream both during use and while in storage. In cosmetic formulations containing lemon and other natural fruit juice products, it is a valuable mold inhibiting agent[72].

The use of propylene glycol in toothpaste manufacture came into vogue about 1944 when it was accepted by the Council on Dental Therapeutics of the American Dental Association[73]. Thomssen[74] described the preparation of a propylene glycol-based paste containing medium quantities of soap. Ammoniated dentifrices may contain up to five per cent of the glycol[69].

Inks

Propylene glycol is the solvent in high-speed, steam-set inks[75] [76] used for printing food wrappers of paper and cloth[20]. Because the food products are in close contact with these wrappers, the inks must be both odorless and harmless, and are so when propylene glycol is used as the solvent.

Miscellaneous

Propylene glycol is employed as a plasticizer and hygroscopic agent in adhesives[1]. Since its vapors are unobjectionable and innocuous, propylene glycol is used to lubricate machinery employed in the packaging of foodstuffs, pharmaceuticals, and beverages. It is also useful in preventing contamination of food equipment during periods of idleness[20], in the preparation of stabilized zein solutions[77], and in the production of fine-textured varnish films from cottonseed oil[78]. Other applications include its use as an oil defoamer[79], ingredient in a carbon-removal compound for aircraft engine parts[80], solvent and spreader in aluminum brazing paste[81], component of a bentonite-sodium silicate pipe-joint compound[82], and solvent in a phosphoric acid base dip coating for aluminum[83]. Normal aliphatic hydrocarbons with 12 to 14 carbon atoms can be separated azeotropically from normal aliphatic alcohols with 8 to 18 carbon atoms by adding a quantity of propylene glycol equivalent to 0.2 to 20 parts per part of hydrocarbons[84]. Propylene glycol has also been used as an air disinfectant (see page 171), but vaporizers installed[85, 86] proved unsatisfactory because of heavy condensation on windows and walls.

Literature Cited

1. Roehm, L. S., *Am. Perfumer Essent. Oil Rev.*, **46** (10), 35–7 (1944).
2. Kern, J. C., *Chem. Inds. Week*, **68** (6), 16 (1951).
3. U. S. Army Specification 4-117, June 15, 1943.
4. *Federal Register*, **10**, 1746 (Feb. 13, 1945).
5. Rae, J., *Mfg. Chemist*, **17**, 53–4 (1946).
6. *Brewers Digest*, **13** (10), 35–6 (1938).
7. Brenner, M. W., Mohr, H., and Chiano G., *Am. Brewer*, **82**, (Oct., 1949).
8. Gucker, F. T., Jr., and Marsh, G. A., *Ind. Eng. Chem.*, **40**, 908–15 (1948).
9. McBride, R. S., *Food Inds.*, **10**, 382 (1938).
10. "Standards for Sprinkler Equipment," National Board of Fire Underwriters, Paragraph 13 (Jan. 13, 1947); "Crosby-Fiske-Forster Handbook for Fire Protection," 10th Ed., Boston, National Fire Protection Association, 1948.
11. "Synthetic Organic Chemicals," U. S. Tariff Commission, Report No. 162, 2nd Series, Table 16B, 1947.
12. Foster, N. C., Hill, L. R., Runk, R. H., and Schulman, E. L. (to Westinghouse Electric Corp.), U. S. Patent 2,477,791 (Aug. 2, 1949); Frosch, J. C. (to Bell Telephone Laboratories, Inc.), U. S. Patent 2,426,994 (Sept. 9, 1947).
13. Biggs, B. S., Erickson, R. H., and Fuller, C. S., *Ind. Eng. Chem.*, **39**, 1090 (1947).
14. Schlaanstine, R. F. (to Hercules Powder Co.), U. S. Patent 2,331,803 (Oct. 12, 1943).
15. Bradley, T. F. (to American Cyanamid Co.), U. S. Patent 1,890,668 (Dec. 13, 1932).
16. Rothrock, D. A., Jr., and Conyne, R. F. (to The Resinous Products & Chemical Co.), U. S. Patent 2,437,046 (March 2, 1948); British Patent 586,826 (April 1, 1947).
17. Beavers, E. M. (to The Resinous Products & Chemical Co.), U. S. Patent 2,445,553 (July 20, 1948).
18. Light, D. W., Bradley, T. F., and Nute, A. D. (to American Cyanamid Co.), U. S. Patent 2,334,107 (Nov. 9, 1943).
19. Fuller, C. S., and Kemp, A. R. (to Bell Telephone Laboratories, Inc.), U. S. Patent 2,349,951 (May 30, 1944).
20. "Propylene Glycol, N. F.," Midland, Michigan, The Dow Chemical Company, 1949.
21. Cooke, G. B., and Ebert, M. S. (to Crown Cork & Seal Co., Inc.), U. S. Patent 2,293,805 (Aug. 25, 1942).
22. Shough, A. H., *Ind. Eng. Chem.*, **34**, 628 (1942).
23. Clark, J. M., and Deventer, R. E. (to Packard Motor Car Co.), U. S. Patent 2,345,585 (April 4, 1944); Morris, R. C., Shokal, E. C., and Snider, A. V. (to Shell Development Co.), U. S. Patent 2,394,251 (Feb. 5, 1946); and Air Corps Specification 3586-C, Feb. 28, 1942.
24. Woodhouse, J. C., and Weber, A. G. (to E. I. du Pont de Nemours & Co.), U. S. Patents 2,102,825 (Dec. 21, 1937) and 2,232,581 (Feb. 18, 1941).
25. Clark, J. M. (to Packard Motor Car Co.), U. S. Patent 2,345,586 (April 4, 1944).
26. Calvery, H. O., *Am. Scientist*, **32**, 108 (1944).
27. Davidson, J. G., *Glass Packers*, **17**, 783–5 (1938).
28. Bruening, C. F., *J. Assoc. Offic. Agr. Chemists*, **33**, 103 (1950).
29. Palmer, E. (to Moorehead Manufacturing Co., Inc.), U. S. Patent 2,515,794 (July 18, 1950).

30. Foulkes, J. H. (to Finer Foods Packaging Corp.), U. S. Patent 2,497,721 (Feb. 14, 1950).
31. Kraybill, H. R., Dugan, L. R., Jr., Beadle, B. W., Vibrans, F. C., Schwartz, V., and Rezabek, H., *J. Am. Oil Chemists' Soc.*, **27,** 449 (1949).
32. Taylor, F. C., Jr. (to The Dow Chemical Co.), U. S. Patent 2,517,734 (Aug. 8, 1950).
33. Kaufman, C. W. (to General Foods Corp.), U. S. Patent 2,338,184 (Jan. 4, 1944).
34. Berg, I. A., U. S. Patent 2,437,150 (March 2, 1948).
35. Ramont, R. E., U. S. Patent 2,474,915 (July 5, 1949).
36. Heine, D. L., Parker, P. F., and Francke, D. E., *Bull. Am. Soc. Hosp. Pharm.*, **7,** 8 (1950).
37. Hanzlik, P. J., Seidenfeld, M. A., and Johnson, C. C., *J. Pharmacol. Exptl. Therap.*, **41,** 387 (1931).
38. Forbring, J. W. (to Winthrop Chemical Co., Inc.), U. S. Patent 1,984,733 (Dec. 18, 1934).
39. Brown, C. L. M., *Quart. J. Pharm. Pharmacol.*, **8,** 390 (1935).
40. Jaros, J. F., *Arch. Phys. Therapy, X-Ray, Radium,* **17,** 346 (1936).
41. Douglas, L. H., and Peyton, F. W., *Am. J. Obstet. Gynecol.*, **33,** 604 (1937).
42. Clark, W. C., *J. Am. Pharm. Assoc., Sci. Ed.*, **26,** 897 (1937).
43. Burnside, C. B., and Kuever, R. A., *J. Am. Pharm. Assoc., Sci. Ed.*, **29,** 373-9 (1940).
44. McGavack, T. H., and Vogel, M., *J. Lab. Clin. Med.*, **29,** 1256-65 (1944).
45. Fleischer, G. A., and Schwenk, E. (to Schering Corp.), U. S. Patent 2,370,154 (Feb. 27, 1945).
46. Brass, H., *J. Am. Pharm. Assoc., Pract. Pharm. Ed.*, **4,** 310 (1943).
47. Roberts, R. G. (to Armour & Co.), U. S. Patent 2,333,581 (Nov. 2, 1943).
48. Rae, J., *Pharm. J.*, **152,** 122 (1944); **135,** 539 (1935); **134,** 590 (1935).
49. Helgren, F. J. (to Abbott Laboratories), U. S. Patent 2,448,180 (Aug. 31, 1948).
50. War Department, Medical Department Tentative Specification 1553-G, Paragraph E-12.
51. Brady, D., Bauer, R., and Yonkman, F. F., *J. Am. Pharm. Assoc., Sci. Ed.*, **32,** 142-3 (1943).
52. Sulzberger, M. B., Shaw, H. C., and Kanof, A., *U. S. Naval Med. Bull.*, **45,** 237 (1945).
53. Thompson, M. R., Accousti, N. J., and Ichniowski, C. T. (to W. R. Warner & Co., Inc.), U. S. Patent 2,415,312 (Feb. 4, 1947).
54. Charney, J. (to Wyeth, Inc.), U. S. Patent 2,449,640 (Sept, 21, 1948).
55. Upham, S. D. (to American Cyanamid Co.), U. S. Patent 2,449,041 (Sept. 7, 1948).
56. Gershenfeld, L., and Witlin, B., *J. Am. Pharm. Assoc., Sci. Ed.*, **39,** 489 (1950).
57. *J. Modern Drug Encyclopedia*, p. 589. April, 1951.
58. Berger, F. M. (to The British Drug Houses, Ltd.), U. S. Patent 2,468,423 (April 26, 1949).
59. Albright, F., Butler, A. M., and Bloomberg, E., *Am. J. Diseases Children,* **54,** 529 (1937).
60. Koppanyi, T., *Federation Proc.*, **9,** 291 (1950).
61. Meleney, F. L., Johnson, B. A., Pulaski, E. J., and Colonna, F., *J. Am. Med. Assoc.*, **130,** 121 (1946).
62. Senger, F. L., Warres, H. L., and Rifkin, I., *J. Urol.*, **55,** 138-42 (1946).
63. Ferlauto, R. J., and Clymer, H. A., *Science*, **105,** 130 (1947).
64. Johnson, B., and Lerrigo, A. F., *Quart. J. Pharm. Pharmacol.*, **20,** 183-97 (1947).

65. Smith, R. M., Joslyn, D. A., Gruhzit, O. M., McLean, I. W., Jr., Penner, M. A., and Ehrlich, J., *J. Bact.*, **55,** 425–48 (1948).
66. *J. Modern Drug Encyclopedia*, p. 591, April, 1951.
67. *Federal Register*, **13,** 5152 (Sept. 3, 1948).
68. Shott, A. N., *Drug & Cosmetic Ind.*, **39,** 185–6 (1936).
69. *J. Am. Dental Assoc.*, **39,** 493 (1949).
70. Cessna, O. C., Ohlmann, E. O., and Roehm, L. S., *Am. Perfumer*, **49,** 369 (1947).
71. Hall, J. H., *Proc. Sci. Sect. Toilet Goods Assoc.*, **1934–44,** No. 1, 2–3.
72. Harry, R. C., *Mfg. Chemist*, **11,** 44–6 (1940).
73. *J. Am. Dental Assoc.*, **31,** 555 (1944).
74. Thomssen, E. G., *Drug & Cosmetic Rev.*, **1946–47,** 109.
75. Lee, E. D. (to Interchemical Corp.), U. S. Patent 2,415,828 (Feb. 18, 1947); and Bernardi, D. J. (to Interchemical Corp.), U. S. Patent 2,285,183 (June 2, 1942).
76. Erickson, R. E., and Thoma, P. J. (to Michigan Research Laboratories), U. S. Patent 2,244,103 (June 3, 1941); and Coleman, R. E. (to The Zein Corp.), U. S. Patents 2,185,112–26 (Dec. 26, 1939).
77. Dunne, J. P. (to Columbian Carbon Company), U. S. Patent 2,489,763 (Nov. 29, 1949).
78. Waldie, W. A. (to New Wrinkle, Inc.), U. S. Patent 2,443,284 (June 15, 1948).
79. Borsoff, V. N., and Clayton, J. O. (to California Research Corp.), U. S. Patent 2,430,858 (Nov. 18, 1947).
80. Navy Aeronautical Specification C-118, May 16, 1942.
81. Miller, M. A. (to Aluminum Co. of America), U. S. Patent 2,403,110 (July 2, 1946).
82. DeLorenzo, J. P., U. S. Patent 2,490,949 (Dec. 13, 1949).
83. Clark, C. W. (to Canadian Copper Refiners, Ltd.), U. S. Patent 2,475,946 (July 12, 1949).
84. Jensen, E. P. (to E. I. du Pont de Nemours & Co.), U. S. Patent 2,360,685 (Oct. 17, 1944).
85. Coey, S. C., and Spiselman, J. W. (to Research Corp.), U. S. Patent 2,344,536 (March 21, 1944).
86. Robertson, O. H., Miller, B. F., and Bigg, E., U. S. Patent 2,333,124 (Nov. 2, 1943).

CHAPTER 11

PROPYLENE OXIDE

R. F. HOLDEN

Propylene oxide is primarily of importance as an intermediate in the production of propylene glycol. Also known as 1,2-epoxypropane and methyloxirane, it has the structural formula

$$CH_2\text{---}CHCH_3$$
$$\diagdown \diagup$$
$$O$$

The compound is produced commercially by Carbide, Dow, and Celanese and, in mixtures with ethylene oxide, by Wyandotte.

Preparation

Propylene oxide was first prepared in 1861 by Oser[1], who dehydro-halogenated 1-chloro-2-propanol with dilute potassium hydroxide. Krasuskii[2] later obtained propylene oxide by reaction of lead oxide and 1-chloro-2-propanol in water solution. Henry[3] reported a similar preparation from 2-chloro-1-propanol, using concentrated potassium hydroxide at 50 to 70°C.

A study of the kinetics of the slightly reversible reaction of 1-chloro-2-propanol with sodium hydroxide has been made by Porret[4], who found both reactions to be approximately second order. The hydrolysis is more rapid than the apparent energy of activation would indicate, and the equilibrium is not displaced with temperature as it would be with a simple bimolecular reversible reaction. It was also observed that 1-chloro-2-propanol is about 20 times more reactive than ethylene chlorohydrin. Advantage of this property is taken in a patent[5] in which ethylene chlorohydrin is separated from propylene chlorohydrin by controlled hydrolysis with lime of the propylene compound to propylene oxide, leaving almost pure ethylene chlorohydrin.

A patent[6] issued in 1927 describes the preparation of propylene and other oxides by the treatment of gas mixtures containing ethylene, propylene, and butylene with hypochlorous acid, followed by distillation over calcium hydroxide, to produce olefin oxides. These are then fractionally distilled under pressure to separate the individual compounds.

The direct catalytic oxidation of propylene with oxygen in an inert gas such as nitrogen or carbon dioxide at 300 to 375°C. with gold, gold-silver, or gold-silver-copper catalysts to produce propylene oxide is also described in the patent literature[7]. Pigulevskii and Gulyaeva[8] have investigated the oxidation of propylene with oxygen at temperatures of 300 to 500°C. The amount of reacted propylene increased with increasing temperature (to 400°C.), oxygen concentration, and contact time. Of the propylene oxidized at 400°C., the yield of propylene oxide was 15 per cent and that of aldehydes, 35 per cent. The catalytic oxidation of propylene, employing ammonium vanadate, gave increased yields of carbon monoxide and carbon dioxide, but no propylene oxide was detected in the reaction products[9].

Propylene oxide is produced commercially from propylene by chlorohydrination processes analogous to those used for the production of ethylene oxide and from natural gas hydrocarbons by vapor-phase, partial oxidation methods (see pages 204 and 205, respectively).

Physical Properties

Propylene oxide is a colorless liquid at ordinary temperatures, with an odor resembling that of ethyl ether. Its important physical properties are listed in Table 11.1. Unless otherwise indicated, the determinations were made on *dl*-mixtures of 99.7 per cent purity in the Carbide laboratories.

Abderhalden and Eichwald[10] have reported the preparation of the pure *d*-isomer (b.p. 36.5–38°C., sp. gr. at 20/20°C. 0.8412, and rotation $[\alpha]_D^{18}$ + 12.72°) and of the *l*-compound (sp. gr. at 20/20°C. 0.8412 and rotation

TABLE 11.1 PHYSICAL PROPERTIES OF PROPYLENE OXIDE

Boiling point at 760 mm.	33.9°C.
at 50 mm.	−24°C.
at 10 mm.	−49°C.
Δb.p./Δ*p*, 740 to 760 mm.	0.036°C./mm.
Coefficient of expansion at 20°C.	0.00151/°C.
Critical temperature	215.3°C.
Explosive limits in air at 760 mm. (upper)	21.5% by vol.
(lower)	2.1% by vol.
Flash point (Cleveland open cup)	−35°F.
Freezing point	−104.4°C.
Heat of combustion	7796 cal./g. (ref. 15)
Heat of vaporization at 1 atm.	160 Btu/lb.
Molal heat of combustion at constant volume	450.5 ± 0.6 kg.cal. (ref. 16)
Molecular weight	58.08
Refractive index, n_D at 20°C.	1.3657
Δn_D/Δ*t*, 20 to 30°C.	0.00053/°C.
Solubility in water at 20°C.	40.5% by wt.
Solubility of water in, at 20°C.	12.8% by wt.
Specific gravity (apparent) at 20/20°C.	0.8304
ΔSp.gr./Δ*t*, 20 to 40°C.	0.00125/°C.
Specific heat	0.51 cal./g./°C.
Vapor pressure at 20°C.	445 mm. (see Fig. 11.1)
Viscosity (absolute) at 20°C.	0.38 cps.

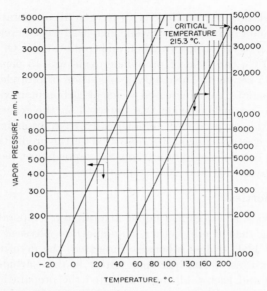

FIGURE 11.1. Vapor pressure of propylene oxide.

$[\alpha]_D^{18} - 8.26°$). Both forms were said to show partial racemization in hot aqueous solutions.

Hibbert and Allen[11] determined the electric moment and oxygen valence angle for propylene oxide as 1.88×10^{18} and 77°, respectively, the "normal" oxygen valence angle being given as $90 \pm 5°$. More recently, Rogers[12] has determined the dipole moment (Debye) of propylene oxide as 1.98.

Ballaus and Wagner[13] obtained the Raman spectrum of propylene oxide and suggested that due to free rotation of the substituted methyl group (i.e., epichlorohydrin), propylene oxide derivatives exist in three different geometric forms.

The system propylene oxide-water forms two liquid phases over a certain compositional range at the atmospheric boiling point, yet does not form an azeotrope[14]. The entire phase relations of this system at atmospheric pressure are shown in Figure 11.2. Figure 11.3 shows the equilibrium data presented as a conventional liquid-vapor equilibrium curve.

Reactions

Propylene oxide is a stable material under ordinary conditions, but when it is passed over pumice at 500°C., propionaldehyde and acetone are produced in a ratio of two to one[17]. Thompson and Meissner[18] have made a more comprehensive study of the kinetics of the thermal decomposition

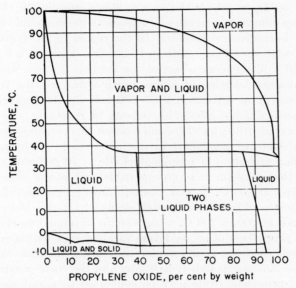

FIGURE 11.2. Phase equilibrium diagram for the system propylene oxide-water at atmospheric pressure.

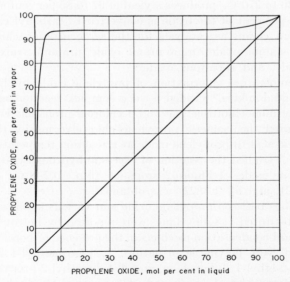

FIGURE 11.3. Liquid-vapor equilibria for the system propylene oxide-water at atmospheric pressure.

of propylene oxide, in which the end products are chiefly ethylene, hydrogen, carbon monoxide, and ethane. This decomposition indicates a quasi-unimolecular homogeneous reaction. In the region of 20 to 300 mm., it is unimolecular with no falling off down to 20 mm. At 490°C., k has a value of 3.125×10^{-3}. The energy of activation for this reaction was calculated as 58,000 calories. Addition of iodine vapor catalyzed the reaction and lowered the energy of activation to 38,000 calories. The addition of inert gases as diluents did not affect the velocity of reaction.

The commercial utility of the isomerization or decomposition reactions of propylene oxide is recognized in the patent art. A German patent[19] illustrates the preparation of propionaldehyde in 70 per cent yield by the vapor-phase isomerization of propylene oxide with steam over a silica gel contact catalyst at 300°C. A later United States patent describes the production of propionaldehyde and allyl alcohol[20] by the isomerization of propylene oxide at 200 to 300°C. using sodium or potassium alum together with a small proportion of an oxidation catalyst such as vanadium oxide. Another patent discloses a process for converting alkylene oxides into a mixture of the monomeric aldehyde isomer and the corresponding paraldehyde[21]. Thus, propylene oxide may be converted to parapropionaldehyde by the use of small amounts of chlorine as a catalyst at 0°C. Still another patent reveals that propylene oxide vapor, passed over a lithium phosphate catalyst at 230 to 270°C., produces a yield of 67 to 85 per cent allyl alcohol. Only 1 to 10 per cent of the oxide is converted to carbonyl compounds[22]. Another patent claims as catalysts for the same reaction chromic oxide, nickel oxide, stannic oxide, urano-uranic oxide, uranium trioxide, molybdenum trioxide, and cobaltous oxide[23].

The low-temperature chlorination of propylene oxide by Dobryanskii, Davydova, and Papkina[24] yielded a very complex reaction mixture containing chiefly monochloroacetone and 1-chloro-2-propanol. Forsberg and Smith[25] prepared the isomeric propylene chlorohydrins by the addition of hydrochloric acid to propylene oxide at a reaction temperature of 80°C. Knunyants[26, 27] studied the reaction of excess anhydrous hydrofluoric acid with propylene oxide. 1-Fluoro-2-propanol (b.p. 107–8°C., sp. gr. at 20/20°C. 1.021, and n_D^{20} 1.3822) was obtained.

Condensations between propylene oxide and various ketones to produce a series of substituted 1,3-dioxolanes were reported by Petrov[28]. Although the predominant condensation products in the presence of boron trifluoride-ether catalyst were polymeric in nature, 2,2,4-trimethyl-1,3-dioxolane, 2,4-dimethyl-2-ethyl-1,3-dioxolane, and 2,4-dimethyl-2-propyl-1,3-dioxolane were isolated and characterized. All were readily hydrolyzed with dilute sulfuric acid at room temperature to propylene glycol and the corresponding ketone.

Levene and Walti[29] reported the direct action of ammonia on propylene oxide to form 1-amino-2-propanol. Krasuskii[30] at a later date studied the reaction of aqueous ammonia with propylene oxide and obtained the same product, along with varying amounts of the di- and tri-substituted amines. The relative proportions of mono-, di-, and triisopropanolamine could be varied, depending on the proportion of reactants taken. Higher ratios of ammonia to propylene oxide served to increase the yields of 1-amino-2-propanol at the expense of the secondary and tertiary amines. Industrially, the isopropanolamines are prepared by diffusing propylene oxide into an aqueous solution of ammonia at a temperature below about 55°C.[31]

Krasuskii[32] also conducted reactions of ethylamine and propylene oxide and obtained both 1-ethylamino-2-propanol and 1-ethylamino-di(2-propanol). The same investigator[33] in 1930 reacted propylene oxide with diethylamine, resulting in a 65 per cent yield of diethylamino-2-propanol. Reaction rates and energies of activation for propylene oxide addition to a number of amines (mono-, di-, and trimethylamines and similar ethyl substituted amines) were determined by Hansson[34].

Propylene oxide and piperazine react in aqueous medium to give a 45 per cent yield of crystalline N,N'-di-(2-propanol)piperazine[35]. Condensation of propylene oxide with benzylamine gives a 62 per cent yield of 1-benzylamino-2-propanol. Similarly, isoamylamine may be used to obtain a 50 to 60 per cent yield of 1-isoamylamino-2-propanol[36].

Tetrahydroquinoline, propylene oxide, and water in equimolar proportions give chiefly 1-tetrahydroquinolino-2-propanol[37]. Decahydroquinoline and tetrahydro-2-naphthylamine have also been condensed with propylene oxide to yield, respectively, 1-decahydroquinolino-2-propanol and 1-tetrahydro-2-naphthylamino-2-propanol, the latter in 29 per cent yield[38].

Propylene oxide has also been reacted with proteins. While studying the action of 1,2-epoxides on proteins, Fraenkel-Conrat[39] found that unusually stable products were formed by reactions of the oxides in aqueous solution at room temperature (chiefly esterification of the carboxyl groups). The decrease in nitrogen content, however, indicated that 80 to 120 mols of reagent per protein molecule were introduced. Fraenkel-Conrat and Olcott[40] prepared propylene glycol 1-monobutyrate in good yields from butyric acid and propylene oxide in the presence of aqueous sodium hydroxide. They reported that amino acids also react, but that crystalline compounds could not be isolated.

Propylene oxide, like ethylene oxide, is capable of reaction with Grignard reagents. Stevens and McCoubrey[41], however, in attempting to prepare 4,4-dimethyl-2-pentanol from propylene oxide and *tert*-butyl magnesium chloride, obtained instead about 11 per cent of 2,2-dimethyl-3-pentanol, indicating isomerization of propylene oxide to propionaldehyde, and later normal addition of the Grignard reagent. No reverse addition resulting in the formation of 2,3,3-trimethyl-1-butanol was encountered. Malinovskii and co-workers[42] prepared 5-methyl-2-hexanol from isobutyl magnesium bromide and propylene oxide. They also obtained 2-heptanol from butyl magnesium bromide and propylene oxide. Ribas[43] has indicated that the action of methyl magnesium bromide on propylene oxide yields, on hydrolysis, 2-butanol, and also that the substitution of a methoxy group for hydrogen in propylene oxide, i. e.,

$$CH_3\text{---}O\text{---}CH_2CH\text{---}CH_2O$$

has no influence on the opening of the epoxide ring by Grignard reagents.

Dialkyl magnesium compounds react with propylene oxide to form addition compounds which yield alcohols on hydrolysis[44, 45]. Thus, with diethyl magnesium, 2-pentanol was obtained in 28 per cent yield and with dimethyl magnesium, 2-butanol in 28 per cent yield. Huston and Bostwick[46] studied the addition of propylene oxide to a number of organomagnesium bromides.

The reaction of propylene oxide with sulfur monochloride was studied by Malinovskii[47], who obtained a 43 per cent yield of bis(2-chloropropyl) sulfite and various by-products. He also reported the reaction of sulfuryl chloride with propylene oxide in ether solution to give 2-chloropropyl chlorosulfonate[48].

Sjoberg[49] reacted thioacetic acid with propylene oxide to produce a mixture of 2-acetoxy-1-propanethiol and 2-hydroxypropyl thioacetate. The former was isolated and hydrolyzed to obtain 2-hydroxypropyl mercaptan.

The condensation of propylene oxide with ethyl cyanoacetate in the presence of sodium ethoxide was studied by Glickman and Cope[50]. They obtained α-cyano-γ-valerolactone in 61 per cent yield.

For a discussion of the alcoholysis and polymerization of propylene oxide, see the sections "Propylene Glycol Ethers" and "Polypropylene Glycols," pages 262 and 277, respectively.

Applications

Like ethylene oxide, propylene oxide is primarily useful as a chemical intermediate. Among its miscellaneous applications, however, are its use as a low-boiling solvent for nitrocellulose, commercial gums, and various resins and its use as a preservative, fumigant, herbicide, and solvent or stabilizer in insecticides.

The use of propylene oxide as an intermediate in the synthesis of various oil additives and anti-oxidants has been patented. Resinous condensation products, obtained by Friedel-Crafts reactions with propylene oxide and such compounds as naphthalene, anthracene, and tetralin, when added in small amounts to lubricating oil, serve as pour-point depressants[51]. Esters of various phosphoric acids, obtained by reaction with propylene oxide, are useful as intermediates in the synthesis of additives for lubricating oils[52]. Such products (which may then be chlorinated) function as sludge and varnish inhibitors. Anti-oxidants, prepared by the condensation of propylene oxide with N,N'-diarylarylenediamines, are also patented[53].

Emulsifiers for cosmetics are obtained by reaction of soya bean lecithin and propylene oxide[54]. De-emulsifying agents for oil-drilling operations are prepared by condensing propylene oxide with iso-octylphenol or cyclo-hexylcyclohexanol to form compounds of the type[55]

$$R—\langle\ \rangle—O—(CH_2CHMeO)_xH$$

Products having surface-active properties are prepared by the condensation of acyl carbamyl guanidines with ethylene, propylene, or butylene oxides[56].

Therapeutic agents are produced when propylene oxide is reacted with a solution of tannic acid at low temperatures and impurities are removed by alcohol precipitation[57]. The oxide also reacts with diphenylacetonitrile to yield 3,3-diphenyl-5-methyl tetrahydro-2-furanoneimine, an intermediate in the preparation of the analgesic, amidone[58].

A resin suitable for use in printing vat dyes is obtained by the equimolar reaction of propylene oxide and ethylenediamine and subsequent heating of the reaction product with one mol of urea[59]. Oil-soluble dyes may be prepared by reacting triethanolamine with propylene oxide, followed by esterification with a fatty acid and condensation with a dye containing an acid group[60].

Compositions useful in the setting of yarn twist are prepared by condensing either ethylene oxide or propylene oxide (or a mixture of the two) with polyhydric compounds and esterifying the product with fatty acids of about 16 carbon atoms[61, 62]. Hydroxypropyl cellulose, useful for coatings and as a pigment binder, has been made by the reaction of propylene oxide with cellulose pulp in aqueous caustic solution[63].

Advantage has been taken of the high solvent power of propylene oxide in its use in various adhesive applications. It is employed as a low-boiling solvent for nitrocellulose adhesive compositions[64] and for vinyl chloride-acetate resins[65]. It has also been claimed as an activator or softener for dried and hardened cellulose derivative type adhesives[66] and as an adhesive or coating for binding neoprene to rubber in the manufacture of golf balls[67]. Nitrocellulose shoe cements for joining soles to uppers are formulated with propylene oxide and 10 per cent of acetone or ester solvents or 1 per cent of dibutyl phthalate[66, 68, 69]. Such cements are sufficiently slow in drying to allow the operators to assemble parts before putting them in the press, yet sufficiently rapid to reduce the necessary drying time while held in the pressure equipment.

Propylene oxide has been used in the separation of pentane from 2-pentene and of some diolefins from mixtures of close-boiling pentenes by azeotropic distillation[70, 71, 72]. Pure amino acids, such as glycine, may be obtained from their acid addition salts by treatment with propylene oxide, followed by alcohol washing[73]. Propylene oxide has also been disclosed as an alkylation catalyst in the high-pressure, high-temperature, gas-phase alkylation of paraffin hydrocarbons with olefins[74].

Whelton, Phaff, Mrak, and Fisher[75] observed that the epoxides are powerful reagents against certain yeasts, molds, and bacteria that attack foods. In this connection, propylene oxide was found to be slightly less effective than ethylene oxide. Fruit juices, such as cider, can be preserved by the addition of 0.5 to 1 per cent by volume of propylene oxide[76]. Its use as a volatile food preservative, particularly with packaged frozen foods, has also been described[77]. The vapor is effective in killing micro-organisms and can penetrate certain packaging materials. At room temperatures the propylene oxide is sufficiently volatile that no preservative remains. Enzymic activity and oxidative deterioration, however, are not inhibited by such treatment.

Roark[78] described the fumigant characteristics of propylene oxide as early as 1929. The oxide is used, for instance, as a mothproofing agent for wool[79].

The germicidal activity of propylene oxide both as a vapor and in dilute water solution was studied by Lepigre[80], who suggested a 0.15 per cent aqueous solution as a soil sterilizing agent. These solutions were found to be effective against *Calandra arizae* and *Pseudococcus adonidum*. Cooper[81] found propylene oxide to be germicidal against *Bacillus lactis aerogenes* at 10 per cent concentration in water and against *Staphylococcus* at 3 per cent concentration.

As a herbicide, propylene oxide was shown to be effective in killing noxious plants such as gooseberries and barberries. Its effect is not lasting in the treated soil. Its advantages are its plant toxicity at low concentrations, the ease with which it can be handled, and its rapid release from the soil, thereby making the period of soil unproductivity shorter than it is with the use of chlorates and chlorides[82]. The mechanism of herbicidal activity was studied by Landon[83] who observed an increased catalase content in the leaves of cabbage plants watered with 0.01 to 1 molar solutions of either ethylene oxide or propylene oxide.

Propylene oxide has also been found useful as a solvent and stabilizer in DDT aerosol-type insecticides[84, 85, 86]. In addition to its effectiveness in such insecticides, propylene oxide in concentrations of 0.1 to 5 per cent by volume will protect unsaturated hydrocarbons from deterioration in storage[87] and also stabilize chlorinated hydrocarbon solvents used for degreasing aluminum and its alloys[88]. The inclusion of a small proportion of propylene oxide during the preparation and storage of vinyl resin lacquers protects them from discoloration. About 0.1 to 0.3 per cent propylene oxide, based on the weight of resin present, is usually sufficient[65].

Literature Cited

1. Oser, B., *Ann., Suppl.*, **1**, 253 (1861).
2. Krasuskii, K. A., *J. Russ. Phys. Chem. Soc.*, **34**, 307 (1902).
3. Henry, L., *Rec. trav. chim.*, **22**, 332 (1903).
4. Porret, D., *Helv. Chim. Acta*, **30, 7**01–6 (1947).
5. Heard, J. R., Jr. (to Wyandotte Chemicals Corp.), U. S. Patent 2,417,685 (March 18, 1947).
6. I. G. Farbenindustrie A.-G., British Patent 292,066 (June 11, 1927).
7. Société française de catalyse généralisée, French Patent 785,149 (Aug. 2, 1935).
8. Pigulevskii, V. V., and Gulyaeva, L. I., *Trans. Exptl. Research Lab. "Khemgas" Leningrad*, **3,** 174–8 (1936).
9. Pigulevskii, V. V., and Yarzhemskaya, E. Ya., *Trans. Exptl. Research Lab. "Khemgas" Leningrad*, **3,** 178–85 (1936).
10. Abderhalden, E., and Eichwald, E., *Ber.*, **51,** 1312 (1918).
11. Hibbert, H., and Allen, J. S., *J. Am. Chem. Soc.*, **54,** 4115 (1932).
12. Rogers, M. T., *J. Am. Chem. Soc.*, **69,** 2544 (1947).
13. Ballaus, O., and Wagner, J., *Z. physik. Chem.*, **45B,** 272 (1939).
14. Wickert, J. N., Tamplin, W. S., and Shank, R. L., Paper presented before the American Institute of Chemical Engineers, Houston, Texas, February, 1950.
15. Moureu, H., and Dodé, M., *Bull. soc. chim. France*, (5) **4,** 637 (1937).
16. Zubow, P. W., and Swientoslawski, W., *Bull. soc. chim. France*, (4) **37,** 271 (1925).
17. Ipatiev, V. N., and Leontowitsch, W., *Ber.*, **36,** 2017 (1903).
18. Thompson, H. W., and Meissner, M., *Trans. Faraday Soc.*, **34,** 1222 (1938).
19. Hoffman, V. (to I. G. Farbenindustrie A.-G.), German Patent 618,972 (Sept. 19, 1935).
20. Law, G. H., and McNamee, R. W. (to Carbide and Carbon Chemicals Corp.), U. S. Patent 2,159,507 (May 23, 1939).
21. Parrish, C. I. (to The Pennsylvania Salt Manufacturing Co.), U. S. Patent 2,435,460 (Feb. 3, 1948).
22. Fowler, G. W., and Fitzpatrick, J. T. (to Carbide and Carbon Chemicals Corp.), U. S. Patent 2,426,264 (Aug. 26, 1947).
23. Lundsted, L. G., Schwoegler, E. J., and Jacobs, E. C. (to Wyandotte Chemicals Corp.), U. S. Patent 2,479,632 (Aug. 23, 1949).
24. Dobryanskii, A. F., Davydova, M. I., and Papkina, Z. T., *J. Gen. Chem. (U.S.S.R.)*, **7,** 291 (1937).
25. Forsberg, G., and Smith, L., *Acta Chem. Scand.*, **1,** 577–80 (1947).
26. Knunyants, I. L., *Compt. rend. acad. sci. U.R.S.S.*, **55,** 223–6 (1947).
27. Knunyants, I. L., Kil'disheva, O. V., and Petrov, I. P., *J. Gen. Chem. (U.S.S.R.)*, **19,** 95–100 (1949).
28. Petrov, A. A., *J. Gen. Chem. (U.S.S.R.)*, **16,** 61–4 (1946).
29. Levene, P. A., and Walti, A., *J. Biol. Chem.*, **71,** 461 (1927).
30. Krasuskii, K. A., *J. Gen. Chem. (U.S.S.R.)*, **6,** 460 (1936).

31. Wickert, J. N. (to Carbide and Carbon Chemicals Corp.), U. S. Patent 1,988,225 (Jan. 15, 1935).
32. Krasuskii, K. A., *J. chim. Ukraine*, **1,** 398 (1925).
33. Krasuskii, K. A., and Pilyugin, G. T., *J. chim. Ukraine*, **5,** 135 (1930).
34. Hansson, J., *Svensk. Kem. Tid.*, **60,** 183–9 (1948); *Chem. Abstracts*, **43,** 926 (1949).
35. Krasuskii, K. A., and Pilyugin, G. T., *J. chim. Ukraine*, **5,** 349 (1930).
36. Krasuskii, K. A., and Pilyugin, G. T., *J. chim. Ukraine*, **5,** 237 (1930).
37. Koroleva, V. I., *J. Gen. Chem. (U.S.S.R.)*, **9,** 2200 (1939).
38. Matskevich, R. M., *J. Gen. Chem. (U.S.S.R.)*, **11,** 1241 (1941).
39. Fraenkel-Conrat, H. L., *J. Biol. Chem.*, **154,** 227 (1944).
40. Fraenkel-Conrat, H. L., and Olcott, H. S., *J. Am. Chem. Soc.*, **66,** 1420 (1944).
41. Stevens, P. G., and McCoubrey, J. A., *J. Am. Chem. Soc.*, **63,** 2847 (1941).
42. Malinovskii, M. S., Volkova, E. E., and Morozova, N. M., *J. Gen. Chem. (U.S.S.R.)*, **19,** 114–17 (1949).
43. Ribas, Ia. I., *Anales soc. españ. fís. y quím.*, **26,** 122 (1928).
44. Norton, F. H., and Hass, H. B., *J. Am. Chem. Soc.*, **58,** 2147 (1936).
45. Golumbic, C., and Cottle, D. L., *J. Am. Chem. Soc.*, **61,** 996 (1939).
46. Huston, R. C., and Bostwick, C. O., *J. Org. Chem.*, **13,** 331–8 (1948).
47. Malinovskii, M. S., *J. Gen. Chem. (U.S.S.R.)*, **9,** 832–9 (1939).
48. Malinovskii, M. S., *J. Gen. Chem. (U.S.S.R.)*, **17,** 1559–63 (1947).
49. Sjoberg, B., *Ber.*, **75B,** 13–29 (1942).
50. Glickman, S. A., and Cope, A. C., *J. Am. Chem. Soc.*, **67,** 1012–6 (1945).
51. Lieber, E., and Thorner, M. E. (to Standard Oil Development Co.), U. S. Patent 2,381,457 (Aug. 7, 1945).
52. Adams, C. E., and Shoemaker, B. H. (to Standard Oil Co.), U. S. Patent 2,372,244 (March 27, 1945).
53. United States Rubber Co., British Patent 570,232 (June 28, 1945).
54. De Groote, M., and Keiser, B. (to Petrolite Corp., Ltd.), U. S. Patent 2,310,679 (Feb. 9, 1943).
55. De Groote, M., and Keiser, B. (to Petrolite Corp., Ltd.), U. S. Patent 2,278,838 (April 7, 1942).
56. Carnes, J. J., and Warner, R. B. (to American Cyanamid Co.), U. S. Patent 2,478,859 (Aug. 9, 1949).
57. Herstein, K. M. (to Skol Co.), U. S. Patent 2,167,073 (July 25, 1939).
58. Easton, N. R., Gardner, J. H., and Stevens, J. R., *J. Am. Chem. Soc.*, **69,** 2941 (1947).
59. Paquin, M. (to General Aniline Works, Inc.), U. S. Patent 2,155,328 (April 18, 1939).
60. Lacey, H. T., and Ness, W. E. (to American Cyanamid Co.), U. S. Patent 2,392,158 (Jan. 1, 1946).
61. Brown, K. R. (to American Viscose Corp.), U. S. Patent 2,418,752 (April 8, 1947).
62. Brown, K. R. (to Atlas Powder Co.), U. S. Patent 2,450,079 (Sept. 28, 1948).
63. Erickson, D. R., U. S. Patent 2,469,764 (May 10, 1949).
64. Boston Blacking & Chemical Co., German Patent 605,725 (Nov. 16, 1934).
65. " 'Vinylite' Copolymer Resins for Surface Coatings," New York, Carbide and Carbon Chemicals Corp., 1942.
66. Clark, P. M., and Taylor, T. T. (to E. I. du Pont de Nemours & Co.), U. S Patent 2,092,050 (Sept. 7, 1937).
67. Macdonald, A. D. (to Boston Blacking & Chemical Co.), U. S. Patent 2,105,697 (Jan. 18, 1938).

68. Pitman, E. C. (to E. I. du Pont de Nemours & Co.), U. S. Patent 2,092,084 (Sept. 7, 1937).

69. Wedger, W. H. (to Boston Blacking & Chemical Co.), U. S. Patents 1,959,320–2 (May 15, 1934).

70. Welling, C. E. (to Phillips Petroleum Co.), U. S. Patent 2,382,119 (Aug. 14, 1945).

71. Short, G. H., and Morris, L. C. (to Phillips Petroleum Co.), U. S. Patent 2,386,274 (Oct. 9, 1945).

72. Welling, C. E. (to Phillips Petroleum Co.), U. S. Patent 2,386,375 (Oct. 9, 1945).

73. Kharasch, M. S., and Fuchs, C. F. (to Eli Lilly and Co.), U. S. Patent 2,404,503 (July 23, 1946).

74. O'Kelly, A. A., Plucker, J., and Work, R. H. (to Socony-Vacuum Oil Co., Inc.), U. S. Patent 2,407,033 (Sept. 3, 1946).

75. Whelton, R., Phaff, H. J., Mrak, E. M., and Fisher, C. D., *Food Inds.*, **18,** 23, 174, and 318 (1946).

76. Haines, E. C., U. S. Patent 2,354,014 (July 18, 1944).

77. Baerwald, F. K. (to Rosenberg Bros. & Co.), U. S. Patent 2,370,768 (March 6, 1945).

78. Roark, R. C., *Dept. Agr. Tech. Bull. No. 162*, March, 1929.

79. Schlack, P. (to I. G. Farbenindustrie A.-G.), U. S. Patent 2,202,169 (May 28, 1940).

80. Lepigre, A. L., *Bull. soc. encour. ind. natl.*, **137,** 367 (1938).

81. Cooper, E. A., *J. Soc. Chem. Ind. (London)*, **66,** 48–50 (1947).

82. Harvey, R. B., *J. Am. Soc. Agron.*, **23,** 481 (1931); *Phytopathology*, **21,** 126 (1931).

83. Landon, R. H., *Am. J. Botany*, **21,** 583 (1934).

84. Goodhue, L. D., and Ballinger, W. R., *Ind. Eng. Chem., Anal. Ed.*, **18,** 131 (1946).

85. Hazen, A. C., and Goodhue, L. D., *Soap Sanit. Chemicals*, **22** (8), 151, 153 (1946).

86. Young, E. G., *Soap Sanit. Chemicals*, **23** (11), 116–7 (1947).

87. Morris, R. C., and Shokal, E. C. (to Shell Development Co.), U. S. Patent 2,364,587 (Dec. 5, 1944).

88. Aitchison, A. G., and Patering, W. H., (to Westvaco Chlorine Products Corp.), U. S. Patent 2,371,645 (March 20, 1945).

CHAPTER 12

DERIVATIVES OF PROPYLENE GLYCOL

R. F. HOLDEN

Like ethylene glycol, propylene glycol is important chemically for its derivatives, the most important of which are discussed in the following sections under the headings ethers, esters, ether-esters and acetals.

Ethers

A wide variety of mono- and diethers of propylene glycol have been prepared, although the industrial utilization of these compounds has been limited by their similarity to the ethylene glycol ethers. While the 1,2-propanediol monoethers may exist in two structurally isomeric forms, little cognizance of this fact has been taken in the patent and industrial literature, and the preparation of isomeric forms has but recently been studied as a problem of academic interest.

Preparation. The monoethers of propylene glycol have been prepared chiefly through the condensation of propylene oxide with alcohols or phenols, usually with either acidic or basic catalysts[1]. They may also be obtained from the reaction of propylene glycol or propylene chlorohydrin with dialkyl sulfates in the presence of sodium hydroxide or potassium hydroxide. This method is used largely for the production of diethers. Investigations of Chitwood and Freure[2] and of Petrov[3, 4] have shown that the base-catalyzed condensation of propylene oxide with alcohols yields almost exclusively the primary monoalkyl ethers, while acid catalyzed or uncatalyzed reactions produce a mixture of primary and secondary monoethers.

The alcoholysis of propylene oxide has been further studied in both the chemical literature and patent art. In 1914 Boyd and Marle[5] prepared a series of glycol aryl ethers by reacting propylene oxide with a number of phenols and related compounds in the presence of their sodium alkoxides. Boyd and Thomas[6] later determined the velocity constants for the reaction of propylene oxide with various phenols. The two isomeric phenoxypropanols were identified by Sexton and Britton[7]. Cox, Nelson, and Cretcher[8] prepared the isomeric n-propoxypropanols from propylene oxide and 1-propanol by an uncatalyzed reaction at 180 to 205°C. Dewael[9] prepared a number of monoalkyl ethers by reacting the oxide with the appropriate alcohols, while Schmidt and Meyer[10] described the preparation of ethers from propylene oxide and polyhydric alcohols such as glycerol, pentaerythritol, sorbitol, and others.

262

Properties. The physical constants of some representative monoethers of propylene glycol are presented in Table 12.1. Previous summaries[11] of physical data for some of these ethers did not specify the structural isomers of the monoethers and are presumed to have been obtained on isomeric mixtures. The present compilation is derived from available data on compounds which may be reasonably assumed to be the individual isomers.

Some additional ethers of propylene glycol include: 1,2-bis(2-cyano-isopropoxy)propane (a pale yellow liquid, b.p. at 1 to 2 mm. 158–162°C., density at 25°C. 0.9995, n_D at 25°C. 1.4462); a mixture of 2-(2-cyano-isopropoxy)-1-propanol and 1-(2-cyanoisopropoxy)-2-propanol (b.p. at 10 mm. 130–137°C.)[15]; 1,2-diphenoxypropane (m.p. 32°C., b.p. at 12 mm. 175–178°C.)[16]; and the trityl ether (m.p. 176.5–177°C.) which is used as

TABLE 12.1. MONOETHERS OF PROPYLENE GLYCOL

R	Boiling Point, °C.	Pressure, mm.	Specific Gravity, 20/4°C.	Refractive Index, n_D at 20°C.	Re'.
Primary Ethers of the Type R—O—CH₂CHOHCH₃					
Methyl	118–118.5	—	0.9312	1.4040	3
Methyl[a]	126–127	760	0.9260	1.40696	9
Ethyl	130–130.8	—	0.896[b]	1.4058	2
Ethyl	130.5–131	—	0.8965	1.4075	3
Ethyl	136	760	0.9028	1.4	9
n-Propyl	148.5–149	730	0.8886	—	8
n-Propyl	148.5–149	—	0.8857–86	1.4130	3
Isopropyl	137–138	—	0.879[b]	1.4070	2
Isopropyl	142–143	765	0.9059	—	9
n-Butyl	74–74.5	20	0.880[b]	1.4170	2
tert-Butyl	151–153	760	0.8707	—	12
2-Ethylhexyl	101.5–102	10	0.871[b]	1.4327	2
Phenyl	130	21	1.0622	1.5232	13
Cyclohexyl	65	2	—	—	
Benzyl	128	12	—	—	14
2-Naphthyl	82–83[c]	—	—	—	13
Secondary Ethers of the Type HOCH₂CHORCH₃					
Methyl	130–132	760	0.9365	1.4072	
Ethyl	140–141	761	0.9044	1.40968	9
Ethyl	137.5–138	—	0.908[b]	1.4100	2
n-Propyl	150.5–151	730	0.8925	—	8
Isopropyl	143–144	—	0.885[b]	1.4094	2
n-Butyl	78–78.5	20	0.888[b]	1.4192	2

[a] 1-Methoxy-2-propanol, possibly a mixture of isomers since H_2SO_4 was used as catalyst in condensation of propylene oxide with methanol; [b] specific gravity, 20/15.6°C.; [c] melting point.

a means of identification for propylene glycol[17], as discussed in Chapter 16, "Analysis and Test Methods." Binkley and Hamilton[18] condensed o-nitrophenol with propylene chlorohydrin to prepare 1-(2-nitrophenoxy)-2-propanol (b.p. at 25 mm. 223–225°C.). The same workers prepared 1-(2-aminophenoxy)-2-propanol (m.p. 75°C.) and 1-(2-arsenophenoxy)-2-propanol (m.p. 167°C).

Physical properties for a series of propylene glycol monoethers offered by Dow are listed in Table 12.2[19]. These compounds are colorless liquids with mild pleasant odors.

TABLE 12.2. PHYSICAL PROPERTIES OF COMMERCIAL PROPYLENE GLYCOL MONOETHERS

	Propylene Glycol Monoether			
	Methyl	Ethyl	Isopropyl	Butyl
Boiling point, °C., at 760 mm.	120.0	132.2	142.2	171.1
at 10 mm.	21.7	30.6	37.8	59.5
Fire point (open cup), °F.,*	102	110	125	160
Flash point (open cup), °F.*	102	110	120	160
Molecular weight	90.1	104.1	118.2	132.2
Pour point, °F.	−142	−130	−134	−130
Refractive index, n_D at 25°C.	1.402	1.405	1.407	1.415
Solubility in water at 25°C., g./100 g. water	∞	∞	∞	6.0
Specific gravity at 25/25°C.	0.921	0.895	0.879	0.878
Specific heat at 25°C.	0.61	0.65	0.62	0.63
Surface tension at 25°C., dynes/cm.	27.7	25.9	23.9	26.5
Vapor pressure at 25°C., mm.	12.5	7.2	4.5	1.2
Viscosity at 25°C., cps.	1.75	1.88	2.27	2.90
Weight per gallon at 25°C., lbs.	7.67	7.45	7.33	7.33

* A.S.T.M.—D92-46.

Applications. The alkyl ethers of propylene glycol are powerful solvents for a wide variety of materials including gums, resins, and cellulose esters, and have been suggested as the solvent components of lacquer formulations[1, 11, 20]. The ability of the lower alkyl monoethers to dissolve both hydrocarbons and water indicates their usefulness as coupling and dispersing agents.

The use of propylene glycol monobutyl ether as a hydraulic brake fluid component has been patented[21]. Its chief advantage is its good low-temperature miscibility with castor oil. As an adhesive-tape remover, propylene glycol monoethyl ether greatly lessens the pain and irritation produced when a firmly adhering plaster is pulled away[22].

1-Phenoxy-2-propanol is useful in preventing the loss of lubricating-oil additives from oil by emulsification with water[23]. Compounds useful as plasticizers for alkyl cellulose or as perfume fixatives are prepared by treating propylene chlorohydrin with the isomeric *o*- and *m*-phenylphenols in the presence of an alkali[24].

In biological applications, 1-(pentachlorophenoxy)-2-propanol (m.p. 57–63°C.) has been suggested as a mildew-proofing agent for textiles[25]. Two high-boiling monoethers of propylene glycol, the 2-methyl-2, 4-pentanediol and 2-ethyl-1,3-hexanediol ethers, are claimed as insect repellents[26]. The 1-(2-allyl chlorophenoxy)-2-propanols (chloro 4 or 6) are claimed as intermediates and as paraciticides[27].

Esters

Commercial production of propylene glycol esters has been largely confined to the higher fatty acid esters. Although the lower esters possess good solvent characteristics, the analogous compounds prepared from ethylene glycol have been more readily available and to some extent have discouraged the industrial development of the propylene glycol esters.

Preparation. Both mono- and diesters of propylene glycol have been prepared by the following methods:

(1) Direct esterification of the glycol with free acids, acyl halides, or acid anhydrides.

(2) Ester exchange (transesterification) reactions[28, 29, 30].

(3) Reactions of propylene dihalides with metallic salts of carboxylic acids[31, 32].

(4) Condensation of propylene oxide with carboxylic acids[33, 34]. These condensation products are primarily monoesters. Propylene glycol monoacetate and diacetate have been prepared by the catalytic oxidation of propylene in the presence of acetic acid[35].

Although the methods employed are common to the preparation of glycol esters in general and ethylene glycol esters in particular, an important difference in the products of esterification exists as a result of the presence of both a primary and a secondary hydroxyl group in propylene glycol, giving rise to isomeric monoesters. In most instances, investigators have failed to define the position of the ester group in these compounds because of the difficulties encountered in their separation.

The preparation of propylene glycol esters of the higher fatty acids has been adequately discussed by Goldsmith[36]. Additional references to the preparation of glycol esters have been reviewed by Ellis[37]. While these reviews are predominantly concerned with ethylene glycol derivatives, many of the same methods are applicable to the preparation of propylene glycol esters.

Properties. The available physical properties of some representative mono- and diesters of propylene glycol are listed in Tables 12.3, 12.4, and 12.5. Variations in the melting points of the fatty acid esters listed by

Goldsmith[36] may be due to the use of impure acids and, in the case of the monoesters, the relative amounts of isomeric reaction products.

In addition to these esters, physical properties have been reported on a

TABLE 12.3. Physical Properties of Common Propylene Glycol Organic Esters

Propylene Glycol Ester	Boiling Point, °C.	Pressure, mm.	Specific Gravity, °C.	Refractive Index, n_D at 20°C.	Ref.
Monoesters					
Acetate	182–183	760	1.055 (20/20)	1.4197	47
1-n-Butyrate	56–57	1	—	1.4246 (25)	33
1-Benzoate	141–143	8	—	—	
Diesters					
Diformate	116	101	1.136[a]	1.4130 (23)	48
Diacetate	190–191	762	1.059 (20/4)	1.4173	9
	189–191	746	1.058 (20/15.6)	1.4148	2
	97–98	28–29	1.0562 (20/4)	1.4146	32
Di-n-butyrate	95–105	15	—	—	49
Dilactate	130–140	1	1.183[b]	—	50
Dicaproate	128	0.8	0.9359 (32/20)	1.4282 (32)	
Dibenzoate	232	12	—	—	38

[a] Density at 25°C.; [b] density at 20°C.

TABLE 12.4. Physical Properties of Propylene Glycol Esters of Some Common Fatty Acids

Propylene Glycol Ester	Melting Point, °C.	Refractive Index
Monoesters		
Laurate	14	—
Oleate	6	—
Palmitate	54.3	1.4405
	95–96	—
Ricinoleate	0	—
Stearate	33–35	—
	37–39	—
	44	—
	59.5	1.4424
	220–230[a]	—
Diesters		
Dilaurate	35	—
Dimyristate	41.5	—
Dipalmitate	68.8	1.4364
	69.5–70	—
	52.5–54.5	—
Distearate	72.3	1.4366
	40	—

[a] Boiling point at 1 mm.

TABLE 12.5. PHYSICAL PROPERTIES OF PROPYLENE GLYCOL INORGANIC ESTERS

Propylene Glycol Ester	Boiling Point, °C.	Pressure, mm.	Density at t°C., g./ml.	Refractive Index, n_D at °C.	Ref.
Arsenite (As$_2$O$_3$)	190	16	1.618 (22)	1.5096 (22)	51
Borate	178	35	1.027 (27)	1.4340 (27)	52
	114–118	1	—	—	53
Carbonate	110	12	1.21 (20)	—	54
Dinitrite	108–110	—	1.144 (0)	—	55
Dinitrate	—	—	1.335 (5)	—	56

series of isomeric dichlorobenzoates[38], diaminobenzoates[39], p-nitrobenzoate (m.p. 126–127°C.)[40], and optical isomers of the diphenyl urethans[41, 42].

Propylene glycol oxalate was prepared by Carothers, Arvin, and Dorough[43]. The monomeric ester (m.p. 142°C.) showed no tendency to condense spontaneously at room temperature, but on heating at 140 to 150°C. for eight hours was converted to a white powder melting at 176–178°C. Evdokimov[44] heated anhydrous oxalic acid and propylene glycol in sealed tubes at temperatures of 100°C. and 240 to 260°C. for various periods, obtaining volatile decomposition products and tarry residues.

Salmi, Merivuori, and Laaksonen[45] have prepared some interesting bicyclo condensation arsenious esters with propylene glycol and alkyl substituted arsonic acids. Physical properties were reported for the methyl and butyl substituted derivatives.

The propylene glycol esters of acrylic and methacrylic acids were prepared by Caldwell[46] from the acids and propylene oxide in the presence of a tertiary amine catalyst. The preparation of propylene glycol 1-methacrylate (b.p. at 7 mm. 90–93°C.) was reported.

Applications. An important use for propylene glycol fatty acid esters (the ricinoleate in particular) has been their inclusion in hydraulic brake fluid formulations. A series of patents issued in the period between 1937 and 1942[29, 30, 57, 58, 59, 60] illustrate the preparation (by ester exchange reactions with castor oil) and use of propylene glycol ricinoleate in hydraulic brake fluids. Their chief advantage over the castor oil-base fluids is said to be a lower freezing point, thus permitting operation of the fluids at relatively low temperatures.

Propylene glycol fatty acid esters have been used in the drug and cosmetic industries. Because of the proper balance between hydrophylic and hydrophobic portions of these molecules, excellent self-emulsifying ointment bases and creams may be prepared. Presslie[61] has reported the preparation of several ointment bases using propylene glycol monostearate and monolaurate and has indicated the good medicinal absorption properties, ease of handling, and emulsifying ability of these esters. Similar results

were obtained by Fiero and Dutcher[62]. The monostearate has also been
suggested as a suppository base[63].

Several monoesters of propylene glycol, the laurate, oleate, ricinoleate,
and stearate, were considered as non-ionic surface active agents by Goldsmith[64], who also patented blends of these with polyglycol fatty esters as
emulsifying agents[65]. The reaction product of propylene glycol and bromo-
stearic acid produces detergents having excellent lathering properties in
hard water[66].

The fatty acid esters of propylene glycol are also used as synergists in
aerosol insecticides[67]. The propylene glycol monoesters of lauric acid and
of coconut fatty acids have been used in formulations applied to fabrics
to improve the "scroop" or "hand" of the finished cloth[68]. The monolaurate
is also used as an anti-spattering agent for fats[69]. The dicaproate ester of
propylene glycol has been found to possess some degree of flea-repellent
activity when tested on cotton twill cloth[70].

Several references to the preparation of propylene glycol alginates from
propylene oxide and alginic acid have appeared. Similar materials prepared from alginic acid by reaction with epoxystearic acid and epoxy-
octadecanols followed by reaction with propylene oxide have also been
reported[71, 72]. The propylene glycol alginates are said to be useful as ice
cream stabilizers[73] and as foam stabilizers for beer[74].

Propylene glycol esters, prepared by a transesterification process from
hydrogenated soybean and castor oils, are useful as anti-foaming agents[28].
Propylene glycol esters of malic acid, salicylic acid, and benzoic acid have
been used as active ingredients in a preparation used for the treatment of
dermatological conditions in animals[75].

Propylene glycol dipropionate has been used as a preservative for cottonseed in storage. Germination of the treated seed was higher than that
of the untreated control[76]. The same ester also acts as a humectant, mold
inhibitor, and flavor retainer in foodstuffs such as doughnuts[77]. It also has
been reported as an excellent fungicide for skin diseases[78].

Propylene glycol diacetate has been pyrolyzed at temperatures of about
500°C. to yield allyl acetate and propionaldehyde[79].

Numerous examples of polymerized propylene glycol esters of dibasic
acids are reported in the literature dealing with the preparation of alkyd-
type resins. These are discussed in Chapter 10, "Commercial Applications
of Propylene Glycol."

A series of glycol carbonates of the general formula $R(O_2COCHR'
CO_2R'')_2$—in which R may be ethylene glycol or propylene glycol, R' a
hydrogen atom or hydrocarbon radical, and R'' an unsaturated alcohol
radical—have been patented[80]. Preparation of the unsaturated carbonate
esters is usually accomplished through the intermediate chloroformates of

the glycol (prepared from the glycol and phosgene). The unsaturated esters thus produced can be utilized as plasticizers or polymerized to form hard transparent resins useful in preparing transparent articles, as impregnating agents, or as adhesives in producing laminated cloth articles.

Water-soluble bismuth compounds having therapeutic value are made by the reaction of propylene glycol and sodium bismuthate to produce brown powders stable in air[81]. An antisyphilitic preparation for oral administration, sold under the trade name "Sobisminol," is prepared by the interaction of sodium bismuthate, propylene glycol, and triisopropanolamine[82, 83].

The reaction product of acetylsalicylic acid and propylene glycol is supposed to have therapeutic characteristics which are superior to those of aspirin[84]. It is effective as a sedative, analgesic, and, in some cases, hypnotic.

Propylene glycol di(benzene sulfonate) has been offered as a plasticizer for resins[85].

In 1921, propylene glycol dinitrate was suggested as a substitute for nitroglycerin, over which it has the advantages of being nonfreezing and more stable[86]. However, there appears to have been no commercial exploitation of this compound in competition with nitroglycerin and ethylene glycol dinitrate.

Ether-Esters

Ether-esters of propylene glycol are known but have not achieved much industrial recognition. Their preparation has usually been accomplished by the esterification of the monoethers of propylene glycol with acids, acid anhydrides, or acyl halides in accord with common esterification methods. The physical properties of some ether-acetate esters of propylene glycol are given in Table 12.6.

The propylene glycol ether-esters are useful as solvents, emulsifying agents, and plasticizers. One patent[87] claims the fatty acid esters of propylene glycol monoethyl ether as softeners for cellulose products.

TABLE 12.6. ETHER-ESTERS OF PROPYLENE GLYCOL

Compound	Boiling Point at 760 mm., °C.	Specific Gravity, 20/4°C.	Refractive Index, n_D at 20°C.	Ref.
1-Methoxy-2-propanol acetate	145.5–146.5	0.9677	1.4028	3
	147 (762)	0.9709	1.40449	9
1-Ethoxy-2-propanol acetate	155.5–156.5	0.9408	1.4042	3
	156–157 (746)	0.9425 (20/15.6)	1.4025	2
1-Propoxy-2-propanol acetate	172.5–174	0.9307	1.4082	3
1-Phenoxy-2-propanol acetate	117–118 (0.5)	—	1.5099 (25)	88

Acetals

Cyclic acetals or 4-methyl-1,3-dioxolanes may be readily produced from propylene glycol by condensation with aldehydes. Thus, with formaldehyde, using a small amount of ferric chloride catalyst, 4-methyl-1,3-dioxolane,

$$CH_3-CH-O$$
$$\quad\quad\quad\quad\quad\searrow$$
$$\quad\quad\quad\quad\quad\quad\quad CH_2$$
$$\quad\quad\quad\quad\quad\nearrow$$
$$CH_2-O$$

can be prepared (b. p. 90°C.)[89]. Another method for preparing the same compound employing a hydrochloric acid catalyst has been described[90]. The product is said to be an excellent solvent for cellulose acetate or other cellulose derivatives. Its use as an intermediate in the preparation of 2-(chloromethoxy)isopropyl acetate (by reaction between the dioxolane and acetyl chloride) has also been described[91].

Cyclic acetals and ketals of propylene glycol have also been prepared by condensing propylene oxide with aldehydes and ketones, respectively (see Chapter 11, "Propylene Oxide").

Literature Cited

1. Davidson, J. G. (to Carbide and Carbon Chemicals Corp.), U. S. Patent 1,730,061 (Oct. 1, 1929).
2. Chitwood, H. C., and Freure, B. T., *J. Am. Chem. Soc.*, **68**, 680–2 (1946).
3. Petrov, A. A., *J. Gen. Chem.* (*U.S.S.R.*), **14**, 1038–43 (1944).
4. Petrov, A. A., *J. Gen. Chem.* (*U.S.S.R.*), **16**, 1206–12 (1946).
5. Boyd, D. R., and Marle, E. R., *J. Chem. Soc.*, **105**, 2117 (1914).
6. Boyd, D. R., and Thomas, D. F., *J. Chem. Soc.*, **115**, 1239 (1919).
7. Sexton, A. R., and Britton, E. C., *J. Am. Chem. Soc.*, **70**, 3606 (1948).
8. Cox, H. L., Nelson, W. L., and Cretcher, L. H., *J. Am. Chem. Soc.*, **49**, 1080 (1927).
9. Dewael, A., *Bull. soc. chim. Belg.*, **39**, 395 (1930).
10. Schmidt, O., and Meyer, E. (to I. G. Farbenindustrie A.-G.), U. S. Patent 1,922,459 (Aug. 15, 1933).
11. Davidson, J. G., *Ind. Eng. Chem.*, **18**, 670 (1926).
12. Evans, T. W., and Edlund, K. R., *Ind. Eng. Chem.*, **28**, 1186–8 (1936).
13. Hurd, C. D., and Perletz, P., *J. Am. Chem. Soc.*, **68**, 38–40 (1946).
14. Butler, C. L., Renfrew, A. G., and Clapp, M., *J. Am. Chem. Soc.*, **60**, 1472–3 (1938).
15. Bruson, H. A. (to The Resinous Products & Chemical Co.), U. S. Patent 2,383,443 (Aug. 28, 1945).
16. Gilta, G., *Bull. soc. chim. Belg.*, **31**, 245–53 (1922).
17. Green, N., and Green, M. W., *J. Am. Chem. Soc.*, **66**, 1610–1 (1944).
18. Binkley, S. B., and Hamilton, C. S., *J. Am. Chem. Soc.*, **60**, 134–5 (1938).
19. "Dowanols," Midland, Michigan, The Dow Chemical Company, 1949.
20. Jordon, O. (to I. G. Farbenindustrie A.-G.), U. S. Patent 1,865,191 (June 28, 1932).
21. Fife, H. R. (to Carbide and Carbon Chemicals Corp.), U. S. Patent 2,169,231 Aug. 15, 1939).

22. *J. Investigative Dermatol.*, **10,** 399 (1948).
23. Zimmer, J. C., and Duncan, G. W. (to Standard Oil Development Co.), U. S. Patent 2,447,607 (Aug. 24, 1948).
24. Vernon, C. C. (to University of Louisville), U. S. Patent 2,140,824 (Dec. 20, 1938).
25. MacMullen, C. W. (to Rohm & Haas Co.), U. S. Patent 2,416,263 (Feb. 18, 1947).
26. Wilkes, B. G. (to Carbide and Carbon Chemicals Corp.), U. S. Patent 2,407,205 (Sept. 3, 1946).
27. Sexton, A. R., and Britton, E. C. (to The Dow Chemical Co.), U. S. Patent 2,500,011 (March 7, 1950).
28. Fritz, J. H. (to National Oil Products Co.), U. S. Patent 2,390,212 (Dec. 4, 1945).
29. Woodhouse, J. C., and Walker, K. E. (to E. I. du Pont de Nemours & Co.), U. S. Patent 2,305,228 (Dec. 15, 1942).
30. Weber, A. G. (to E. I. du Pont de Nemours & Co.), U. S. Patent 2,249,800 (July 22, 1941).
31. Coleman, G. H., and Moore, G. V. (to The Dow Chemical Co.), U. S. Patents 2,115,905 (May 3, 1938) and 2,021,852 (Nov. 19, 1935).
32. Pukirev, A. G., *Trans. Inst. Pure Chem. Reagents* (*U.S.S.R.*), **15,** 45–50 (1937).
33. Fraenkel-Conrat, H. L., and Olcott, H. S., *J. Am. Chem. Soc.*, **66,** 1420–1 (1944).
34. Schuette, H., and Wittwer, M. (to I. G. Farbenindustrie A.-G.), U. S. Patent 2,174,760 (Oct. 3, 1939).
35. Gresham, W. F. (to E. I. du Pont de Nemours & Co.), U. S. Patent 2,497,408 (Feb. 14, 1950).
36. Goldsmith, H. A., *Chem. Revs.*, **33,** 257–349 (1943).
37. Ellis, C., "The Chemistry of Petroleum Derivatives," Vol. **I,** p. 518, New York, The Chemical Catalog Co., Inc. (Reinhold Publishing Corp.), 1934; Vol. **II,** p. 539, 1937.
38. Heim, H. C., and Poe, C. F., *J. Org. Chem.*, **9,** 299–301 (1944).
39. Jacquemain, R., and Devillers, G., *Compt. rend.*, **206,** 1305–7 (1938).
40. Edlund, H., and Price, C. C., *J. Am. Chem. Soc.*, **67,** 693 (1945).
41. Levene, P. A., and Haller, H. L., *J. Biol. Chem.* **67,** 329–32 (1926).
42. Levene, P. A., and Walti, A., *J. Biol. Chem.*, **68,** 415–24 (1926).
43. Carothers, W. H., Arvin, J. A., and Dorough, G. L., *J. Am. Chem. Soc.*, **52,** 3292 (1930).
44. Evdokimov, A. G., *Chem. Abstracts*, **33,** 3760 (1939).
45. Salmi, E. J., Merivuori, K., and Laaksonen, E., *Suomen Kemistilehti*, **19B,** 102–8 (1946); *Chem. Abstracts*, **41,** 5440 (1947).
46. Caldwell, J. R. (to Eastman Kodak Co.), U. S. Patent 2,484,487 (Oct. 11, 1949).
47. Henry, L., *Bull. acad. roy. méd. Belg.*, **445,** 535 (1902); *Chem. Zentr.*, **74,** II, 486 (1903).
48. Bartlett, E. P. (to E. I. du Pont de Nemours & Co.), U. S. Patent 2,405,936 (Aug. 20, 1946).
49. Abderhalden, E., and Eichwald, E., *Ber.*, **51,** 1312–22 (1918).
50. Meyer, L. W. A. (to Eastman Kodak Co.), U. S. Patent 2,231,729 (Feb. 11, 1941).
51. Dupire, A., *Compt. rend.*, **214,** 82–4 (1942).
52. Dupire, A., *Compt. rend.*, **202,** 2086–7 (1936).
53. Rippere, R. E., and La Mer, V. K., *J. Phys. Chem.*, **47,** 204–34 (1943).
54. Steinmig, G., and Wittwer, M. (to I. G. Farbenindustrie A.-G.), U. S. Patent 1,907,891 (May 9, 1933).
55. Bertoni, G., *Gazz. chim. ital.*, **16,** 519 (1886).
56. Henry, L., *Ann. chim. et. phys.*, (4) **27,** 261 (1872); *Ber.*, **4,** 602 (1871).

272 GLYCOLS

57. Woodhouse, J. C., and Weber, A. G. (to E. I. du Pont de Nemours & Co.), U. S. Patents 2,102,825 (Dec. 21, 1937); 2,205,183 (June 18, 1940); and 2,232,581 (Feb. 18, 1941).
58. Wagner Electric Corp., German Patent 661,738 (June 25, 1938).
59. Fife, H. R. (to Carbide and Carbon Chemicals Corp.), U. S. Patents 2,200,494 (May 14, 1940) and 2,255,208 (Sept. 9, 1941).
60. Smith, W. P. (to Automotive Products Co.), British Patent 539,560 (Sept. 16, 1941).
61. Presslie, R., *Pharm. J.*, **157,** 185–6 (1946).
62. Fiero, G. W., and Dutcher, M. W., *J. Am. Pharm. Assoc., Sci. Ed.*, **34,** 56–9 (1945).
63. Bird, J. C., *J. Am. Pharm. Assoc., Sci. Ed.*, **26,** 475–9 (1937).
64. Goldsmith, H. A., *Chem. Inds.*, **52,** 326–8 (1943).
65. Goldsmith, H. A. (to H. Bennett), U. S. Patent 2,269,529 (Jan. 13, 1942).
66. Guest, H. H. (to The J. B. Williams Co.), U. S. Patent 2,435,829 (Feb. 10, 1948).
67. Sullivan, W. N., and Goodhue, L. D. (to the United States of America), U. S. Patent 2,345,892 (April 4, 1944).
68. Kaplan, S. (to Onyx Oil & Chemical Co.), U. S. Patent 2,410,382 (Oct. 29, 1946).
69. Cahn, F. J., and Harris, B. R. (to The Emulsol Corp.), U. S. Patents 2,236,516–7 (April 1, 1941).
70. Linduska, J. P., Cochran, J. H., and Morton, F. A., *J. Econ. Entomol.*, **39,** 767–9 (1946).
71. Steiner, A. B. (to Kelco Co.), U. S. Patent 2,426,125 (Aug. 19, 1947).
72. Steiner, A. B., and McNeely, W. H. (to Kelco Co.), U. S. Patents 2,463,824 (March 8, 1949) and 2,494,912 (Jan. 17, 1950).
73. Steiner, A. B., and Sperry, G. D. (to Kelco Co.), U. S. Patent 2,485,935 (Oct. 25, 1949).
74. Wallerstein, J. S., Schade, A. L., and Levy, H. B. (to Wallerstein Co.), U. S. Patent 2,478,988 (Aug. 16, 1949).
75. Haubrich, L. R., and Haubrich, W. R., *J. Am. Vet. Med. Assoc.*, **108,** 169–71 (1946).
76. Lambou, M. G., King, G. S., and Condon, M. Z., *Science*, **108,** 563 (1948).
77. Arenson, S. W. (to Doughnut Corp. of America), U. S. Patent 2,446,505 (Aug. 3, 1948).
78. Bereston, J., *J. Investigative Dermatol.*, **8,** 227 (1947).
79. Chitwood, H. C. (to Carbide and Carbon Chemicals Corp.), U. S. Patent 2,251,983 (Aug. 12, 1941).
80. Muskat, I. E., and/or Strain, F. (to Pittsburgh Plate Glass Co.), U. S. Patents 2,403,113 (July 2, 1946); 2,399,287 and 2,399,285 (Apr. 30, 1946); 2,397,630 (Apr. 2, 1946); 2,392,621 (Jan. 8, 1946); 2,385,934 (Oct. 2, 1945); 2,384,115 (Sept. 4, 1945); 2,379,250 (June 26, 1945); and 2,370,572 (Feb. 27, 1945).
81. Kuever, R. A. and Wheeler, L. M. (to the State of Iowa), U. S. Patent 2,414,650 (Jan. 21, 1947).
82. Hanzlik, P. J. (to Board of Trustees of Leland Stanford, Jr., University), U. S. Patent 2,125,561 (Aug. 2, 1938).
83. Hanzlik, P..J., Lehman, A. J., and Richardson, A. P., *Am. J. Syphilis, Gonorrhea, Venereal Diseases*, **21,** 1 (1937).
84. Ruben, S., U. S. Patent 2,070,240 (Feb. 9, 1937).
85. Jackson, D. R. (to Wyandotte Chemicals Corp.), U. S. Patent 2,486,416 (Nov. 1, 1949).
86. Barab, J. (to The Commercial Research Corp.), U. S. Patent 1,371,215 (March 15, 1921).

87. Buckley, J. R. (to E. I. du Pont de Nemours & Co.), U. S. Patent 1,869,660 (Aug. 2, 1932).

88. Newman, M. S., Magerlein, B. J., and Wheatley, W. B., *J. Am. Chem. Soc.*, **68,** 2112 (1946).

89 Trillat, A., and Cambier, R., *Compt. rend.*, **118,** 1277 (1894).

90. Seymour, G. W. (to Celanese Corp. of America), U. S. Patent 2,031,619 (Feb. 25, 1936).

91. Gresham, W. F. (to E. I. du Pont de Nemours & Co.), U. S. Patent 2,377,878 (June 12, 1945).

CHAPTER 13

PROPYLENE GLYCOL CONDENSATION POLYMERS

R. F. HOLDEN

Condensation polymers of propylene glycol have the general formula $HO(C_3H_6O)_nC_3H_6OH$. They are discussed here under the headings dipropylene glycol (where $n = 1$) and polypropylene glycols (where $n = 2,3,4,\ldots$). A discussion of the closely related mixed polyethylene-polypropylene glycols follows.

Dipropylene Glycol

Three structural isomers of dipropylene glycol, corresponding to the structural formulas below, are possible:

$$\begin{array}{cc} CH_3 & CH_3 \\ | & | \\ HOCH_2CH-O-CHCH_2OH \end{array}$$

$$\begin{array}{cc} CH_3 & CH_3 \\ | & | \\ HOCH_2CH-O-CH_2-CHOH \end{array}$$

$$\begin{array}{cc} CH_3 & CH_3 \\ | & | \\ HOCH-CH_2-O-CH_2CHOH \end{array}$$

However, no data that describe or identify the separate compounds are available in the literature. Levene and Walti[1] prepared dipropylene glycol by the condensation of propylene oxide and propylene glycol, but it is believed, in the light of further studies on propylene oxide alcoholysis, that the products obtained were mixtures of isomers since acid catalysis was used in their preparation[2, 3].

Properties. Dipropylene glycol is similar to the other glycols in general characteristics. It has, however, a greater solvency for certain organic materials such as castor oil than do the other glycols. The physical constants of commercial dipropylene glycol are summarized in Table 13.1. No information is available on the ratio of isomers contained in this material.

Chemically, dipropylene glycol undergoes reactions typical of hydroxyl bearing compounds. A number of ester and ether derivatives of this glycol are known.

The diacetate of dipropylene glycol (b.p. at 761 mm. 248°C., sp. gr. at 20/4°C. 1.050) was prepared by Dewael[4]. The dipropionate and diisobutyr-

TABLE 13.1. PHYSICAL PROPERTIES OF COMMERCIAL DIPROPYLENE GLYCOL

Boiling point at 760 mm.	231.8°C.
at 50 mm.	151°C.
at 10 mm.	114°C.
Δb.p./Δp	0.050°C./mm.
Coefficient of expansion at 20°C.	0.00073/°C.
at 55°C.	0.00075/°C.
Flash point (open cup)	280°F.
Heat of vaporization at 1 atm.	308 Btu/lb.
Molecular weight	134.17
Refractive index, n_D at 20°C.	1.4440
Solubility in water	complete
Specific gravity (apparent) at 20/20°C.	1.0252
ΔSp.gr./Δt	0.00075
Specific heat at 25°C.	0.650 cal./g./°C.
Vapor pressure at 20°C.	<0.01 mm.
Viscosity (absolute) at 20°C.	107 cps.

ate esters have been suggested as plasticizers for cellulose derivatives[5, 6]. The dinitrate is useful in accelerating the ignition of diesel fuels[7]. The monosalicylate has been suggested as an ultraviolet absorber for use in cosmetics and paints[8]. The ricinoleic ester (obtained by transesterification from castor oil) has been proposed as a base for hydraulic fluid formulations[9, 10].

The preparation of unsaturated diesters from dipropylene glycol through the intermediate chloroformates has been described in the patents of Muskat and Strain[11]. The unsaturated esters thus obtained may be polymerized to resins useful in coating paper, cloth, and metals, or as molding compositions[12].

The properties of a series of commercial-grade monoalkyl ethers of dipropylene glycol are given in Table 13.2[13]. These materials are suggested as solvents and coupling agents for general use[8]. Vehicles for wood-graining inks may be prepared by reacting the monoethyl ether with maleic anhydride and drying oil[14]. This ether is also useful as an intermediate in the preparation of anthraquinone acetate dyestuffs[15].

Nichols and Yanovsky[16] prepared the diallyl ether of dipropylene glycol using allyl bromide in a modified Williamson reaction. Physical constants reported for the diallyl ether were: b.p. at 1 mm. 75–77°C., sp. gr. at 20/4°C. 0.9093, n_D^{20} 1.4380. The polymerization of this ether was also studied.

Linduska, Cochran, and Morton[17] found that the monocyclohexyl ether of dipropylene glycol was an effective flea repellent on cotton-twill cloth. The dipropylene glycol ether of 2-methyl-2,4-pentanediol has also been suggested as an insect repellent[18].

TABLE 13.2. Physical Properties of Commercial Dipropylene Glycol Monoethers

	Dipropylene Glycol Monoether		
	Methyl	Ethyl	Butyl
Boiling point, °C.. at 760 mm.	190	197.8	228.9
at 10 mm.	76.1	81.7	105.0
Fire point (open cup), °F.*	182	200	245
Flash point (open cup), °F.*	182	195	235
Molecular weight	148.2	162.2	190.3
Pour point, °F.	−117	−141	−116
Refractive index, n_D at 25°C.	1.419	1.419	1.425
Solubility in water at 25°C., g./100 g. water	∞	∞	4.3
Specific gravity at 25/25°C.	0.950	0.930	0.913
Specific heat at 25°C.	0.59	0.59	0.59
Surface tension at 25°C., dynes/cm.	28.8	27.7	28.2
Vapor pressure at 25°C., mm.	0.4	0.3	0.06
Viscosity at 25°C., cps.	3.33	1.06	1.33
Weight per gallon at 25°C., lbs.	7.94	7.75	7.62

* ASTM—D92-46.

Applications. Dipropylene glycol itself has found application in several fields. It has been used in printing ink formulations[19], particularly as a water-miscible solvent in the "steam-setting" types of printing ink[20, 21, 22].

A mixture of 65 per cent dipropylene glycol and 35 per cent ethylene glycol is used in the solvent extraction of aromatic hydrocarbons from a hydrocarbon mixture. Dipropylene glycol acts as the "primary" solvent in this process[23].

Dipropylene glycol compositions with diethylene glycol are useful as low freezing-point fluids for heat or pressure transmission[24]. The glycol is also useful as a high-temperature reaction medium in the decarboxylation of quinolinic acid to nicotinic acid[25].

Dipropylene glycol vapor exhibited a high degree of germicidal activity when tested by Robertson, Puck, Lemon, and Loosli[26, 27], illustrating its possibilities as an air treatment agent. Under laboratory conditions the minimum vapor concentration necessary to kill 95 per cent of airborne *Staphylococcus albus* within ten minutes was found to be 0.027 mg./l. at 72°F. and a relative humidity of 28 per cent as compared with 0.006 mg./l. for triethylene glycol (see also page 171).

Dipropylene glycol, in conjunction with small amounts of isopropanol, has been proposed as a safe, powerful vapor germicide in liquefied-gas aerosol formulations[28].

Polypropylene Glycols

Polypropylene glycols are more oil soluble and less hygroscopic than the comparable polyethylene glycols. Two series of polypropylene glycols available commercially from Carbide and Dow are designated by numbers that approximate their average molecular weights.

Preparation. The polymerization of propylene oxide has received considerable attention, as evidenced by the extensive patent literature. The earliest reported polymerization was that of Levene and Walti[1], who heated propylene oxide in a sealed tube for several weeks at 165°C. and obtained a mixture of various polyethers and small amounts of dimethyldioxane (believed to be the 2,6-isomer). However, two-thirds of the starting material was recovered unchanged. The same investigators heated propylene oxide with propylene glycol in a sealed tube at 117°C. for 12 days and isolated both dipropylene glycol and tripropylene glycol from the reaction mixture.

The dimethyl-1,4-dioxanes, which may be considered the simplest ethers of propylene glycol, are prepared by heating the glycol with dehydration catalysts such as sulfuric acid or phosphoric acid[29, 30, 31]. The "dimethyl-dioxane" thus obtained is reported to boil at 115–117°C. at 745 mm. pressure and probably consists of a mixture of at least two structural isomers:

2,6-Dimethyl-1,4-dioxane   2,5-Dimethyl-1,4-dioxane

No data have been reported in the literature on the properties of the pure 2,5-dimethyl isomer. Pure 2,6-dimethyl-1,4-dioxane (b.p. 120–121°C., sp. gr. at 20/4°C. 0.9244, and n_D^{20} 1.4169) has, however, been prepared with allyl ether and mercuric acetate as starting materials[32].

Other cyclic ethers have been prepared by treating dry propylene oxide with a boron trifluoride catalyst (see Table 13.3). The reaction was strongly exothermic at the boiling point of the reaction mixture, with intermittent addition of boron trifluoride etherate. After careful rectification, the fractions showed very low hydroxyl content upon analysis by acetylation. Only monocyclic structures seem consistent with the properties of the products and the method of preparation. The dimer appeared to differ from those previously reported. The tetramer was produced in largest yield and contained by analysis 61.9 per cent carbon and 10.0 per cent hydrogen compared to theoretical values of 62.0 per cent and 10.4 per cent,

TABLE 13.3. PROPERTIES OF CYCLIC PROPYLENE OXIDE POLYMERS

	Dimer	Trimer[a]	Tetramer	Pentamer	Hexamer
Boiling range at 5 mm., °C.	122–125 (760)	53–58	104–104.8	134–138	155
Refractive index, n_D at 30.5°C.	1.4135	1.4240	1.4431	1.4425	1.4389
Specific gravity at 30.5/20°C.	0.936	0.978	0.991	0.993	0.993
Molecular refraction					
Found	31.0	41.8	62.2	77.5	92.3
Calculated	31.0	42.2	62.0	77.5	93.0
Molecular weight					
By Menzies-Wright	116[b]	—	234	286	315
Calculated	116	—	232	290	348
Hydroxyl equivalents per 100 grams	0.024	0.42	0.002	—	0.16

[a] Contained 16 per cent glycol as proplyene glycol; [b] by freezing point depression of benzene.

respectively. Range finding tests indicated it to be similar to propylene oxide in toxicity (see page 321).

Staudinger[33] mentions the polymerization of propylene oxide by means of a tin tetrachloride catalyst. Liquid polymers of relatively low molecular weight resulted, although a semi-solid substance of higher molecular weight was isolated by fractionation methods.

A series of patents assigned to I. G. Farbenindustrie A.-G., concerned with the polymerization of propylene oxide, were issued during the period 1930–1935[34, 35, 36, 37]. Two general methods are described. In the first, propylene oxide vapors are passed over alkaline catalysts such as potassium hydroxide at temperatures of 40 to 60°C. or over acid catalysts such as acid phosphates and sodium bisulfate at temperatures usually between 100 and 160°C. Acid catalysts are particularly useful when 2,5-dimethyldioxane is the desired product. The second general method employs similar catalysts and temperatures, but differs in that an inert solvent is used. A wide variety of such solvents is disclosed, ranging from aromatic hydrocarbons and chlorinated compounds to various esters, ethers, and similar materials which contain no hydroxyl or other group capable of reaction with the epoxide ring. In one instance, polymers of propylene oxide are used as diluents, and if these are in a low stage of polymerization, further polymerization occurs so as to produce a homogeneous product. The polymers thus produced are usually described as viscous liquids.

A later patent[38] describes the preparation of polypropylene glycols having a specific viscosity in benzene solution (4 per cent) of between 0.083 and

0.138. Such products are prepared by polymerizing propylene oxide in water with sodium hydroxide catalyst at 100°C. in a closed system until a pressure drop to atmospheric is attained.

For further details on the production of polyalkylene glycols, see Chapter 7, "Ethylene Glycol Condensation Polymers."

Properties. Physical properties of commercial polypropylene glycols are listed in Table 13.4. They are colorless to light yellow, nonvolatile, viscous liquids. The lower molecular weight compounds are completely soluble in water; the higher molecular weight compounds are only slightly soluble in water. Because of their higher carbon-to-oxygen ratios, they are more widely compatible with vegetable oils and natural waxes and resins than

TABLE 13.4. PHYSICAL PROPERTIES OF SOME COMMERCIAL POLYPROPYLENE GLYCOLS

	Polypropylene Glycol					
	150	425	750[a]	1025	1200[b]	2025
Average molecular weight	140–160	400–450	750	975–1075	1200	1950–2100
Specific gravity, 20/20°C.	1.02	1.0103	1.004[c]	1.0072	1.003[c]	1.0055
Freezing point, °C.[d]	—	−60	—	−50	—	−45
Solubility in water at 20°C., % by wt.	∞	∞	15.25[e]	1.5	1.96[e]	0.15
Viscosity at 210°F., centistokes	—	4.2	7.62	10.94	12.70	23.9
Flash point (open cup), °F.	320	385	>440	455	>440	450

[a] Sold as Polyglycol P750; [b] sold as Polyglycol P1200; [c] at 25/25°C.; [d] sets to a glass below this temperature; [e] at 25°C.

the polyethylene glycols. They are completely soluble in aliphatic ketones, alcohols, esters, glycol ethers, most chlorinated solvents, phthalic ester plasticizers, and a large number of hydrocarbons.

The terminal hydroxyl groups of the polypropylene glycols can be esterified, and with dibasic acids the reaction products are resins of the alkyd type. The dinitrates are effective in decreasing the ignition time of diesel fuels, thus increasing the cetane number. When esterified with only one molecule of a fatty acid, the polypropylene glycols form emulsifying agents that are not affected by hard water. These esters are useful as petroleum emulsion breakers and as emulsifiers in insecticidal preparations.

Ethers of polypropylene glycols have been described by Fife and Roberts[39, 40]. These products are water insoluble and are used as lubricants and hydraulic fluids (see also "Mixed Polyethylene-Polypropylene Glycols," page 280). Two butoxy polypropylene glycols of 400 and 800 average molecular weights are considered to be promising fly repellents for use on livestock[41].

Ether-esters of the polypropylene glycols, the butoxy polypropylene glycol stearates in particular, are useful as lubricants for the production of metal foil[42].

Applications. The polypropylene glycols themselves are useful in hydraulic fluids and automobile radiator compounds. They are utilized as mold lubricants for rubber, antidusting agents for powdered dyestuffs, and antifoaming agents for ceramic glaze solutions[43].

Mixed Polyethylene-Polypropylene Glycols

Mixed polyethylene-polypropylene glycols[34, 35, 36, 37] and their derivatives have been described in the literature[44, 45, 46]. Such mixtures are sold commercially under the trade-marks "Ucon" and "Prestone" as lubricants for industrial and automotive use. The products have molecular weights as high as 13,000 to 15,000 and vary from mobile to highly viscous liquids. They are available in both water-soluble and water-insoluble forms.

Preparation. Roberts and Fife[47] declare that aldehyde-free ethylene oxide and propylene oxide may be added to aliphatic monohydric alcohols at substantially anhydrous conditions at 80 to 160°C. and a pressure of 5 to 50 psi to prepare a mixed oxyethylene-oxypropylene polymer derivative. These same products may be converted to esters and diethers which are useful lubricants and show improved viscosity-temperature relations[48, 49]. Toussaint and Fife[50] claim a polymeric substance of oxyethylene and oxypropylene glycols in which ethylene oxide and propylene oxide are combined therein as oxyalkylene groups. These products may be converted to esters[51].

Applications. These polymeric mixtures and similar polypropylene glycol derivatives resist the formation of sludge and carbon deposition when applied as lubricants for internal combustion engines, industrial machinery, calenders and mills for resins and rubber, electric motors, and refrigerating equipment[52]. Because they have high viscosity indexes and possess extremely low pour points, they may be employed for sub-zero temperature applications. They are utilized as lubricants in forming various metals into rods, sheets, bars, metal foil, and certain types of wire. These materials have low solvent power for most synthetic and natural rubber compositions, and therefore may be used for lubricating rubber and rubber-metal combinations. They are also useful for lubricating textile fibers and as industrial hydraulic fluids. Other uses include: defoaming of aqueous and nonaqueous liquids; demulsifying of water-hydrocarbon mixtures; softening of paper, textiles, and leather; plasticizing nitrocellulose coatings; and preparing hair dressings. Detergent applications of the mixed poly-

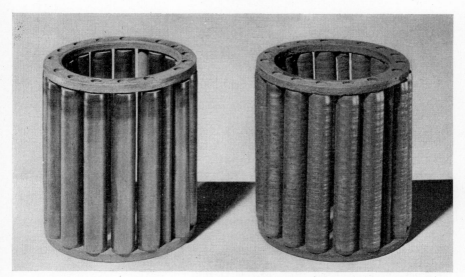

Courtesy of Carbide and Carbon Chemicals Company

FIGURE 13.1. Kiln car wheel bearings lubricated (right) with conventional oil and graphite and (left) with mixed polyethylene-polypropylene glycols and their derivatives.

ethylene-polypropylene glycol derivatives have been discussed by Mc-Cutcheon[53] and by Schwartz and Perry[54].

Literature Cited

1. Levene, P. A., and Walti, A., *J. Biol. Chem.*, **75,** 325–36 (1927).
2. Chitwood, H. C., and Freure, B. T., *J. Am. Chem. Soc.*, **68,** 680–2 (1946).
3. Petrov, A. A., *J. Gen. Chem.* (*U.S.S.R.*), **14,** 1038–43 (1944).
4. Dewael, A., *Bull. soc. chim. Belg.*, **39,** 395 (1930).
5. Holt, H. S., (to E. I. du Pont de Nemours & Co.), U. S. Patent 2,031,603 (Feb. 25, 1936).
6. Izard, E. F. (to Dupont Viscoloid Co.), U. S. Patent 2,014,381 (Sept. 17, 1935).
7. Curme, G. O., Jr. (to Carbide and Carbon Chemicals Corp.), U. S. Patent 2,378,466 (June 19, 1945).
8. *Chem. Inds.*, **61,** 447 (1947).
9. Woodhouse, J. C., and Weber, A. G. (to E. I. du Pont de Nemours & Co.), U. S. Patent 2,102,825 (Dec. 21, 1937).
10. Fife, H. R. (to Carbide and Carbon Chemicals Corp.), U. S. Patents 2,200,494 (May 14, 1940) and 2,255,208 (Sept. 9, 1941).
11. Muskat, I. E., and Strain, F. (to Pittsburgh Plate Glass Co.), U. S. Patents 2,384,125 (Sept. 4, 1945); 2,370,568 (Feb. 27, 1945); and 2,399,286 (April 30, 1946).
12. Nichols, P. L., Jr., Hamilton, R. M., Smith, L. T., and Yanovsky, E., *Paint Ind. Mag.*, **60,** 84 (1945).
13. "Dowanols," Midland, Michigan, The Dow Chemical Co., 1949.
14. Swain, R. A. (to Interchemical Corp.), U. S. Patent 2,365,363 (Dec. 19, 1944).

282 GLYCOLS

15. Slinger, F. H. (to Imperial Chemical Industries, Ltd.), British Patent 571,663 (Sept. 4, 1945).
16. Nichols, P. L., Jr., and Yanovsky, E., *J. Am. Chem. Soc.*, **67,** 46–9 (1945).
17. Linduska, J. P., Cochran, J. H., and Morton, F. A., *J. Econ. Entomol.*, **39,** 767–9 (1946).
18. Wilkes, B. G. (to Carbide and Carbon Chemicals Corp.), U. S. Patent 2,407,205 (Sept. 3, 1946).
19. Kline, B. L. (to The Western Union Telegraph Co.), U. S. Patent 2,375,230 (May 8, 1945).
20. Jeuck, F. J., and Rietz, C. A. (to Interchemical Corp.), U. S. Patent 2,390,102 (Dec. 4, 1945).
21. Lee, E. D. (to Interchemical Corp.), U. S. Patent 2,415,827 (Feb. 18, 1947).
22. Denton, R. A. (to Sun Chemical Corp.), U. S. Patent 2,436,954 (May 2, 1948).
23. Smith, A. S. (to Blaw-Knox Co.), U. S. Patent 2,444,582 (July 6, 1948).
24. Cox, H. L. (to Carbide and Carbon Chemicals Corp.), U. S. Patent 2,003,429 (June 4, 1935).
25. Lee, J., and Heineman, S. D. (to Hoffman-LaRoche, Inc.), U. S. Patent 2,389,065 (Nov. 13, 1945).
26. Robertson, O. H., Puck, T. T., Lemon, H. F., and Loosli, C. G., *Science*, **97,** 142–4 (1943).
27. Puck, T. T., *J. Exptl. Med.*, **85,** 743 (1947).
28. Fulton, J. D., Nichols, M. E., Woehler, J., Shrewsbury, C. L., Goodhue, L. D., and Wilkins, P., *Soap Sanit. Chemicals*, **24** (5), 125 (1948).
29. Jordan, O. (to I. G. Farbenindustrie A.-G.), U. S. Patent 1,919,727 (July 25, 1933).
30. Steimmig, G., and Hambsch, O. (to I. G. Farbenindustrie A.-G.), U. S. Patent 1,939,189 (Dec. 12, 1933).
31. I. G. Farbenindustrie A.-G., German Patent 516,844 (Dec. 28, 1927).
32. Nesmeyanov, A. N., and Lutsenko, I. F., *Bull. acad. sci. U.R.S.S., Classe sci. chim.*, **1943,** 296–304.
33. Staudinger, H., "Die Hochmolekularen Organischen Verbindungen, Kautschuk und Cellulose," p. 294, Berlin, J. Springer, 1932.
34. I. G. Farbenindustrie A.-G., British Patents 346,550 (March 20,1930) and 406,443 (March 1, 1934); French Patent 750,520 (Aug. 11, 1933); and German Patents 613,261 (May 15, 1935) and 616,428 (July 27, 1935).
35. Webel, F. (to I. G. Farbenindustrie A.-G.), U. S. Patent 1,921,378 (Aug. 8, 1933).
36. Winkler, F., Haeuber, H., and Feiler, P. (to I. G. Farbenindustrie A.-G.), U. S. Patent 1,922,918 (Aug. 15, 1933).
37. Wittwer, M. (to I. G. Farbenindustrie A.-G.), U. S. Patent 1,976,678 (Oct. 9, 1934).
38. Schlosser, P. H., and Gray, K. R. (to Rayonier, Inc.), U. S. Patent 2,362,217 (Nov. 7, 1944).
39. Fife, H. R., and Roberts, F. H. (to Carbide and Carbon Chemicals Corp.), U. S. Patent 2,448,664 (Sept. 7, 1948).
40. Roberts, F. H., and Fife, H. R. (to Union Carbide and Carbon Corp.), U. S. Patent 2,520,612 (Aug. 29, 1950).
41. Granett, P., Haynes, H. L., Connola, D. P., Bowery, T. G., and Barber, G. W., *J. Econ. Entomol.*, **42,** 281–6 (1949).
42. Fife, H. R. (to Carbide and Carbon Chemicals Corp.), British Patent 606,407 (Feb. 6, 1945).
43. "Dow Polypropylene Glycols," Midland, Michigan, The Dow Chemical Co., 1950.

44. Kratzer, J. C., Green, D. H., and Williams, D. B., *Petroleum Refiner*, **25** (2), 79–90 (1946).

45. Russ, J. M., Jr., *Lubrication Eng.*, **2**, 151–7 (1946).

46. Millett, W. H., *Iron Steel Engr.*, **25** (8), 51 (1948).

47. Roberts, F. H., and Fife, H. R. (to Carbide and Carbon Chemicals Corp.), U. S. Patent 2,425,755 (Aug. 19, 1947).

48. Fife, H. R., and Roberts, F. H. (to Carbide and Carbon Chemicals Corp.), U. S. Patent 2,480,185 (Aug. 30, 1949).

49. Roberts, F. H., and Fife, H. R. (to Union Carbide and Carbon Corp.), U. S. Patent 2,520,611 (Aug. 29, 1950).

50. Toussaint, W. J., and Fife, H. R. (to Carbide and Carbon Chemicals Corp.), U. S. Patent 2,425,845 (Aug. 19, 1947).

51. Fife, H. R., and Toussaint, W. J. (to Carbide and Carbon Chemicals Corp.), U. S. Patent 2,457,139 (Dec. 28, 1948).

52. " 'Ucon' Brand Fluids and Lubricants," New York, Carbide and Carbon Chemicals Corp., 1949.

53. McCutcheon, J. W., *Soap Sanit. Chemicals*, **25** (8, 9, 10), 33, 42, 40 (1949).

54. Schwartz, A. M., and Perry, J. W., "Surface Active Agents," New York, Interscience Publishers, Inc., 1949.

CHAPTER 14

HIGHER GLYCOLS

S. M. LIVENGOOD

A large number of glycols containing four or more carbon atoms have been reported in the literature. Of these, 2-methyl-2,4-pentanediol, 2-ethyl-1,3-hexanediol, 1,3-butanediol, and 2,3-butanediol are produced commercially. 1,4-Butanediol, 2-butene-1,4-diol, and 2-butyne-1,4-diol have also been produced on commercial or semi-commercial sales and, if a demand arose, could be produced in substantial quantities with existing knowledge. These latter glycols were utilized during World War II in Germany as chemical raw materials for conversion into such essentials as butadiene and polyurethanes, useful as polyamide resin replacements.

Among the other diols which have been manufactured in small commercial amounts are: 1,5-pentanediol; 2,4-pentanediol; 2-methyl-1,3-pentanediol; 1,6-hexanediol; 2,5-hexanediol; 2,4-heptanediol; 2,2-diethyl-1,3-propane-diol; and 2-ethyl-2-butyl-1,3-propanediol. Large-scale uses for these compounds, however, have not as yet been established. 2,3-Dimethyl-2,3-butanediol (pinacol) was important during World War I as an intermediate in the production of synthetic rubber. Physical properties for all these higher glycols are listed in Table 1.1, Chapter 1. Their reactions are, in general, those typical of aliphatic glycols.

2-Methyl-2,4-pentanediol

2-Methyl-2,4-pentanediol is a mild-odored liquid that is soluble in water, alcohol, ether, and aromatic and aliphatic hydrocarbons. Its physical properties are listed in Table 14.1. This diol was first prepared in 1901 by Zelinsky and Zelikow[1], who reduced diacetone alcohol with sodium amalgam under an atmosphere of carbon dioxide, and by Franke[2], who reduced an aqueous solution of the same compound in the presence of aluminum amalgam.

2-Methyl-2,4-pentanediol is produced commercially by the liquid-phase hydrogenation of diacetone alcohol with conventional hydrogenation catalysts. The major producers are Carbide and Shell Chemical Corporation.

A series of mono- and diesters of 2-methyl-2,4-pentanediol have been prepared by Tryon[3]. He made the monoesters of acetic, propionic, and butyric acids by reacting the diol with the corresponding anhydrides, and the diesters of acetic, propionic, isobutyric, benzoic, and stearic acids by reacting the diol with the corresponding acid chlorides.

TABLE 14.1. Physical Properties of Commercial 2-Methyl-2,4-pentanediol

Boiling point at 760 mm.	197.1°C.
at 50 mm.	125°C.
at 10 mm.	94°C.
Δb.p./Δp, 740 to 760 mm.	0.043°C./mm.
Coefficient of expansion at 20°C.	0.00078
Flash point (Cleveland open cup)	215°F.
Freezing point	sets to a glass below -50°C.
Heat of vaporization at 1 atm.	208 Btu/lb.
Molecular weight	118.17
Refractive index, n_D at 20°C.	1.4263
Solubility in water at 20°C.	∞
Solubility of water in, at 20°C.	∞
Specific gravity (apparent) at 20/20°C.	0.9234
Δsp.gr./Δt	0.00072
Vapor pressure at 20°C.	0.05 mm.
Viscosity (absolute) at 20°C.	34.4 cps.

Pines and Ipatieff[4] condensed 2-methyl-2,4-pentanediol with propylene under 10 to 100 atmospheres pressure at 150 to 275°C. to form 1,3,5-trimethylcyclohexene, which was subsequently hydrogenated to the alkyl substituted cyclohexane. Employing a ferric chloride catalyst under similar conditions, they also obtained 1,3,5-trimethylcyclohexane by the reaction of 2-methyl-2,4-pentanediol with propanol[5].

2-Methyl-2,4-pentanediol has been used as a starting material in the synthesis of 2,4-dimethylsulfolane. The diol is dehydrated to 2-methyl-1,3-pentadiene[6], which is then reacted with sulfur dioxide to form 2,4-dimethyl-3-sulfolene[7]. The latter compound is then hydrogenated to 2,4-dimethylsulfolane. This compound is effective as a non-corrosive selective solvent for liquid-vapor and liquid-liquid extraction processes employed in the petroleum industry[8]. It can be used to effect the separation of aromatics from paraffins, naphthenes, and olefins, to desulfurize petroleum fractions, and to refine vegetable oils.

2-Methyl-2,4-pentanediol is employed to advantage as a blending agent or mutual solvent in the compounding of certain hydraulic fluids[9]. It has been used in the formulation of dry cleaning soaps and emulsions[10], in detergent compositions for polishing glass surfaces[11], and as a penetrating and wetting agent in alkaline mercerizing baths[12]. It has been described as a good resin solvent for printing and duplicating inks[13, 14]. Scripture[15] demonstrated the efficacy of 2-methyl-2,4-pentanediol as a cement additive and gained its acceptance by the ASTM C-1 committee on cement[16]. Its function is to prevent the formation of coatings on the balls and mill lining and to break up previously formed linings of this kind.

The 1,3-isomer of 2-methyl-2,4-pentanediol has been prepared by the chemical[17, 18] and catalytic reduction of propionaldol. 2-Methyl-1,3-pentanediol is a water-white, viscous liquid, miscible in all proportions with methanol, ethanol, acetone, and benzene[19]. It has been offered in limited quantities by Celanese Corporation of America.

2-Ethyl-1,3-hexanediol

2-Ethyl-1,3-hexanediol is a colorless liquid soluble in alcohol and ether, but only slightly soluble in water. Its physical properties are listed in Table 14.2. It was first isolated in 1928 by Grignard and Fluchaire[20], who obtained 2-ethyl-1,3-hexanediol dibutyrate as a by-product of the con-

TABLE 14.2. PHYSICAL PROPERTIES OF COMMERCIAL 2-ETHYL-1,3-HEXANEDIOL

Boiling point at 760 mm.	244.2°C.
at 50 mm.	163°C.
at 10 mm.	129°C.
Δb.p./Δp, 740 to 760 mm.	0.49°C./mm.
Coefficient of expansion at 20°C.	0.00080
Flash point (Cleveland open cup)	265°F.
Freezing point	sets to a glass below −40°C.
Heat of vaporization at 1 atm.	184 Btu/lb.
Molecular weight	146.22
Refractive index, n_D at 20°C.	1.4511
$\Delta n_D/\Delta t$	0.00037
Solubility in water at 20°C.	4.2% by wt.
Solubility of water in, at 20°C.	11.7% by wt.
Specific gravity (apparent) at 20/20°C.	0.9422
ΔSp.gr./Δt	0.00074
Vapor pressure at 20°C.	<0.01 mm.
Viscosity (absolute) at 20°C.	323 cps.

densation of butyraldehyde with ethoxy magnesium iodide. By saponification of this diester, they obtained 2-ethyl-1,3-hexanediol in sufficient purity to establish its properties. In 1943 Kulpinski and Nord[21] recovered 2-ethyl-1,3-hexanediol by hydrolyzing its monobutyrate prepared by the reaction of butyraldehyde with magnesium aluminum butoxide. Carbide produces it commercially by the hydrogenation of butyraldol.

Bland, oily, complex esters are formed by reacting 2-ethyl-1,3-hexanediol and dibasic acids with either monobasic acids or monohydric alcohols. These reaction products are useful as low-temperature lubricants[22, 23] or as plasticizers for thermoplastic resins[24].

High purity 2-ethyl-1,3-hexanediol is considered one of the best compounds ever developed as an insect repellent[25, 26, 27, 28, 29]. It affords excellent protection from mosquitoes, black flies, gnats, chiggers, and other biting insects, and was widely used for this purpose during World War II.

Although usually applied as a liquid, it can be spread effectively when incorporated into a transparent soap stick[30].

2-Ethyl-1,3-hexanediol is used as a resin and dyestuff solvent for printing inks[13]. It serves as a plasticizer for nylon molding powders. It has been employed as an intermediate for alkyd resins in the formulation of fast-drying paints, as a starting material in the preparation of polyurethane resins for electrical coatings, and as a coupling agent in metal cleaners, industrial soaps, and dry-cleaning fluids.

1,3-Butanediol

1,3-Butanediol is a colorless liquid that is miscible with water and alcohol but only slightly soluble in ether. It finds application as a plasticizer, humectant, coupling agent, and component of printing inks. Physical constants for 1,3-butanediol are listed in Table 14.3.

TABLE 14.3. PHYSICAL PROPERTIES OF COMMERCIAL 1,3-BUTANEDIOL

Boiling point at 760 mm.	207.5°C.
at 50 mm.	132°C.
at 10 mm.	98°C.
Δb.p./Δp, 740 to 760 mm.	0.044°C./mm.
Flash point (Cleveland open cup)	250°F.
Freezing point	below −50°C.
Heat of vaporization at 1 atm.	279 Btu/lb.
Molecular weight	90.12
Refractive index, n_D at 20°C.	1.4401
Solubility in water at 20°C.	∞
Solubility of water in, at 20°C.	∞
Specific gravity (apparent) at 20/20°C.	1.0059
ΔSp.gr./Δt	0.00068
Surface tension at 25°C.	37.8 dynes/cm.
Vapor pressure at 20°C.	0.06 mm.
Viscosity at 35°C.	89 cps.

1,3-Butanediol is manufactured commercially by the reduction of acetaldol[31, 32] under a wide variety of conditions with the usual hydrogenation catalysts. Yields are good and the process is relatively simple. Delbrück and Meisenberg[33] reduced acetaldol electrolytically, and Hibbert[34] accomplished the reduction with reducing metals such as aluminum and magnesium amalgams. Celanese manufactures 1,3-butanediol by a process presumed to be hydrocarbon oxidation[35, 36].

Fitzky[37] prepared 1,3-butanediol by the reaction of propylene and formaldehyde hydrate using a hydrogen- or metal-halide catalyst and superatmospheric pressures. Baker[38] saponified the diacetate of 1,3-butanediol. Lincoln and Drewitt[39] obtained a 70 per cent yield of the diol by hydrogenation of the mixed aldol of formaldehyde and acetone.

Optically active forms of 1,3-butanediol have been isolated. Neuberg and Kerb[40] prepared a dextrorotatory form by the reduction of acetaldol with yeast. Levene and Haller[41] obtained a dextrorotatory form [b.p. at 0.8 mm. 60–65°C., $[\alpha]_D^{22}$ 7.5° (abs. EtOH)] by reduction of D-methyl-3-hydroxybutyrate and by deamination of D-1-amino-3-butanol. Levene and Walti[42] reduced 4-hydroxy-2-butanone with fermenting yeast, obtaining a 50 to 60 per cent yield of levorotatory glycol [b. p. at 23 mm. 107–110°C., $[\alpha]_D^{25}$ −18.8° (abs. EtOH)].

Reactions. Butadiene can be prepared by the dehydration of 1,3-butanediol with phosphate catalysts, such as cerium phosphate and ammonium phosphate. Yields of 75 to 90 per cent are claimed[43, 44, 45, 46]. Synthesis of butadiene from ethanol (or acetylene) through acetaldehyde, acetaldol, 1,3-butanediol, to butadiene offers an alternate route to the direct synthesis of the diene from ethanol and acetaldehyde.

Oxidation of 1,3-butanediol with nitric acid gives acetic acid, oxalic acid, crotonaldehyde, and acetaldehyde[47]. Halasz[48] obtained a 50 per cent yield of crotonaldehyde by heating the diol with a nickel catalyst. Hanschke[49] prepared a cyclic acetal (b.p. 117–118°C., n_D at 20°C. 1.4140) by reacting 1,3-butanediol with acetaldehyde.

Moll[50] prepared thick, oily polymers of 1,3-butanediol and adipic acid in the presence of acid catalysts. The dibenzoate (b.p. at 3 mm. 132–133°C., n_D at 20°C. 1.5130) was obtained in 52 per cent yield by McElvain and Carney[51], who reacted the diol and benzoyl chloride in pyridine. Fatty esters of 1,3-butanediol, including the dilaurate, dimyristate, and dipalmitate, are described in a review by Goldsmith[52].

Cold concentrated hydrochloric acid with 1,3-butanediol gives 3-hydroxybutyl 3-chlorobutyl ether; hydrogen chloride at 100°C. gives 1,3-dichlorobutane[53]. Rippere and La Mer[54] prepared a borate by heating 1,3-butanediol with boric acid. By similar reactions Dupire[55] obtained a borate (b.p. at 17 mm. 212°C., density at 17°C. 1.092, n_D at 17°C. 1.446) and an arsenite (b.p. at 15 mm. 215°C., density at 21°C. 1.462, n_D at 21°C. 1.4967).

2,3-Butanediol

Depending on the isomeric form, 2,3-butanediol is a crystalline solid or a viscous liquid. The physical properties of the commercial product are summarized in Table 14.4 and of the isomeric forms in Table 14.5[56, 57]. Additional physical properties data that have been reported include: specific heat[58]; absorption and velocity of sound in the diol[59]; infrared absorption spectra[60]; Raman spectra[61]; vapor-liquid equilibrium data[62]; density, optical rotatory power, and refraction of aqueous solutions[63].

TABLE 14.4. Physical Properties of Commercial 2,3-Butanediol[a]

Boiling point at 760 mm.	182°C.
Flash point (Tag open cup)	185°F.
Freezing point	19°C.
Molecular weight	90.12
Refractive index, n_D at 20°C.	1.4377
Specific gravity at 20/20°C.	1.0093
Specific heat at 30°C.	0.60 cal./g.
Vapor pressure at 20°C.	0.17 mm.
Viscosity at 25°C.	121 cps.

[a] A mixture of 85 per cent *meso* and 15 per cent *dextro-levo* isomers: Celanese Corporation of America, New Products Bulletin N-27-1, June 1, 1951.

TABLE 14.5. Physical Properties of 2,3-Butanediol Isomers

	Levo	Dextro	Meso	Dextro-Levo
Specific rotation at 26°C.	−13.34	—	0.00	0.00
Boiling point, °C.	178	—	182	177
Melting point, °C.	18	—	34.4	7.6
Freezing point of 50% aq. soln., °C.	−30	—	+14	—
Refractive index, n_D	1.4318 (26°)	1.4306 (25°)	1.4325 (35°)	—
Density at 20°C.	0.991	0.987 (25°)	1.004	—
Density of 50% aq. soln. at 20°C.	1.023	—	1.027	—
Viscosity, cps.	41.1 (25°) 21.8 (35°)	—	65.6 (35°)	—

Preparation. The preparations of 2,3-butanediol may be divided into biochemical methods and chemical methods, with the former receiving the greater attention to date. Ethanol or 2,3-butanediol can be produced by fermentation from the same raw materials in approximately the same yields, but the preparation of the diol is inherently more costly because the diol is more difficult to recover from the fermentation liquor, due to its high boiling point. The materials which may be fermented to 2,3-butanediol include most sugars, malted potatoes, molasses, wheat mash, enzyme mash, barley mash, corn mash, wood mash, wood sugar, and corn starch. The products of the fermentation depend on the species of bacteria used and may include (besides 2,3-butanediol) carbon dioxide, hydrogen, formic acid, glycerol, ethanol, and lactic acid[56]. The diol is usually recovered from the fermentation liquors by simple distillation[64], but other feasible methods include solvent extraction[65], steam stripping[66], dialysis[67], and a chemical method based on the formation, recovery, and purification of the formal followed by alcoholysis[68].

The optical isomers of 2,3-butanediol are produced in different proportions by various species of bacteria. Thus the diol produced by *Aerobacter aerogenes* is approximately 90 to 95 per cent the *meso* isomer and 5 to 10 per cent the *dextro* isomer, while *Aerobacillus polymyxa* gives practically pure *levo* diol. This may be important in some applications because of differences in the properties of the isomers. For example, the *levo* isomer has been considered as a permanent type anti-freeze. A 50 per cent aqueous solution has a freezing point of $-30°C$. A 50 per cent solution of the *meso* form, on the other hand, has a freezing point of $+14°C$.

The chemical preparations of 2,3-butanediol are primarily of academic interest. Methods include: hydrolysis of the diacetate obtained by reacting silver acetate and 2,3-dibromobutane[69]; hydrolysis of 2,3-dichlorobutane with lime at 75°C.[70]; reduction of acetoin and biacetyl[71, 72]; and hydration of 2,3-epoxybutane[73]. Celanese, however, produces 2,3-butanediol by oxidation of natural gas hydrocarbons[35, 36].

Reactions. The production of butadiene from 2,3-butanediol has been investigated extensively in the United States and Canada[74, 75]. In general, the direct dehydration to butadiene is rather difficult. Winfield[76] obtained a 60 per cent single pass yield of butadiene and an 80 per cent combined yield of butadiene and vinylmethylcarbinol by passing 2,3-butanediol over thorium oxide at elevated temperatures and reduced pressures. Hale and Miller[77] used an aluminum-silicon-tungsten catalyst in the presence of amines and added methyl ethyl ketone to the charge to depress the formation of additional methyl ethyl ketone.

The preferred method for producing butadiene from 2,3-butanediol involves the preparation and pyrolysis of the diacetate of the diol[78, 79, 80]. This process has been investigated thoroughly and has been operated successfully on a pilot plant scale. The acetylation of 2,3-butanediol can be accomplished in a continuous process with a yield of 97 per cent[81]. The pyrolysis of the diacetate to butadiene is accomplished at 550°C. with a yield of 83 per cent. Much of the remainder is usable by-product and the acetic acid may be recovered almost quantitatively[82, 83, 84].

2,3-Butanediol can be dehydrogenated to biacetyl and acetoin using a copper catalyst at elevated temperatures[85]. Methyl ethyl ketone and methyl vinyl ketone can be produced from 2,3-butanediol by dehydration and dehydrogenation[74]. Isobutyraldehyde has been prepared by a pinacol rearrangement of the diol[86]. Neish and Macdonald[87] characterized 19 cyclic acetals and ketals of 2,3-butanediol. Liebmann[64] prepared halogenated derivatives, esters, nitrogen derivatives, oxide derivatives, ethers, ketonic derivatives, and olefinic derivatives.

Resins can be prepared by the reaction of 2,3-butanediol and polybasic acids. Staudinger and Schmidt[88] give analytical, molecular-weight, osmotic-pressure, and viscosity data for a polymer of 2,3-butanediol and sebacic acid.

Morell and Lathrop[89] prepared the monoacid borate of 2,3-butanediol (b. p. 266–269°C.) in 58 per cent yield and the diorthoborate in 90 per cent yield by dehydrating, respectively, equimolar and 3:2 mol ratio mixtures of 2,3-butanediol and boric acid. The cyclic carbonate (b. p. at 8 mm. 96°C., b. p. at 740 mm. 240°C., density at 26°C. 1.129, n_D at 26°C. 1.4226) was prepared in 75 per cent yield by Kolfenbach, Fulmer, and Underkofler[90] by reacting 2,3-butanediol and phosgene at 150°C. Toy[91] prepared the cyclic phenylphosphonate (b. p. at 15 mm. 210–215°C.) in 79 per cent yield by the reaction of phenylphosphonyl chloride and the diol.

1,4-Butanediol

1,4-Butanediol is a viscous liquid, miscible with water and slightly soluble in ether. Its physical properties are summarized in Table 14.6. It is produced commercially in Germany by hydrogenation of 2-butyne-1,4-

TABLE 14.6. PHYSICAL PROPERTIES OF 1,4-BUTANEDIOL

Boiling point at 760 mm.	230°C.
at 20 mm.	127°C.
Melting point	16°C.
Molecular weight	90.12
Specific gravity at 20/4°C.	1.020

diol, which is in turn prepared by the reaction of acetylene and formaldehyde. The hydrogenation is accomplished at temperatures between 15 and 200°C. and at 200 to 400 atmospheres pressure over a catalyst such as nickel or cobalt on a pumice carrier[92, 93].

1,4-Butanediol has been obtained by other methods. The process for preparing adiponitrile from furfural though furan, tetrahydrofuran, 1,4-dichlorobutane, to adiponitrile may be altered to give the diol[94]. Adkins and Folkers[95] reduced diethyl succinate with hydrogen over copper chromite at 250°C. and 220 atmospheres pressure, obtaining 1,4-butanediol in yields of 80 to 98 per cent. By a similar process Lazier[96] obtained the diol from the catalytic reduction of the diesters of succinic acid and alcohols of four or more carbon atoms. Dreyfus[97] prepared it by refluxing ethylene chlorohydrin for 48 hours with five times the stoichiometric quantity of copper and a catalytic amount of methylamine.

Reactions. Dehydration of 1,4-butanediol may be controlled to give either butadiene or tetrahydrofuran. At 250 to 350°C. with a catalyst such as trisodium phosphate, tetrahydrofuran is the principal product. At 400 to 450°C. with catalysts such as sodium dihydrogen phosphate or cuprous oxide, butadiene is produced. The preferred procedure for the production of butadiene from 1,4-butanediol is first to prepare tetrahydro-furan and then to dehydrate it catalytically to butadiene[46, 98, 99, 100, 101]. This process was used commercially in Germany during World War II.

Oxidation of 1,4-butanediol with nitric acid gives succinic acid[102]. Brenner and Jones[103] prepared butyrolactone by passing the diol over copper chromite at 200°C. Bennett and Heathcoat[104] obtained 4-chlorobutyl acetate from the reaction of 1,4-butanediol and acetyl chloride. Paden and Adkins[105] prepared 1-benzylpyrrolidine in 76 per cent yield by heating a mixture of the diol and benzylamine over a copper chromite catalyst at 250°C. for one hour. When 1,4-butanediol and ammonia are passed over alumina at 400°C., a 35 per cent yield of pyrrolidine is obtained[106]. Under the same conditions, the use of hydrogen sulfide instead of ammonia gives a 62.5 per cent yield of tetrahydrothiophene. The action of hydrogen bromide on the diol gives 1,4-dibromobutane, di(4-bromobutyl) ether, and tetrahydrofuran[107]. 1,4-Butanediol forms a bis-α-naphthylurethane (m. p. 198°C.)[104].

Muskat and Strain[108] prepared and polymerized the bis(chloroallyl carbonate) of 1,4-butanediol. A polymeric condensation product of adipic acid and a mixture of the diol and methyldiethanolamine has been recommended as a soaking bath for rayon fiber[109]. Carothers and Van Natta prepared 1,4-butanediol carbonate as a polymer from the diol and diethyl carbonate[110, 111]. Heating the cream-colored, powdery polymer (mol. wt. 1300–1450, m.p. 55–60°C.) at 300 to 325°C. gave a small quantity of di-molecular material (m.p. 175–176°C.). Hill and Carothers[112] prepared a cyclic formal (b.p. 112–117°C., density at 20°C. 1.0022, n_D at 20°C. 1.4310) from trioxymethylene and 1,4-butanediol and polymerized it by heating to 150°C. with camphorsulfonic acid. Spanagel and Carothers[113] prepared polymeric esters of 1,4-butanediol and depolymerized them to cyclic monomers and dimers using salts, e.g., magnesium nitrate, as catalysts. The melting points, boiling points, densities, and refractive indexes are given by these authors for the cyclic esters of the diol and succinic, azelaic, and sebacic acids.

Most important of the polymeric products derived from the four carbon glycols are the polyurethane resins[114, 115]. They are prepared by reacting a diol—usually 1,4-butanediol— and a diisocyanate in monochlorobenzene:

$$HO(CH_2)_4OH \; + \; O{=}C{=}N{-}(CH_2)_6{-}N{=}C{=}O \; \rightarrow$$

$$\left[{-}O{-}(CH_2)_4{-}O{-}\overset{\overset{\displaystyle O}{\|}}{C}{-}NH{-}(CH_2)_6{-}NH{-}\overset{\overset{\displaystyle O}{\|}}{C}{-} \right]_n$$

mol. wt. 10,000

The polymer separates from solution as a powder and the yield is almost quantitative. This development began in Germany in 1937, and two of these resins—"Igamid" U for plastics and "Perlon" U for fibers—were produced commercially in Germany during World War II.

The physical properties of the polymers depend on the number of methylene groups in the structural unit. The water resistance increases but the tensile strength and melting point decrease as the number of methylene groups in the chain increases. These resins are said to be similar to polyamide resins in general properties but superior in acid resistance, outdoor durability, and electrical properties. Polymers obtained from a mixture of diisocyanates and glycols, unlike the simple polymers, are readily soluble in chlorinated solvents; they are softer, more compatible with plasticizers, and have lower melting points. The reactions of linear glycol polyesters with diisocyanates have been reviewed[116].

The polyurethane resins are very versatile and have been recommended for many types of applications. The linear polymers are suitable for fibers, bristles, and plastics. Lacquers may be prepared from low molecular weight polymers which contain alcohols with more than two hydroxyl groups. Resin solutions containing a diisocyanate are applied and the reaction continues on the surface. Although the adhesion and rate of conversion are very good, the pot life of the lacquers is short, solvents containing no water or molecules with active hydrogen must be used, and the odor and toxicity of the diisocyanates are undesirable. The pot life of lacquers can be increased by adding bis-phenyl urethanes or malonic or acetoacetic ester adducts of diisocyanates which break down on baking the coatings.

2-Butene-1,4-diol

2-Butene-1,4-diol has been prepared by reducing 2-butyne-1,4-diol with zinc in alkaline solution or with palladium and hydrogen[117, 118, 119], by hydrolysis of 1,4-dichloro-2-butene obtained by chlorination of butadiene[120], and by saponification of 1,4-dibromo-2-butene with sodium bicarbonate at 80°C.[121] The diol exists in *cis* and *trans* forms, and there is some disagreement as to the physical properties of the two. In Table 14.7 are given the values considered the most reliable.

TABLE 14.7. PHYSICAL PROPERTIES OF 2-BUTENE-1,4-DIOL

	Cis[119]	Trans[122]
Melting point	—	25°C.
Boiling point	134–135°C. at 15 mm.	131.5°C. at 12 mm.
Refractive index, n_D	1.4716 at 25°C.	1.4772 at 20°C.
Density at 20°C.	—	1.0687

Reactions. Reppe and Drossbach[123] prepared maleic acid by passing a gaseous mixture of 2-butene-1,4-diol and oxygen over oxidation catalysts. Dehydration of the diol with catalysts such as aluminum oxide, thorium oxide, aluminum phosphate, or acids gives dihydrofurans[124, 125]. Valette[126] reports that dehydration of the *trans* diol gives only crotonaldehyde, whereas dehydration of the *cis* diol gives 35 per cent 2,5-dihydrofuran and 65 per cent crotonaldehyde.

Prevost and Valette[127] prepared meso-erythritol by reacting *cis*-2-butene-1,4-diol and potassium permanganate. Addition of bromine to the *cis*-diol followed by hydrolysis of the resulting dibromo diol gave racemic erythritol. Deebel[128] obtained diesters of 2-butene-1,4-diol by the reaction of the sodium salt of the acid with 1,4-dichloro-2-butene. Shilov and Kanyaev[129] studied the kinetics of the addition of hypochlorous acid to 2-butene-1,4-diol.

2-Butyne-1,4-diol

2-Butyne-1,4-diol is a colorless, crystalline solid (m.p. 64°C.)[101, 130]. Since impurities may cause explosive decomposition, it is best distilled under reduced pressure (b. p. at 15 mm. 145°C.). Its physical properties are listed in Table 14.8.

TABLE 14.8. PHYSICAL PROPERTIES OF 2-BUTYNE-1,4-DIOL

Boiling point at 760 mm.	238°C.
at 100 mm.	194°C.
at 10 mm.	140°C.
Melting point	64°C.[a]
Molecular weight	90.12
Refractive index, n_D at 25°C.	$\alpha = 1.450 \pm 0.002$
	$\beta = 1.528 \pm 0.002$
Solubility in water at 25°C.	374 g./100 ml.
at 0°C.	121 g./100 ml.

[a] Melting points of 57.5°C. and 58°C. have also been reported: General Aniline & Film Corporation, New Product Bulletin No. 301A, July 10, 1950.

Commercial production of 2-butyne-1,4-diol was practiced in Germany where the acetylenic diol was a precursor of 1,4-butanediol used to produce butadiene and polyurethane resins. An almost quantitative yield of the diol is produced by the reaction of acetylene and formaldehyde in the presence of metallic acetylides such as copper acetylide[131, 132]. It is desirable to have a bismuth compound present during the synthesis to suppress cuprene formation[133]. Propargyl alcohol, an intermediate in this synthesis, can also be converted to 2-butyne-1,4-diol by condensation with formaldehyde in the presence of a metallic acetylide catalyst[134].

2-Butyne-1,4-diol has been prepared by other methods. Iozitsch[135] produced it by reacting acetylene bis magnesium bromide and formaldehyde. Lespieau[136] obtained it by the action of zinc dust on 2,3-dibromo-2-butene-1,4-diol.

Reactions. Reduction of 2-butyne-1,4-diol with nickel and hydrogen gives 1,4-butanediol[101]. Reduction with palladium and hydrogen or with zinc in alkaline solution gives 2-butene-1,4-diol[130]. Johnson[130] investigated thoroughly the reactions of 2-butyne-1,4-diol and gives the preparation and properties of esters, ethers, amino compounds, and halogen compounds derived therefrom. The preparation of ethers by the reaction of the diol and a dialkyl sulfate has been described by Rapp[137].

2,3-Dimethyl-2,3-butanediol

2,3-Dimethyl-2,3-butanediol (pinacol) has been of importance only as an intermediate in the production of synthetic *methyl rubber* during World War I in Germany. Acetone was converted to pinacol, which was then dehydrated to 2,3-dimethylbutadiene:

$$2(CH_3)_2C{=}O \ + \ H_2 \ \xrightarrow{Al-Hg} \ CH_3{-}\underset{\underset{OH}{|}}{\overset{\overset{CH_3}{|}}{C}}{-}\underset{\underset{OH}{|}}{\overset{\overset{CH_3}{|}}{C}}{-}CH_3 \ \xrightarrow{-2H_2O}$$

$$CH_2{=}\overset{\overset{CH_3}{|}}{C}{-}\overset{\overset{CH_3}{|}}{C}{=}CH_2$$

This latter compound was polymerized into rubber-like substances. These materials were far from satisfactory, however, and production ceased immediately after the war.

Literature Cited

1. Zelinsky, N., and Zelikow, J., *Ber.*, **34,** 2858 (1901).
2. Franke, A., *Monatsh.*, **22,** 1070 (1901).
3. Tryon, P. F., *J. Am. Chem. Soc.*, **69,** 972–3 (1947).
4. Pines, H., and Ipatieff, V. N. (to Universal Oil Products Co.), U. S. Patents 2,366,126 (Dec. 26, 1944) and 2,406,630 (Aug. 27, 1946).
5. Pines, H., and Ipatieff, V. N. (to Universal Oil Products Co.), U. S. Patent 2,406,631 (Aug. 27, 1946).
6. Schelling, W. T., and Anderson, J. (to Shell Development Co.), U. S. Patent 2,422,802 (June 24, 1947).
7. Morris, R. C., and Finch, H. de V. (to Shell Development Co.), U. S. Patent 2,420,834 (May 20, 1947).
8. Staaterman, H. G., Morris, R. C., Stager, R. M., and Pierotti, G. J., *Chem. Eng. Progress*, **43** (4), 148 (1947).
9. Dolian, F. E. (to Commercial Solvents Corp.), U. S. Patent 2,337,650 (Dec. 28, 1943).
10. Guest, H. H. (to The J. B. Williams Co.), U. S. Patent 2,435,829 (Feb. 10, 1948).

11. Gangloff, W. C. (to The Drackett Co.), U. S. Patent 2,386,106 (Oct. 2, 1945).
12. Robinette, H., Jr. (to Commercial Solvents Corp.), U. S. Patent 2,352,409 (June 27, 1944).
13. Chiappe, C. F., and Kroeger, J. W. (to Frederick H. Levey Co., Inc.), U. S. Patent 2,437,908 (March 16, 1948).
14. Bjorksten, J. (to Ditto, Inc.), U. S. Patent 2,294,711 (Sept. 1, 1942).
15. Scripture, E. W., Jr., U. S. Patent 2,364,555 (Dec. 5, 1944).
16. *ASTM Bull. No. 152*, **1948,** 29.
17. Thalberg, A., *Monatsh.*, **19,** 157 (1898).
18. de Montmollin, M., and Martenet, M., *Helv. Chim. Acta.*, **12,** 606 (1929).
19. "New Products Bulletin N-010-1," New York, Celanese Corp. of America.
20. Grignard, V., and Fluchaire, M., *Ann. chim.*, (10) **9,** 5–54 (1928).
21. Kulpinski, M. S., and Nord, F. F., *J. Org. Chem.*, **8,** 256–70 (1943).
22. Beavers, E. M. (to Rohm & Haas Co.), U. S. Patent 2,449,983 (March 7, 1950).
23. Beavers, E. M., and Conyne, R. F. (to Rohm & Haas Co.), U. S. Patent 2,449,984 (March 7, 1950).
24. Lanham, W. M. (to Union Carbide and Carbon Corp.), U. S. Patents 2,512,722–3 (June 27, 1950).
25. Wilkes, B. G. (to Carbide and Carbon Chemicals Corp.), U. S. Patent 2,407,205 (Sept. 3, 1946).
26. Travis, B. V., and Jones, H. A. (to the United States of America), U. S. Patent 2,356,801 (Aug. 29, 1944).
27. Granett, P., and Haynes, H. L., *J. Econ. Entomol.*, **38,** 671–5 (1945).
28. Granett, P., *New Jersey Mosquito Extermination Assoc., Proc. Ann. Meeting,* **25,** 51–7 (1938).
29. Setterstrom, C. A., *Chem. Inds.*, **59,** 474 (1946).
30. Omohundro, A. L., Neumeier, F. M., and Zeitlin, B. R. (to McKesson & Robbins, Inc.), U. S. Patent 2,465,470 (March 29, 1949).
31. Balcar, F. R. (to Air Reduction Co., Inc.), U. S. Patent 2,421,451 (June 3, 1947).
32 Metzger, F. J. (to Air Reduction Co., Inc.), U. S. Patent 2,419,275 (April 22, 1947)
33. Delbrück, K., and Meisenburg, K. (to Farbenfabriken vorm. Friedr. Bayer & Co.), U. S. Patent 1,094,539 (April 28, 1914).
34. Hibbert, H. (to E. I. du Pont de Nemours & Co.), U. S. Patent 1,008,333 (Nov. 14, 1911).
35. Robertson, N. C. (to Celanese Corp. of America), U. S. Patent 2,477,087 (July 26, 1949).
36. Michael, V. F., and Phinney, J. A. (to Stanolind Oil and Gas Co.), U. S. Patent 2,482,284 (Sept. 20, 1949).
37. Fitzky, W. (to I. G. Farbenindustrie A.-G.), U. S. Patent 2,143,370 (Jan. 10, 1939).
38. Baker, J. W., *J. Chem. Soc.*, **1944,** 296.
39. Lincoln, J., and Drewitt, J. G. N. (to British Celanese, Ltd.), U. S. Patent 2,395,414 (Feb. 26, 1946).
40. Neuberg, C., and Kerb, E., *Biochem. Z.*, **92,** 96 (1918).
41. Levene, P. A., and Haller, H. L., *J. Biol. Chem.*, **69,** 165, 569 (1926).
42. Levene, P. A., and Walti, A., *J. Biol. Chem.*, **94,** 361 (1931).
43. Reppe, W., and Hoffmann, U. (to I. G. Farbenindustrie A.-G.), German Patent 578,994 (June 21, 1933).
44. Lorch, A. E. (to Air Reduction Co., Inc.), U. S. Patent 2,371,530 (March 13, 1945).

45. Manninen, T. H. (to U. S. Industrial Chemicals, Inc.), U. S. Patent 2,399,049 (April 23, 1946).
46. Copenhaver, J. W., and Bigelow, M. H., "Acetylene and Carbon Monoxide Chemistry," New York, Reinhold Publishing Corp., 1949.
47. Kekule, A., *Ann.*, **162,** 310 (1872).
48. Halasz, A., *Ann. chim.*, (11) **14,** 318 (1940).
49. Hanschke, E., *Ber.*, **76B,** 180-2 (1943).
50. Moll, F. (to I. G. Farbenindustrie A.-G.), German Patent 566,519 (May 20, 1930).
51. McElvain, S. M., and Carney, T. P., *J. Am. Chem. Soc.*, **68,** 2592 (1946).
52. Goldsmith, H. A., *Chem. Revs.*, **33,** 257 (1943).
53. Fargher, R. G., and Perkin, W. H., *J. Chem. Soc.*, **105,** 1356 (1914).
54. Rippere, R. E., and La Mer, V. K., *J. Phys. Chem.*, **47,** 204 (1943).
55. Dupire, A., *Compt. rend.*, **202,** 2086 (1936).
56. Neish, A. C., *Am. Perfumer Essent. Oil Rev.*, **48** (10), 59 (1946).
57. Knowlton, J. W., Schieltz, N. C., and MacMillan, D., *J. Am. Chem. Soc.*, **68,** 208 (1946).
58. Khokhlovkin, M. A., and Kalacheva, A. V., *Sintet. Kauchuk*, **1936,** No. 1, 25.
59. Willard, G. W., *J. Acoust. Soc. Am.*, **12,** 438 (1941).
60. Barnes, R. B., Liddel, U., and Williams, V. Z., *Ind. Eng. Chem., Anal. Ed.*, **15,** 83 (1943).
61. Taufen, H. J., Murray, M. J., and Cleveland, F. F., *J. Am. Chem. Soc.*, **65,** 1130 (1943).
62. Othmer, D. F., Shlechter, N., and Koszalka, W. A., *Ind. Eng. Chem.*, **37,** 895 (1945).
63. Clendenning, K. A., *Can. J. Research*, **24B,** 269 (1946).
64. Liebmann, A. J., *Oil & Soap*, **22,** 31 (1945).
65. Walmesley, R. A., and Davis, W. R. (to Imperial Chemical Industries, Ltd.), U. S. Patent 2,397,065 (March 19, 1946).
66. Blom, R. H., Reed, D. L., Efron, A., and Mustakas, G. C., *Ind. Eng. Chem.*, **37,** 865 (1945).
67. Cornwell, R. T. K. (to Sylvania Industrial Corp.), U. S. Patent 2,390,779 (Dec. 11, 1945).
68. Senkus, M., *Ind. Eng. Chem.*, **38,** 913 (1946).
69. Bainbridge, E. G., *J. Chem. Soc.*, **105,** 2291 (1914).
70. Schering, E. (to Chemische Fabrik auf Aktien), German Patent 246,572 (Sept. 20, 1910).
71. Kling, A., *Compt. rend.*, **140,** 314, 1457 (1905).
72. Sabatier, P., and Mailhe, A., *Compt. rend.*, **144,** 1086 (1907).
73. Batalin, V. S., and Ugryumov, P. G., *Sintet. Kauchuk*, **1936,** No. 6, 8-16.
74. Neish, A. C., *Can. Chem. Process Inds.*, **28,** 862 (1944).
75. Neish, A. C., Haskell, V. C., and Macdonald, F. J., *Can. J. Research*, **23B,** 281 (1945).
76. Winfield, M. E., *J. Council Sci. Ind. Research*, **18,** 412 (1945).
77. Hale, W. J., and Miller, H. (to National Agrol Co., Inc.), U. S. Patent 2,400,409 (May 14, 1946).
78. Schniepp, L. E., Dunning, J. W., and Lathrop, E. C., *Ind. Eng. Chem.*, **37,** 872 (1945).
79. Morell, S. A. (to the United States of America), U. S. Patent 2,372,221 (March 27, 1945).

80. Shlechter, N., Othmer, D. F., and Marshak, S., *Ind. Eng. Chem.*, **37,** 900 (1945).
81. Grubb, H. W., *Chem. Eng. Progress*, **43,** 437 (1947).
82. Shlechter, N., Othmer, D. F., and Brand, F., *Ind. Eng. Chem.*, **37,** 905 (1945).
83. Morell, S. A., Geller, H. H., and Lathrop, E. C., *Ind. Eng. Chem.*, **37,** 877 (1945).
84. Schniepp, L. E., Dunning, J. W., Geller, H. H., Morell, S. A., and Lathrop, E. C., *Ind. Eng. Chem.*, **37,** 884 (1945).
85. McAllister, S. H., and de Simo, M. (to Shell Development Co.), U. S. Patent 2,051,266 (Aug. 18, 1936).
86. Akabori, S., *J. Chem. Soc. Japan*, **59,** 1132 (1938).
87. Neish, A. C., and Macdonald, F. J., *Can. J. Research*, **25B,** 70 (1947).
88. Staudinger, H., and Schmidt, H., *J. prakt. Chem.*, **155,** 129 (1940).
89. Morell, S. A., and Lathrop, E. C., *J. Am. Chem. Soc.*, **67,** 879 (1945).
90. Kolfenbach, J. J., Fulmer, E. I., and Underkofler, L. A., *J. Am. Chem. Soc.*, **67,** 502 (1945).
91. Toy, A. D. F. (to Victor Chemical Works), U. S. Patent 2,382,622 (Aug. 14, 1945).
92. Reppe, W., Schmidt, W., Schulz, A., and Wenderlein, H. (to General Aniline & Film Corp.), U. S. Patent 2,319,707 (May 18, 1943).
93. Schmidt, W., and Manchen, F. (to General Aniline & Film Corp.), U. S. Patent 2,222,302 (Nov. 19, 1940).
94. Cass, O. W., *Chem. Inds.*, **60,** 612 (1947).
95. Adkins, H., and Folkers, K., *J. Am. Chem. Soc.*, **53,** 1095 (1931).
96. Lazier, W. A. (to E. I. du Pont de Nemours & Co.), U. S. Patent 2,040,944 (May 19, 1936).
97. Dreyfus, H. (to Celanese Corp. of America), U. S. Patent 2,389,347 (Nov. 20, 1945).
98. Reppe, W. (to General Aniline & Film Corp), U. S. Patent 2,251,292 (Aug. 5, 1941).
99. Reppe, W., and Trieschmann, H. G. (to General Aniline & Film Corp.), U. S. Patent 2,251,835 (Aug. 5, 1941).
100. Reppe, W., and Trieschmann, H. G. (to General Aniline & Film Corp.), German Patent 711,709 (Sept. 4, 1941).
101. "Advances in Acetylene Chemistry," Technical Report from Reconstruction Finance Corporation, Office of Rubber Reserve, Research and Development Section.
102. Hamonet, J., *Compt. rend.*, **132,** 632 (1901).
103. Brenner, J. G. M., and Jones, D. G. (to Imperial Chemical Industries, Ltd.), British Patent 583,344 (Dec. 16, 1946).
104. Bennett, G. M., and Heathcoat, F., *J. Chem. Soc.*, **1929,** 268.
105. Paden, J. H., and Adkins, H., *J. Am. Chem. Soc.*, **58,** 2487 (1936).
106. Yur'ev, Yu. K., and Medovshchikov, N. G., *J. Gen. Chem. (U.S.S.R.)*, **9,** 628 (1939).
107. Müller, A., and Vanc, W., *Ber.*, **77B,** 669 (1944).
108. Muskat, I. E., and Strain, F. (to Pittsburgh Plate Glass Co.), U. S. Patent 2,403,113 (July 2, 1946).
109. Nelles, J., Bayer, O., Tischbein, W., and Baehren, F. (to the United States of America), U. S. Patent 2,417,513 (March 18, 1947).
110. Carothers, W. H., and Van Natta, F. J., *J. Am. Chem. Soc.*, **52,** 314 (1930).
111. Carothers, W. H. (to E. I. du Pont de Nemours & Co.), U. S. Patent 1,995,291 (March 26, 1935).
112. Hill, J. W., and Carothers, W. H., *J. Am. Chem. Soc.*, **57,** 925 (1935).
113. Spanagel, E. W., and Carothers, W. H., *J. Am. Chem. Soc.*, **57,** 929 (1935).

114. Bayer, O., *Modern Plastics*, **24** (10), 149 (1947).

115. Kline, G. M., *Modern Plastics*, **23** (2), 152A (1945).

116. Bayer, O., Müller, E., Petersen, S., Piepenbrink, H. F., and Windemuth, E., *Angew. Chem.*, **62**, 57–66 (1950).

117. I. G. Farbenindustrie A.-G., British Patent 508,543 (June 29, 1939).

118. I. G. Farbenindustrie A.-G., French Patent 49,861 (Aug. 22, 1939).

119. Johnson, A. W., *J. Chem. Soc.*, **1946,** 1014.

120. Arbusov, B. A., and Zoroastrova, V. M., *Compt. rend. acad. sci.* (*U.S.S.R.*,) **53,** 41 (1946).

121. Prevost, C., *Bull. soc. chim. France*, (5) **11**, 218 (1944).

122. Prevost, C., *Compt. rend.*, **183,** 1291 (1926).

123. Reppe, W., and Drossbach, O. (to I. G. Farbenindustrie A.-G.), German Patent 709,370 (July 10, 1941).

124. Reppe, W., and Schnabel, R. (to I. G. Farbenindustrie A.-G.), German Patent 695,218 (July 18, 1940).

125. I. G. Farbenindustrie A.-G., British Patent 510,949 (Aug. 8, 1939).

126. Valette, A., *Compt. rend.*, **223,** 907 (1946).

127. Prevost, C., and Valette, A., *Compt. rend.*, **222,** 326 (1946).

128. Deebel, G. F. (to Monsanto Chemical Co.), U. S. Patent 2,366,667 (Jan. 2, 1945).

129. Shilov, E. A., and Kanyaev, N. P., *J. Phys. Chem.* (*U.S.S.R.*), **10,** 123 (1937).

130. Johnson, A. W., *J. Chem. Soc.*, **1946,** 1009.

131. I. G. Farbenindustrie A.-G., British Patent 508,062 (June 20, 1939).

132. Reppe, W., and Keyssner, E. (to General Aniline & Film Corp.), U. S. Patent 2,232,867 (Feb. 25, 1941).

133. Reppe, W., Steinhofer, A., Spaenig, H., and Locker, K. (to General Aniline & Film Corp.), U. S. Patent 2,300,969 (Nov. 3, 1942).

134. Keyssner, E., and Eichler, E. (to General Aniline & Film Corp), U. S. Patent 2,238,471 (April 15, 1941).

135. Iozitsch, Z. I., *J. Russ. Phys. Chem. Soc.*, **38,** 252 (1906).

136. Lespieau, R., *Compt. rend.*, **158,** 708 (1914).

137. Rapp, W. (to I. G. Farbenindustrie A.-G.), German Patent 742,650 (Oct. 21, 1943).

CHAPTER 15

PHYSIOLOGICAL ASPECTS OF THE GLYCOLS AND RELATED COMPOUNDS

H. F. SMYTH, JR.

The physiological properties of many of the glycols and other compounds discussed in previous chapters have been thoroughly studied and recorded in the literature. The references discussed below represent the most complete investigations which have a bearing upon technical applications of these materials. In most instances regular commercial products, rather than specially purified samples, have been reported upon.

Ethylene Glycol and Related Compounds

Ethylene Glycol. Large single doses of ethylene glycol injure by depression of the central nervous system, but small repeated doses manifest a toxic action which centers chiefly in the kidney.

Conventional industrial applications appear to be free from danger to health from vapor inhalation because of the low vapor pressure of the compound. The most extensive experimental study of inhalation is that of Wiley, Hueper, and von Oettingen[1], who exposed mice and rats to concentrations of 0.35 to 0.40 mg./l. of air (140 to 160 ppm.) for 80 periods of 8 hours each during 16 weeks, without producing any injury. This concentration is only slightly less than saturation at room temperature, and it can hardly be exceeded by industrial exposures, except when a fog is created from hot vapors or by high-speed mechanical action. The safety of fog inhalation, which would cause higher glycol intake than does vapor inhalation, has not been studied and must be regarded with caution.

Ethylene glycol manifests a negligible irritant action upon the skin, and there is no evidence that it is absorbed by this route in dangerous amounts; but in view of the modification in skin permeability which may be brought about by surface-active agents or other ingredients, the use of this solvent in cosmetic preparations intended to be applied over extensive areas of the body is probably unwise.

There have been more than 40 fatalities reported as a result of the ingestion of notable volumes of ethylene glycol, usually in the form of antifreeze. From these it is deduced that the single lethal dose for man is approximately 100 ml. The first severe poisonings were described by Hansen[2] and Brekke[3], both in 1930. Pons and Custer[4] list no less than 18. From very large doses death was due to respiratory failure after a few hours of coma following cyanosis, vomiting, and convulsions. Severe lesions were found in the central nervous system, but kidney damage was less serious. One of the earlier persons who swallowed a large volume of the glycol suffered hemorrhagic nephritis and his life was saved, apparently only as a result of the surgical decapsulation of one kidney.

Aside from these ingestion episodes, reports of injury in the literature are confined to one note[5] of slight urinary abnormalities, such as urobilinuria, albuminuria, and red blood cells in the urine, among assemblers of electrolytic condensers.

In dogs and rabbits approximately one-half per cent of a large nonfatal dose is found in the urine as oxalic acid, and deposits of calcium oxalate crystals have been frequently noted in the kidneys[6]. Mulinos, Pomerantz, and Lojkin[7] have shown that a single intravenous dose of sodium oxalate equal to 20 times the oxalate formed from a fatal dose of ethylene glycol does not injure rabbits. They conclude that oxalic acid formation is irrelevant to the acute toxicity of ethylene glycol; however, they explain the chronic toxicity of the glycol on the basis of obstruction of the secreting tubules of the kidney by deposits of calcium oxalate crystals, with a consequent suppression of urine flow and resulting death from uremia. It has been shown[8] that rats will tolerate 1.2 per cent of oxalic acid in their diet for two years. This report further weakens the evidence that ethylene glycol is toxic by virtue of oxidation to oxalic acid. The ingestion of ethylene glycol does not increase urinary glucuronates[9].

Quantitative toxiological data obtained with laboratory animals must be regarded with caution because man is more susceptible to injury from ethylene glycol. Human fatalities have indicated a lethal dose of about 1.4 ml./kg., but Laug, Calvery, Morris, and Woodard[10] report the oral LD_{50}* values for guinea pigs, rats, and mice to be 7.35, 5.50, and 13.1 ml./kg., respectively. Others have reported comparable data. They report that small animals die with hydropic degeneration of the epithelium of renal convoluted tubules and focal necrosis of the liver, but this pathological interpretation is disputed by Mulinos, Pomerantz, and Lojkin[7].

The most complete study of chronic toxicity is that of Morris, Nelson, and Calvery[11], who maintained white rats for two years upon diets containing 1 and 2 per cent of ethylene glycol, probably equivalent to 0.5 and 1 g. per kilo per day. The glycol shortened the life span of the rats, produced calcium oxalate bladder stones, severe renal tubular atrophy, and fatty degeneration in the liver with slight centrolobular atrophy. Remembering the greater human susceptibility to single doses of the glycol, these authors, working in the laboratories of the United States Food and Drug Administration, concluded that the toxicity of ethylene glycol is too great to be tolerated in any product intended for internal consumption. This

---

* LD_{50} = the dose lethal to 50 per cent of the animals being tested.

conclusion is apparently not shared in some other countries where the employment of small amounts, as in flavoring extracts, is tolerated. Injuries from this application have not been reported.

Diethylene Glycol. The physiological action of diethylene glycol is somewhat similar to that of ethylene glycol, but quantitatively the former is slightly less toxic. There have been no studies reported upon the effect of inhalation, but injury would be even less likely than in the case of ethylene glycol because of lower vapor pressure and a lower degree of toxicity.

Diethylene glycol produces a negligible degree of irritation when applied to the skin, and while there is no evidence that it is absorbed by this route in dangerous amounts, the use of the solvent in preparations intended to be applied over extensive areas of the body is probably unwise.

In 1937 there were 105 fatalities in the United States from the use of a solution of sulfanilamide in an aqueous mixture containing 72 per cent of diethylene glycol intended for oral therapy. From this misfortune it has been estimated that the fatal human dose is about 1 ml. per kilo[12]. However, there were concurrent complicating factors. At about the same time there was a similar episode on a smaller scale in Japan, where at least four died from injection of a solution of bufotoxin in diethylene glycol[13]. The pathology in human victims resembles closely that reported for laboratory animals, consisting of hydropic degeneration of the renal cortex with less severe but similar lesions in the liver[14]. Urine was suppressed because of the compression resulting from swollen epithelium of the convoluted tubules, and death followed the onset of anuria by two to seven days. Aside from these acute episodes the only report of injury from diethylene glycol is a dermatitis case on the fingers, blamed upon the use of the glycol as a humectant in tobacco[15].

In laboratory animals, most of a single dose was found unchanged in the urine by Haag and Ambrose, but small amounts of oxalic acid were also present[16]. On the other hand Wiley, Hueper, Bergen, and Blood[6] could not demonstrate oxalic acid formation following large single doses of diethylene glycol to rabbits and dogs. Morris, Nelson, and Calvery[11] consider that the presence of calcium oxalate bladder concretions in chronically fed rats proves that the ether linkage splits to form ethylene glycol in the body. However, it remains debatable whether the small amounts of oxalic acid reported may not have arisen from ethylene glycol present in commercial lots of the diglycol.

Single oral dose data for small animals indicate a toxicity considerably less than that quoted above for man and justify conservatism in interpreting quantitative results obtained from animal studies. Laug, Calvery, Morris, and Woodard[10] report the LD_{50} values for guinea pigs, rats, and mice to be, respectively, 7.76, 14.8, and 23.7 ml./kg.

The first publication of an experimental study of the chronic toxicity of diethylene glycol is that of Haag and Ambrose[16]. The most extensive and protracted study is that made by the United States Food and Drug Administration[11, 17] in which, for a period of two years, oral doses of 1, 2, and 4 per cent of the glycol were given to albino rats. The lowest dosage level slightly retarded growth and produced a low incidence of calcium oxalate bladder calculi, with slight kidney and infrequent liver damage. The larger doses produced the same effects to a greater degree, and some bladder tumors of unproved etiology were observed. Some mortality resulted from the greatest dosage.

In the United States it is generally believed that diethylene glycol is unsafe in any preparation intended for internal consumption, but it is understood that a limited use in flavoring extracts and the like has taken place without injuries in some other countries. All available evidence indicates that the use of the glycol as a humectant in cigarettes results in such a small intake into the body that no physiological effect can result.

Triethylene Glycol. Triethylene glycol is less toxic than diethylene glycol. Robertson *et al.*[18] have reported extensive experiments with monkeys and rats, showing that prolonged inhalation of saturated vapors, as in air disinfection, are without physiological effects. During trials of disinfection large numbers of persons have been exposed without ill effect[19]. It is generally concluded that indefinitely long exposures to vapors substantially saturated at room temperature are harmless.

The first report of a study of the oral toxicity of triethylene glycol is that of Latven and Molitor[20], who conclude that its single dose toxicity is less than that of ethylene glycol and more than that of propylene glycol. Lauter and Vrla[21] conclude that triethylene glycol is less toxic than diethylene glycol in repeated doses to rats, for a 3 per cent solution in place of water had no effect during a few weeks. Fitzhugh and Nelson[17] reached a similar conclusion on the basis of an experiment in which parallel groups of rats were fed the two latter glycols over a two-year period. They found no effect from 4 per cent triethylene glycol in the drinking water, and their results with diethylene glycol have been given above. It is their view, on the basis of their laboratory's study of the three lower ethylene glycols, that toxicity decreases with increasing molecular weight.

Liquid Polyethylene Glycols. Gross[22] reported briefly upon a polyglycol mixture, possibly equivalent to what is known in the United States as polyethylene glycol 200. He found it caused no irritation of human skin, and reported a fairly low single dose oral toxicity to rabbits, with death from large doses due to kidney injury, and no injury from moderate oral doses repeated for 12 days.

The only other publications on the toxicity of liquid polyethylene glycols are those of Smyth, Carpenter, and Shaffer[23, 24], who studied commercial products with mean molecular weights of 200, 300, and 400. These materials were about equivalent in toxicity to published data on triethylene glycol, but they continue the trend toward lower toxicity with increased molecular weight by a slightly lower single dose toxicity.

Rats were not injured by 4 per cent solutions of the three products given in place of drinking water for a 90-day period, which resulted in a daily intake of about 5 g./kg.; but at 16 per cent concentrations there was a material reduction in fluid intake and two-thirds of the animals died with severely injured kidneys. The survivors also showed in some degree kidney injury similar to that produced by lower glycols.

Daily inunction of 2 ml./kg. of each of the three compounds on rabbits with a total of 90 applications resulted in no internal injury or skin irritation.

Daily intravenous injection of 1 g. per rabbit for a total of 30 doses resulted in no deaths from polyethylene glycols 200 and 300, while one of five receiving polyethylene glycol 400 died. Among survivors a small number revealed light cloudy swelling of the kidneys. Samples of polyethylene glycol 400 injected into man were readily excreted in the urine[25].

Solid Polyethylene Glycols. Middendorf[26] described toxicity studies with a polyethylene glycol suitable for a suppository base. He found no irritation on the rabbit ear or in the eye, and there was no effect seen after 25 oral doses of 10 g. each to dogs. Friedman[27], studying the use of polyethylene glycol 1500 as a vehicle for intravenous use, gave single injections to dogs without effect.

In single dose oral toxicity the solid polyethylene glycols follow the pattern of decreased toxicity with increased molecular weight, being less toxic than the liquid polyethylene glycols[24, 28, 29, 30]. Indeed one must give a dose close to the entire stomach content to kill even a portion of a group of small animals. Victims succumb to kidney damage and die with very high blood nonprotein nitrogen concentrations. Survivors have kidneys which are substantially normal. Single doses are absorbed from the rat and human digestive tract to a negligible extent, if at all, and intravenously injected samples are eliminated from the bloodstream of the dog and man by the kidney. The compounds can be recovered from the urine[29]. Absorption through the skin is negligible if it occurs at all, and sensitization of the human skin is unlikely[28], although isolated cases have been observed[31].

When administered in the drinking water of albino rats over a two-year period, 1.5 g./kg. per day (2 per cent in the water) of polyethylene glycol 1500 produced in 1941 did not injure the animals, nor did 0.06 g./kg. per day (0.08 per cent in the water) of polyethylene glycol 4000[24, 30]. Material produced in 1947 and later years is considerably less toxic chronically than the earlier products discussed in publications before 1950. Rats have tolerated for 90-day periods 2.5 per cent levels in the diet of polyethylene glycols 1500, 4000, 6000, and 10,000 with no adverse effect whatever[30]. It is concluded that currently produced solid polyethylene glycols show the same decreased toxicity as molecular weight is increased for both chronic and acute administration.

Small amounts of polyethylene glycol 4000 or 6000 have been used for some time as binders in pills. The most complete report of human administration in this fashion concerns the sublingual administration of desoxycorticosterone acetate for Addison's disease in tablets of polyethylene glycol 4000, the daily intake of the polyethylene glycol being 0.45 g.[32]. Fourteen patients were followed upon this regimen for periods of eighteen months to two years, with no evident effects from the polyethylene glycol vehicle. The daily dosage in this series of observations approximated 0.01 g./kg. per day.

The acute oral toxicities for rats of ethylene glycol and its condensation polymers are listed in Table 15.1[30]. The values are given in terms of the LD_{50} in grams dose per kilo body weight. The compounds were administered by stomach tube as approximately 50 per cent solutions in water. The values were calculated by the Bliss method of probits[33], except for the four values marked "RF," which were estimated graphically from the data on a small number of rats.

TABLE 15.1. SINGLE ORAL DOSE TOXICITIES OF ETHYLENE GLYCOL AND ITS CONDENSATION POLYMERS

Compound	LD_{50} for Rats, g./kg.
Ethylene glycol	8.5
Diethylene glycol	20.8
Triethylene glycol	22.1
Polyethylene glycol 200	34.0
Polyethylene glycol 300	38.9
Polyethylene glycol 400	43.6
"Carbowax" 1000	42 RF
"Carbowax" 1500	44.2
"Carbowax" 1540	51.2
"Carbowax" 4000	59* RF
"Carbowax" 6000	>50 RF
"Carbowax" 10,000	50 RF

* Data obtained from divided doses.

Ethylene Glycol Ethers. In single oral doses to animals the ethers of ethylene glycol are several times as toxic as the glycol itself, but in repeated doses they are quantitatively no more toxic than the glycol. There is no reason to believe that they are hydrolyzed in the body, and Wiley, Heuper,

Bergen, and Blood[6] could demonstrate no formation of oxalic acid from doses of ethylene glycol monomethyl ether or ethylene glycol diethyl ether given to rabbits and dogs. The ingestion of these ethers is not followed by immediate symptoms; and unless the dose is very large, death is delayed for four to six days, ultimately resulting from injury to kidney tubular epithelium. Hematuria is frequent from excessive doses, and hemorrhages in the digestive tract are found. Narcosis is marked only with certain aromatic ethers such as ethylene glycol monobenzyl ether. The ethers differ quantitatively among themselves in toxicity, but all the evidence points to qualitative similarity in action.

Laug, Calvery, Morris, and Woodard[10], on the basis of studies of the acute oral toxicity of ethylene glycol monoethyl ether, concluded that this ether is not suitable for internal consumption, and their view has been generally accepted as applying to all ethers of ethylene glycol. Morris, Nelson, and Calvery[11] have reported upon doses of ethylene glycol monoethyl ether in the diet of rats over a two year period, at the single dosage level of 1.45 per cent, probably equivalent to about 0.9 g./kg. per day. They found none of the oxalate concretions in kidney or bladder which they reported for ethylene glycol. Livers were normal, kidneys only slightly damaged, and the only significant effect was marked tubular atrophy in the testes with interstitial edema. It appears from this that the chronic toxicity of ethylene glycol monoethyl ether is less than that of ethylene glycol.

The single oral dose toxicities for rats of a number of ethylene glycol ethers[34] are listed in Table 15.2 in terms of the LD_{50} in grams dose per kilo body weight. These data are to be regarded only as comparative because small differences in character of the animals will change slightly the numerical values.

TABLE 15.2. SINGLE ORAL DOSE TOXICITIES OF ETHYLENE GLYCOL ETHERS

Ethylene Glycol Ether	LD_{50} for Rats, g./kg.
Methyl	2.46
Ethyl	3.00
Butyl	1.48
Isopropyl	4.35
n-Propyl	4.89
Diethyl	4.39
Dibutanyl	4.5
Allyl phenyl	4.26
Benzyl	1.19
Phenyl	1.26
Phenyl ethyl	3.2
α-Methyl benzyl	2.29

It has been found that the ethers penetrate the intact skin of animals. The LD_{50} values by this route in guinea pigs and rabbits are about twice the corresponding oral values in the same species when the applications remain in contact with the skin 24 hours or longer. Locally the skin reveals erythema but not necrosis.

The only human fatality which has been reported is that described by Young and Woolner[35]. A young man drank approximately 240 ml. of ethylene glycol monomethyl ether mixed with rum. He was admitted to a hospital in a comatose condition and died five hours later. His urine contained ethanol but no methanol, confirming the absence of hydrolysis of glycol ethers. Examination of organs revealed marked toxic degeneration in kidney tubules and fatty degeneration of the liver. This case is inadequate for estimating the fatal human dose because there is no assurance that a much smaller imbibition would not have been equally disastrous.

Browning[5] mentions three human instances of minor complaints as a result of exposure to ethylene glycol monobutyl ether vapors. One man had hematuria twice during five months, and two girls suffered irritation of nose and eyes, with headache.

The other reports of transient industrial injuries concern ethylene glycol monomethyl ether vapors. Donley[36] described one case with anemia, drowsiness, disorientation, and psychopathic symptoms as a result of "fusing" shirt collars by dipping them in a mixture containing 3 per cent ethylene glycol monomethyl ether and 74 per cent isopropanol. Vapor exposure was considerable because the wet collars were then pressed with heat. Two years later the Parsons[37] reported two similar cases in the same industry. There was a depression of the bone marrow activity, nausea, and symptoms resembling low-grade narcosis, described as encephalopathy. As a result of this report, Greenburg, Mayers, Goldwater, Burke, and Moskowitz[38, 39] investigated this factory and another having a similar installation but using acetone and methanol in place of the ethylene glycol monomethyl ether-denatured alcohol formula. All 19 workers with the glycol ether revealed abnormalities in the blood picture, suggesting macrocytic anemia, with some degree of lassitude, tremors, and abnormal reflexes; those in the other plant were normal. It was obvious that before the two men previously affected had sought medical aid, the local exhaust system at the pressing machines had become clogged with lint, and vapor concentrations inhaled must have been excessive. This neglect had been remedied before the survey of Greenburg, and analysis of the atmosphere revealed 25 to 76 ppm. ethylene glycol monomethyl ether vapors at that time. Despite ignorance of the concentrations which had caused the injuries, the authors concluded that human exposures should be kept below 25 ppm.

Waite, Patty, and Yant[40] concluded from experiments with guinea pigs that 1000 ppm. ethylene glycol monoethyl ether vapors would cause slight symptoms if inhaled for several hours, but that 6000 ppm., substantial saturation at room temperatures, would not kill within one hour. This concentration was irritating to human eyes and had a disagreeable odor. Accordingly, those authors felt that the warning power of the vapors was adequate to protect workers.

Werner and co-workers[41] determined the concentrations of five ethers which were 50 per cent lethal to mice after a single 7-hour inhalation. The values were: methyl, 1480 ppm.; ethyl, 1820; n-propyl, 1530; isopropyl, 1930; and butyl, 700. The concentrations are all appreciable fractions of saturation at room temperature, from one-seventh for methyl to 70 per cent for butyl. Death was due to lung and kidney injury, mostly within 24 hours of the exposure, but sometimes four weeks later. The same authors[42] exposed rats seven hours a day for 25 days to concentrations of the six ethers of 300 to 400 ppm., and concluded that the effects were qualitatively similar. There were no external signs of toxic action, and no kidney or lung pathology. There were reversible changes in the bone marrow, evidence of red blood cell destruction in the spleen, anemia, and a shift in the white cell picture toward immature forms. They concluded that the first signs of industrial injuries would be found in the blood picture.

These authors next reported[43] on the exposure of two dogs each for 60 seven-hour periods to concentrations of 750 ppm. ethylene glycol monomethyl ether, 840 ppm. ethylene glycol monoethyl ether, and 415 ppm. ethylene glycol monobutyl ether (7, 16, and 42 per cent of saturation, respectively). These exposures produced no irreversible changes. Microcytic anemia was found with the methyl ether, and a shift to immature white cell forms was seen.

These animal studies confirmed the character of the effects from ethylene glycol monomethyl ether reported in the shirt collar industry, but the concentrations required to injure animals were several times that suggested by Greenburg as a maximum permissable limit. It is usual that concentrations based on animal work agree more closely than this with those derived from human observation. One can conclude that the improvement in ventilation in the plant studied by Greenburg produced a major change in concentration from the time the injuries were suffered to the time of the survey. In accord with this view, Cook[44] suggests 100 ppm. as the maximum permissable concentration for the methyl ether vapors in industry. He suggests 200 ppm. for the ethyl and butyl ethers of ethylene glycol.

Diethylene Glycol Ethers. In single oral doses to animals, the ethers of diethylene glycol are two or more times as toxic as the glycol but less toxic than the ethers of ethylene glycol. In repeated doses they are several times less toxic than the glycol. The ingestion of these ethers in large doses produces prostration and coma, with death in usually one or two days, due chiefly to kidney injury.

Laug, Calvery, Morris, and Woodard[10] reported upon the acute oral toxicity of diethylene glycol monoethyl ether to animals, the LD_{50} for rats being 5.54 g./kg., for mice 6.58, and for guinea pigs 3.87. As a result of this study, the group concluded that the compound should not be employed in preparations intended for internal consumption, and apparently this view applies equally to other ethers of diethylene glycol.

The single dose toxicities for rats of several of the diethylene glycol ethers[34] are listed in Table 15.3 in terms of the LD_{50} in grams dose per kilo body weight. The values are to be taken as revealing the relative toxicity between members of the group, but differences in technique cause dif-

TABLE 15.3. SINGLE ORAL DOSE TOXICITIES OF DIETHYLENE GLYCOL ETHERS

Diethylene Glycol Ether	LD_{50} for Rats, g./kg.
Methyl	9.21
Ethyl (pure)	8.69
Ethyl (commercial)	9.05
Butyl	6.56
n-Hexyl	4.9
2-Ethylhexyl	6.0
Cyclohexyl	3.2
Trimethylcyclohexyl	3.2
α-Methylbenzyl	3.6
Diethyl	4.97

ferences in the absolute values between these and some figures from other sources.

The same laboratory found that the absorption through intact skin of animals is high; in some cases a given amount held on the skin for 24 hours was more injurious than the same amount administered in a single dose by mouth.

Two groups agree[45, 46] that diethylene glycol monoethyl ether is practically nonirritating to the skin of humans and that its sensitizing power is so weak that no large incidence of contact dermatitis should follow its use in preparations to be applied to the skin. Meininger[46] was unable to find any evidence of skin penetration when large doses were applied repeatedly to human skins. This report serves to discount other observations of skin penetration in experimental animals.

The first report upon the chronic toxicity of diethylene glycol monoethyl ether was that of Morris, Nelson, and Calvery[11], who administered 2.16 per cent of a purified preparation[47] in the diet of rats for two years. No kidney injury was found and there was no adverse effect upon growth or life span, but oxalate concretions and edematous testes reported for ethylene glycol and its ethyl ether occurred to a very limited extent. In the absence of details of the degree of purification of the sample, it is possible to debate that these adverse effects may have been due to small amounts of ethylene glycol or even of the ethyl ether of ethylene glycol, present as impurities. Such effects have not been confirmed by others.

More extensive studies of the ethyl ether of diethylene glycol have recently appeared from the laboratories of Hanzlik[48, 49, 50, 51]. These workers found slight, if any, effect upon rats receiving 1 per cent in the drinking water or mice receiving 5 per cent in the diet over a two-year period. They conclude that the pure ether is comparatively noninjurious, but with the commercial product, which contains a notable amount of ethylene glycol, they obtained injury proportional to the glycol content and typical of the action of the latter compound. These workers studied skin penetration in rabbits and concluded that 0.04 ml./kg. per day was harmless over a 30-day period. They report that the ether is largely oxidized in the body, is not hydrolyzed to the glycol, and causes an increase in glucuronates in the urine. Indeed, they find many similarities between the behavior of propylene glycol and pure diethylene glycol monoethyl ether in the body. They conclude that moderate use of the diethylene glycol ether in cosmetics is harmless, but that a pure product is preferable to the commercial grade.

Several years ago the United States Food and Drug Administration[52] stated that ethylene glycol, diethylene glycol, or the ethyl ether of diethylene glycol should not be used in excess of 5 per cent in a preparation for topical application to small areas of the body, and that where large areas were to be treated any content of these compounds might be a hazard.

Other diethylene glycol ethers have been less thoroughly studied. There are no reports of human injuries due to any of them. Kesten, Mulinos, and Pomerantz[53] found that the methyl and butyl ethers had effects on rats similar to those of the ethyl ether and diethylene glycol when administered over a brief period. Another laboratory[54] found the relative subacute oral toxicity for rats during 30 days of dosing to be as follows: pure diethylene glycol monoethyl ether, one; commercial diethylene glycol monoethyl ether, two; diethylene glycol monobutyl ether, four; and diethylene glycol monomethyl ether, eight. The same group in an unpublished two-year oral dose study on rats found the chronic toxicity of commercial diethylene glycol monoethyl ether to be 20 times that of the pure grade.

The only information on inhalation of diethylene glycol monoethyl ether vapors is that of Gross[22], who found no injury to mice, cats, rabbits, and guinea pigs from 12 days inhalation of nearly saturated vapors.

Ethers of Polyethylene Glycols. The only data available on the toxicity of ethers of polyethylene glycols are largely unpublished. Some scattered data are listed in Table 15.4 in terms of the rat oral LD_{50} from single doses[34, 54].

In doses administered to rats in the diet for 30 days, 0.75 g./kg. per day of ethoxytriethylene glycol had no effect[54], indicating a lower toxicity than that of diethylene glycol monoethyl ether. Larger doses produced kidney injury.

Esters. Esters of the ethylene glycols are readily saponified in the body and produce effects similar to the individual actions of the glycol and acid.

The quantitative acute oral toxicities of a few esters are listed in Table 15.5[34] in terms of the LD_{50} for rats. It will be seen that there is no regularity in the relationship between the toxicity of ester and glycol, ethylene glycol monoacetate being half as toxic as the glycol, and the diacetate almost the same as the glycol.

Ethylene glycol monoacetate forms oxalic acid in the body to about the same extent as does ethylene glycol, and it is equally injurious to the

TABLE 15.4 SINGLE ORAL DOSE TOXICITIES OF POLYETHYLENE GLYCOL ETHERS

Polyethylene Glycol Ether	LD_{50} for Rats, g./kg.
Ethoxytriethylene glycol	10.61
Hexoxytriethylene glycol	2.2
Dimethoxytetraethylene glycol	5.14
Dibutoxytetraethylene glycol	6.5
Methoxypolyethylene glycol 370	22.0
Methoxypolyethylene glycol 550	40.0
Methoxypolyethylene glycol 750	40.0
Butoxypolyethylene glycols	5.6 to 15.2 (depending on molecular weight)

TABLE 15.5. SINGLE ORAL DOSE TOXICITIES OF ESTERS OF ETHYLENE GLYCOL AND ITS CONDENSATION POLYMERS

Ethylene Glycol Ester	LD_{50} for Rats, g./kg.
Ethylene glycol monoacetate	8.25
Ethylene glycol diacetate	6.85
Ethylene glycol diformate	1.51
Diethylene glycol diacetate	8.0
Diethylene glycol dipropionate	4.5
Triethylene glycol di(2-ethylbutyrate)	8.42
Triethylene glycol di(2-ethylhexanoate)	31.37
Tetraethylene glycol di(2-ethylhexanoate)	18.0
Polyethylene glycol 400 mono-oleate	78.0
Polyethylene glycol 400 monostearate	100.0

kidneys[6]. The inhalation of saturated vapors by animals[22] for eight hours on twelve days gave albuminuria, lung irritation, and kidney damage, but no death among cats, guinea pigs, and monkeys. One rabbit, however, died. Inhalation of a mist of 28 mg./l. by cats[55] for 6 hours on two days killed the animals.

Ethylene glycol diacetate in single and repeated doses to animals behaves like ethylene glycol, and quantitatively its effects are nearly identical[7, 53].

Lard fatty acid esters of glycols were studied by Lepkovsky, Ouer, and Evans[56] in regard to nutrition. It appears that they are saponified in the digestive tract and the fatty acids utilized for nutrition. However, ethylene and diethylene glycol esters were so toxic at levels of 25 and 60 per cent in the diet of rats that serious kidney injury and sometimes death resulted. Propylene glycol esters were not toxic. Using a similar method, Shaffer and Critchfield[57] showed that the fatty acid of polyethylene glycol 400 monostearate is utilized for nutrition.

During a 30-day experiment rats were not affected in any way by the presence of 8 per cent of polyethylene glycol 400 monostearate in their diet, resulting in the consumption of 6.2 g./kg. per day.

Ethylene glycol dinitrate lowers blood pressure by dilation of the blood vessels and forms notable amounts of methemoglobin[58]. It is more readily absorbed through the skin than nitroglycerin[59], and in cats by various routes is about twice as toxic as the latter. Inhalation of 2 ppm. (0.013 mg./l.) eight hours a day for 1000 days causes only transient blood changes in cats, while 21 ppm. (0.134 mg./l.) for the same period causes no other injury than marked blood changes. In the formation of methomoglobin and Heinz bodies it is four times as active as nitroglycerin and 10 to 20 times as active as ethylene glycol mononitrate. Chronic poisoning involves anemia, irreversible red blood cell changes, fatty changes in heart muscle, liver, and kidney, and hyperplasia of the bone marrow. Human fatalities that resulted suddenly 24 to 48 hours after exposure have not been adequately explained[59].

Ether-Esters. Esters of ethylene glycol ethers are apparently saponified in the body and produce effects similar to those of the glycol ether and the acid. The acute oral toxicities of a few esters are listed in Table 15.6[34] in terms of the LD_{50} for rats. Each of these esters is somewhat less toxic acutely than the corresponding ether.

Skin absorption as measured by mortality following 24-hour contact with the rabbit skin is appreciable, but the LD_{50} by this route is one-third or less than the oral LD_{50} for the same species. There has been one report of human injury from skin absorption of one of these compounds[60]. A three-year-old child suffered nephrosis which was blamed upon excessive use of an insect repellent containing diethylene glycol monobutyl ether acetate as active ingredient.

TABLE 15.6 SINGLE ORAL DOSE TOXICITIES OF ETHER-ESTERS OF
ETHYLENE GLYCOL AND DIETHYLENE GLYCOL

Ether-Ester	LD$_{50}$ for Rats, g./kg.
Of Ethylene Glycol	
Ethyl ether acetate	5.1
Methyl ether acetate	3.93
α-Methylbenzyl ether acetate	5.6
Di(butyl ether phthalate)	8.38
Methyl ether oleate	11.21
Of Diethylene Glycol	
Ethyl ether acetate	11.0
Methyl ether acetate	11.96
Butyl ether acetate	11.92

Cook[44] considers that a reasonable maximum allowable vapor concentration for industrial exposure to ethylene glycol monoethyl ether acetate or ethylene glycol monomethyl ether acetate is 100 ppm.

Flury and Wirth[61] conclude on the basis of animal experiment that ethylene glycol monomethyl ether acetate vapor is ten times as toxic as ethylene oxide but one-tenth as toxic as methanol. It is irritating to eyes and nose and reduces hemoglobin level and red blood cell count.

Ethylene Chlorohydrin. The toxicity of ethylene chlorohydrin is sufficiently great so that the material must be handled with special precautions to prevent inhalation of the vapor or wetting of the skin. New installations should be designed with preventive measures in mind. Rubber gloves are inadequate protection for the skin because the chemical, even in aqueous solution, easily penetrates them[62].

The literature carries reports of eight deaths and 21 serious poisonings by ethylene chlorohydrin among industrial workers[63, 64, 65, 66, 67, 68, 69]. These were caused by inhalation of vapors, skin penetration of fluid, or a combination of the two. Only one of the deaths[69] occurred as a result of normal operations in the manufacture of the compound, the victim having been injured by chronic action during a two-month period. The other seven were the result of abuse of the chemical, such as its use for cleaning machinery, or of neglect of ordinary precautions.

For only one accident was a sufficiently complete description of the exposure published to allow estimation of the fatal human dose[68]. It was established that the victim died as the result of working two and one-quarter hours without respiratory protection in an atmosphere containing 1 mg. of ethylene chlorohydrin vapor per liter (305 ppm.). If the very doubtful points are granted, *i.e.*, that his rubber gloves prevented all skin penetration and that all vapor in the inhaled air was absorbed by the lungs, then this man was killed by a dose of approximately 3.5 g. Animal experi-

ment[62, 70] indicates that an amount of fluid of this order might also have
been fatal if it were allowed to absorb through the skin without any inhalation or if it had been swallowed.

The symptoms and pathology of severe and fatal poisoning by ethylene
chlorohydrin are described by Goldblatt and Chiesmann[69]. They conclude
that the compound is a violent cerebral and vascular poison, also injurious
to the liver and kidney. Such poisoning is characterized by a delay of
several hours in the development of symptoms and may have a chronic
effect. Men in poor physical condition are more readily injured than
those in good health, and personal idiosyncrasy plays a role in the sever-
ity of symptoms. They consider that no measurable concentration of the
vapor is safe to inhale if exposure is a daily occurence.

These authors and Goldblatt[70] believe vapor inhalation is the chief hazard in the production of ethylene chlorohydrin, but they warn of the dangers
of skin absorption from wearing soiled garments. Skin contact is particularly dangerous because the absence of irritation prevents any warning
when the skin is wetted. They state that one segment of British industry
is in accord with their view that frequent analyses of the working atmosphere should be performed with a view to keeping vapor concentrations
below 2 ppm. They believe that persons working with the chemical should
receive frequent medical examinations because the onset of poisoning is
subtle and irreparable damage may be done before clinical symptoms are
marked.

American experience in the production of ethylene chlorohydrin has
been more favorable than that in Britain. The only reported fatalities
occurring in this country resulted from the abuse of the compound by substituting it as a metal cleaner for a petroleum product[68] and in careless
handling in the treatment of seed potatoes to produce sprouting[71].
McLaughlin[72] reported, however, that when the fluid or its concentrated
aqueous solutions are splashed into the eye serious corneal injury may
result which, if not treated properly, will cause loss of vision.

Ethylene Oxide. Ethylene oxide is an irritant anesthetic vapor[73]. Anesthesia may result in prompt death from respiratory paralysis, from lung
edema somewhat later, or after a few days from liver and kidney damage.
It is stated that concentrations used in fumigation are not highly toxic for
man, but that they can cause cyanosis[74]. In many parts of the world the
use of ethylene oxide in fumigation is regulated by law, and injuries from
this use are rare.

Waite, Patty, and Yant[75] reported that guinea pigs are killed in a short
time by 50,000 to 100,000 ppm., that 3000 to 6000 ppm. is dangerous in
30 to 60 minutes, and that 250 ppm. caused slight symptoms in several
hours. Prompt death was due to respiratory paralysis and lobar pneumonia,

with kidney damage responsible for later deaths. *The odor of ethylene oxide is inadequate to serve as a warning of dangerous concentrations.* Walker and Greeson[76] reported that 2500 ppm. is not unpleasant to man. Flury[77] reported that 250 ppm. has some effect upon humans, 500 ppm. is dangerous, and that 1000 ppm. irritates the mucous membrane at once. In injured animals he found lung edema, hyperemia in the brain, and fatty degeneration of liver and kidney. He explained delayed injury on the basis of oxidation to aldehydes in the body.

The few reported cases of human injury[78, 79] show the first signs of excessive exposure to be irritation of the pharynx, nose, and eyes, with a peculiar taste evident. Later come headache, vertigo, nausea, dyspnea, dullness, respiratory and heart disturbances. Pulmonary edema has been produced, lymphocytosis is found, and bile pigments are excreted in the urine.

Skin exposure to liquid ethylene oxide, concentrated or dilute, can cause severe delayed burns. Sexton and Henson[80] reported three cases of second-degree burns which resulted from prolonged contact with a 1 per cent aqueous solution of ethylene oxide. Very large blebs formed within 6 to 12 hours after the exposure and appeared without significant redness, itching, burning, or pain. The onset was sudden and rapidly progressive to the maximum involvement. The magnitude of the dermatological manifestations was roughly proportional to the length of exposure time and was usually greater on hairy than on smooth skin.

Dioxane. In 1933 the death of five British workmen[81] called attention to the toxicity of dioxane, but no later incidents have been reported. These men worked in an experimental unit treating cellulose acetate yarn with the solvent, and all died at about the same time, shortly after a change in the operation had increased exposure. One of the victims succumbed only five days after he started work. Apparently a few intense exposures were responsible, not chronic toxicity. The illnesses developed over two weekends, following 12-hour work shifts in place of the 8-hour shifts performed early in the week. The men inhaled nearly saturated vapors for brief periods several times a day as they manipulated yarn in tanks of the solvent without the protection of local exhaust ventilation. The cause of death was hemorrhagic nephritis with central necrosis of the liver. Eighty men on other operations nearby were examined and mild symptoms were found, such as coughing, misty vision, drowsiness, dizziness, headache, gastrointestinal distress, poor appetite, nausea, tender liver, increased leucoytes, and neutrophiles.

Experiments with animals partly confirm the observations upon the five fatalities. A vapor concentration of 30,000 ppm., substantial saturation, kills guinea pigs after three hours' inhalation[82, 83], but 10,000 ppm. is not fatal in eight hours. The authors believe health hazard from vapors is slight until saturation is approached, but they fail to study micropathology. They also believe eye and nose irritation is adequate to warn humans against excessive inhalation. This fact is disputed by Fairley, Linton, and Ford-Moore[84], who exposed a variety of species repeatedly for $1\frac{1}{2}$ hours a day to approximate the exposure of the human victims. They found 10,000 ppm. killed all with lung edema or toxic pneumonia, 5000 ppm. killed most with kidney and liver injury, while 1000 and 2000 ppm. were not fatal but produced severe injury to those organs and elevated blood urea.

Fairley and his colleagues[85] believed the formation of oxalic acid in the body is largely responsible for the toxicity of dioxane, but Wiley, Heuper, Bergen, and Blood[6] found no oxalic acid in the urine after repeated injections. They state that this absence proves no more than that no large part of the dose is oxidized to oxalic acid, but they state that hydrolysis to ethylene glycol is impossible because that compound does result in detectable oxalic acid in the urine. Their finding of calcium-bearing debris in pyramidal kidney tubules probably represents calcification of necrotized tissue.

De Navasquez[86] studied oral and intravenous doses of dioxane in guinea pigs, rabbits, and cats. The first effect of a fatal dose was narcosis, then greatly increased urine flow. Within two days urine flow ceased entirely, blood urea rose, and death from uremia followed in three to four days more. In animals, kidney injury was confined to the secreting tubular epithelium, leading to hydropic degeneration, swelling, and consequent anuria. The human victims suffered instead necrosis of the interlobular arteries and parenchyma. This author is convinced that the liver injury reported by others in animals, and perhaps also in humans, is no more than the presence of excessive glycogen, but this is disputed by Kesten, Mulinos, and Pomerantz[53]. They found that animal livers returned completely to normal soon after a nonfatal dose, and thus concluded that the toxicity of dioxane to humans is low and that large doses are needed to produce fatal effects.

Laug, Calvery, Morris, and Woodard[10] studied the effect of single oral doses upon small animals and found the LD_{50} to vary from 4 to 6 ml./kg. with the species. Micropathology from the doses resembled that from diethylene glycol—hydropic degeneration of kidney convoluted tubular epithelium and similar degeneration of liver parenchymatous cells with vacuoles. Fatty degeneration of the liver was not produced. Kesten, Mulinos, and Pomerantz[53] studied the effect of repeated oral doses upon rats. Five per cent in the drinking water (about 1 ml./kg. per day intake) killed most rats in 5 to 12 days, with liver and kidney damage like that described above. One per cent for 110 days followed by 3 per cent for 48 days did not kill, but caused liver and kidney injury. These authors disagree with De Navasquez[86] on the subject of liver injury. They were unable to show the presence of glycogen and hence dispute his explanation of what all others describe as central necrosis. Fairley, Linton, and Ford-Moore[84] showed clearly that dioxane is absorbed through the intact skin of animals.

The present-day attitude toward the safety of the use of dioxane is dictated by the five unfortunate deaths caused by gross abuse of the solvent. Wirth and Klimmer[87] state that dioxane is unsuited for use in cosmetics and pharmaceuticals and hazardous in surface coatings. It is doubtful if the preponderance of evidence fully justifies the sceptical regard given to this solvent. Certainly applications would be safe where infrequent or brief inhalation of low vapor concentrations are possible, for no investigator has uncovered evidence of marked chronic toxicity, and all recorded human injury has followed the inhalation of nearly saturated vapors.

Glyoxal. In single oral doses to rats the LD_{50} of glyoxal is 2.02 g./kg., corresponding to 40 per cent of the acute toxicity of formaldehyde[34]. When both aldehydes are applied as 40 per cent aqueous solutions to rabbit skins to evaluate the hazard by skin absorption, the LD_{50} of glyoxal is 6.6 g./kg. and formaldehyde is about ten times as toxic. In addition, the latter necroses the skin while glyoxal does not. Hynd[88] points out that glyoxal in the monomeric state is no different in action from that in the polymeric state, that symptoms of injury are delayed in onset, and that convulsions do not precede death.

Acetals. Nothing was found in the literature on the toxicity of the glycol acetals. Diethylene glycol monomethyl ether formal, however, has an oral LD_{50} for rats of 7.2 g./kg. It is only slightly more toxic than the methyl ether of diethylene glycol. Bloody urine and delayed death were prominent symptoms.

Glycolic Acid. In single oral doses, the LD_{50} of glycolic acid for rats is 1.95 g./kg., about twice the acute toxicity of lactic acid[34]. The maximum nontoxic daily oral dose of the sodium salt to cats is 100 ml./kg., but dogs tolerate five times as much for four months[89]. Larger amounts cause kidney injury. Glycolic acid does not form glycogen in the rat[90] nor increase glucuronic acid excretion[91], but it does somewhat increase citric acid in the urine of rats[92]. Oral doses do not increase urinary oxalic acid in humans[93], but two-thirds of an intramuscular injection in rabbits is found in the urine in the form of oxalic acid[94], although injection of oxalic acid itself results in a very little in the urine.

Propylene Glycol and Related Compounds

Propylene Glycol. The physiological properties of propylene glycol (1,2-propanediol) may be summarized in the words used in "New and Non-Official Remedies"[95]—"Its toxicity is similar to that of glycerin. As ordinarily applied, it may be called practically non-toxic."

The oral and intravenous LD_{50} values for small animals are close to 20 ml./kg.[10, 20, 96, 97]. Large oral doses produce minimal kidney changes[10], while large intravenous doses injure this organ more severely[53] in addition to causing hemolysis of red blood cells[53, 96, 98]. The narcotic action of propylene glycol is about one-third that of ethanol[99], and the anesthetic dose for dogs is about four-fifths of the fatal dose[97]. The glycol is rapidly absorbed from the intestinal tract of dogs and distributed throughout the tissues[96]. From one-fourth to one-half of an oral or intravenous dose to rats, dogs, or human beings appears unchanged in the urine within 24 hours[96, 97, 98, 99, 100]. In rats, propylene glycol can partially replace carbohydrate in the diet, and in doses greater than 0.75 ml./kg. about 15 per cent of the glycol fed is stored in the liver in the form of glycogen for future energy requirements[101, 102].

Rats and rabbits have been maintained for long periods of time upon diets or drinking water containing up to 10 per cent of propylene glycol without injury[53, 97, 103, 104, 105, 106], although Holck[107] reported injury from 3.58 per cent in the drinking water in an 11-week experiment. By adding very high levels of propylene glycol and glycerol to the diet of rats, Whitlock, Guerrant, and Dutcher[100] have shown that glycerol is less injurious. The difference between the actions of the two compounds is not evident until the concentration is raised to 30 per cent. At this level rats receiving the glycol grow slowly and fail to wean their young, while animals on the same level of glycerol were normal to the fifth generation. The authors account for part of the difference on the grounds that glycerol is the more completely metabolized, very little appearing in the urine. They point out that the dosage levels employed are so high that the results have no bearing upon practical use of the glycol. Air saturated with propylene glycol vapors has proved to result in no ill effects in animals exposed for periods of 12 to 18 months[18].

Since 1942, propylene glycol has been included in "New and Non-Official Remedies" as a proper ingredient for pharmaceutical products. It is accepted as an ingredient of dental preparations[108], and the United States Food and Drug Administration does not object to its use as a solvent in food products to replace other solvents[109]. A rather wide usage has resulted in foods, drugs, and preparations for topical application, and no evidence of injury to humans has been reported. One notable clinical report[110] discusses the treatment of a 15-year-old boy with a vitamin preparation, during which a total of 2400 ml. of propylene glycol was administered as a solvent within a period of five months without causing injury.

There is reason to suspect that propylene glycol enhances the skin absorption of other compounds. Due to its low toxicity, however, it is not itself objectionable upon the skin[47].

Trimethylene Glycol. Trimethylene glycol (1,3-propanediol) is about twice as toxic as propylene glycol to small animals in single and repeated doses. It does not form glycogen in the liver[111].

Dipropylene Glycol. Dipropylene glycol does not share the toxicological inactivity of propylene glycol. Hanzlik and his colleagues[97] reported that in single doses to small animals it is about twice as toxic as the latter, although it is less harmful than ethylene glycol and diethylene glycol. The single dose toxicity of *redistilled* samples appears to be identical with that of propylene glycol (see Table 15.7). A sample of dipropylene glycol having an oral LD_{50} of 14.8 g./kg. to rats had an LD_{50} of 10.3 and 5.7 g./kg. by the intraperitoneal and intravenous routes, respectively. It is therefore possible that only the effects of material less pure than could be made available if the need were shown, have been reported hitherto.

Dipropylene glycol is not utilized by the liver nor is it stored as glycogen[102, 112]. While propylene glycol stimulates the voluntary running activity of rats, dipropylene glycol depresses this index of well-being, although the latter has less effect than do ethylene glycol and diethylene glycol[113]. Rats were not affected by 5 per cent dipropylene glycol in their drinking water for 77 days; at a level of 10 per cent, some died with hydropic degeneration of kidney tubular epithelium and liver parenchyma. These effects were similar to those of diethylene glycol, but less severe and less uniformly produced[53].

Tripropylene Glycol. No investigation has been made of the toxicity of tripropylene glycol. One sample known to consist of 85 per cent dipropylene glycol and 15 per cent tripropylene glycol, sold for a commercial application, was found to be twice as toxic as propylene glycol in single oral doses to rats (matching data in the literature for dipropylene glycol). However, it produced no effect when fed to rats in the drinking water for 90 days at a dosage of 2.45 g./kg. per day.

Polypropylene Glycols. Polypropylene glycols are available in a range of molecular weights extending from 425 to 2025. A comparative study was made on their acute toxicity to rats by the oral, intraperitoneal, and intravenous routes. Calculated on a molar basis, these data indicate a peak in toxicity somewhere near the middle of this range:

	LD_{50}, millimols/kg.		
	Oral	I.P.	I.V.
Polypropylene glycol 425	6.85	1.08	0.96
Polypropylene glycol 1025	2.10	0.22	0.10
Polypropylene glycol 2025	4.82	2.21	0.35

A polypropylene glycol with an average molecular weight of 750 produced ventricular extrasystoles when administered intravenously in an anesthetized dog[114]. The total amount required to produce the extrasystoles varied (10 to 90 mg./kg.) from animal to animal, but the duration appeared to depend on the total amount of polypropylene glycol administered rather than on the size of a single dose. The polymer of average molecular weight 425 was found to be similar to that of 750 molecular weight in its ability to produce ventricular extrasystoles in dogs, and was effective at a low dosage either by injection or by mouth.

Ethers. Ethers of propylene glycol are similar to those of ethylene glycol in being narcotic agents and causing kidney injury. Their toxicity is greater than that of propylene glycol, and they do not share its lack of injurious effect. Only fragmentary information upon toxicity of these and other propylene glycol derivatives is available.

Gross[22] found that single inhalation of the monoethyl ether of propylene glycol by small animals at 30 mg./l. (7000 ppm.) for two hours produced no injury beyond albumin and red blood cells in the urine. Eight-hour inhalations at 5 mg./l. (1180 ppm.) for 12 days killed four of six small animals with lung and kidney injury.

In single oral doses to rats, one sample of the mixed isomers of the monoethyl ether was about one-third as toxic as the corresponding ethylene glycol ether. Both the *alpha* and *beta* isomers had similar toxicities[34]. Large single doses produced marked narcosis, and the kidneys of victims revealed necrosis of tubular epithelium. When given to rats in the drinking water for 30 days, 0.68 g./kg. per day had no effect and 2.14 g./kg. per day caused kidney pathology but not death[54]. This represents about one-fourth the subacute toxicity of the corresponding ethylene glycol ether.

The single oral dose toxicity to rats of the monomethyl ether, *alpha* isomer, was the same as that of the ethyl ether, but the *beta* isomer was a little more toxic[34]. Both were from one-half to one-third as toxic as the monomethyl ether of ethylene glycol.

The monoethyl ether of dipropylene glycol, a mixture of isomers, had the same single dose oral toxicity to rats as the corresponding ethylene glycol ether[34].

The monomethyl ether of dipropylene glycol is a central nervous system depressant of low toxicity[115]. When administered either orally or intravenously to an unanesthetized dog in amounts as large as 5 ml./kg., loss of righting reflexes and first plane anesthesia occur, with uniform recovery in 24 hours or less without any evidence of delayed toxicity. The lethal intravenous dose in the artificially respired anesthetized animal is approximately 1.3 ml./kg. The most interesting pharmacological action of this compound occurs in the artificially respired dog at a dose level of 0.65

to 0.75 ml./kg. At this dosage, auricular fibrillation occurs quite consistently.

Monobutyl ethers of polypropylene glycols are promising repellents for various species of flies[116]. They are synergists for pyrethrum. A butoxy polypropylene glycol with an average molecular weight of 546 was found to be slightly to moderately toxic on the basis of single oral doses to rats and rabbits. The LD_{50} for rats was 5.84 g./kg. when diluted with water 50 per cent; the LD_{50} for rabbits was 3.39 ml./kg. for the undiluted compound. By skin penetration, the compound was only one-fourth as toxic for rabbits as by the oral route. Single doses on the order of 2 g./kg. were well absorbed from the gastrointestinal tract of rabbits, and 25 to 55 per cent of the dose was excreted in the urine during the first 24 hours. Concentrations of this compound up to 4 per cent have been fed in the diet of rats for a period of 90 days. Judged by several criteria, the dosage level that produced no effect lies between 0.16 and 0.67 g./kg. per day. No storage of this compound was detected in the liver lipids of rats fed a 5 per cent level in the diet for 30 days. It is estimated that a minimum of 20 ppm. could have been determined.

Esters. In single oral doses to rats the toxicity of propylene glycol monoacetate is one and one-half times that of the glycol, and the toxicity of the diacetate is twice that of the glycol[34]. These acetates produce narcosis, and victims have necrosis of kidney tubular epithelium and liver parenchyma, unlike victims of large doses of propylene glycol.

Propylene glycol monostearate as available commercially was fed to rats for 30 days in the diet at a level of 0.54 g./kg. per day without producing any injury.

Propylene Oxide. In single oral doses to rats the LD_{50} of propylene oxide is 1.14 g./kg. and to guinea pigs 0.70 g./kg.[34]. Skin absorption is poor, the LD_{50} for a four-day poultice application to guinea pigs being 8.64 ml./kg. The inhalation of 400 ppm. vapors for two hours killed none of six guinea pigs while four hours' inhalation killed all with lung and kidney injury[34]. The vapors therefore are somewhat less toxic than those of ethylene oxide for the same concentration, and oral toxicity is one-fifth that of the ethylene compound dissolved in water.

The tetramer of propylene oxide (see page 277) was found to have a single dose oral toxicity for rats close to that of the monomer.

Dimethyl Dioxane. The acute toxicity of dimethyl dioxane is about twice that of dioxane, the rat oral LD_{50} being 3 g./kg. The inhalation of 8000 ppm. vapors for two hours killed two of six rats within 14 days, again about twice the toxicity of dioxane. Skin absorption is poor because 10 ml./kg. poulticed upon guinea pigs for four days killed none of six animals[34]. Nothing is known of its chronic toxicity.

TABLE 15.7. Single Dose Oral Toxicities of Propylene Glycol
AND Related Compounds

Compound	LD$_{50}$ for Rats, g./kg.
Propylene glycol[a]	26.4
Polypropylene glycol (85% di-, 15% triglycol)[a]	14.1
Polypropylene glycol 425	2.91
Polypropylene glycol 1025	2.15
Polypropylene glycol 2025	9.76
Ethyl ether of propylene glycol (mixed isomers)[a]	8.41
Ethyl ether of propylene glycol (*alpha* isomer)	7.11
Ethyl ether of propylene glycol (*beta* isomer)	7.0
Methyl ether of propylene glycol (*alpha* isomer)	7.51
Methyl ether of propylene glycol (*beta* isomer)	5.71
Ethyl ether of dipropylene glycol (mixed isomers)[a]	9.06
Propylene glycol monoacetate[a]	18.0
Propylene glycol diacetate[a]	13.5
Propylene oxide[a]	1.14
Propylene oxide tetramer[a]	1.8 RF
Dimethyl dioxane[a]	3.0 RF

[a] Commercial or pilot plant product. [b]

Tabulation. Table 15.7 lists for comparison the single dose oral toxicity
for rats of a number of propylene glycol derivatives. The tabulated data
are given in terms of the LD$_{50}$ calculated by the Bliss method of probits[33],
except for the two values marked "RF," which were estimated graphically
from the data on a small number of rats.

Higher Glycols

Only fragmentary toxicity data are available on most of the higher
glycols. About half of those mentioned in Chapter 14 have not been mentioned in the toxicology literature, and it is not known whether their
physiological properties have been studied. It is reasonable to assume that
their acute toxicity is low, but it would be rash to judge chronic toxicity
on the basis of those isomers which have been investigated.

1,3-Butanediol. In single doses 1,3-butanediol is about as toxic acutely
as diethylene glycol. In rabbits 15 g./kg. is fatal, resulting in death within
24 hours, accompanied by gastrointestinal irritation, with cloudy swelling
and glomerular congestion of the kidney but without albumin in the urine.
A dog was not injured by 2.4 g./kg., but 0.2 g./kg. given 14 times within
two weeks produced albuminuria[117].

The oral LD$_{50}$ for rats is given as 18.61 g./kg. and for guinea pigs as
11.46 g./kg.[34]. More recently, the LD$_{50}$ for rats has been found to be 22.8
g./kg.; 20 ml./kg. killed no rabbits by skin absorption in a 24-hour cuff

test. Eight per cent in the diet of rats, equivalent to about 5.6 g./kg. per day, over a 90-day period, did not cause death and had no effect upon appetite, weight increase, or weight of liver and kidney. Two of nine rats had light cloudy swelling of convoluted kidney tubules.

1,4-Butanediol. 1,4-Butanediol causes in animals a deep narcosis and damage to the kidneys. In acute poisoning, death is due to paralysis of the respiratory center[118].

2,3-Butanediol. 2,3-Butanediol is not oxidized to any considerable extent by the rabbit, but is excreted as a glucuronic acid conjugate. Rabbits tolerate doses of 5 ml./kg. without injury[119]. It is stated to be unsuited to internal use, injuring the kidney[120].

2,5-Hexanediol. The acute toxicity of 2,5-hexanediol is about twice that of ethylene glycol, the oral LD_{50} for rats being 5.0 g./kg. Skin absorption is poor, the LD_{50} for rabbits in a 24-hour cuff test being 16.3 ml./kg.[54].

2-Methyl-2,4-pentanediol. The acute toxicity for rats of 2-methyl-2,4-pentanediol is stated to be slightly less than that of dimethylphthalate, but its toxicity by skin absorption is considerably greater[121]. Its acute toxicity is about twice that of ethylene glycol, the rat oral LD_{50} being 4.7 g/kg. Skin absorption is poor, the rabbit LD_{50} in a 24-hour cuff test being 13.3 ml./kg.[54].

2,3-Dimethyl-2,3-butanediol (Pinacol). A single dose of 3 g. of pinacol had no effect on a large rabbit, while 10 g. caused sleep of 5 to 6 hours' duration. The compound was found in the urine as a glucuronic acid conjugate[119].

2,2-Diethyl-1,3-propanediol. The 2,2-diethyl derivative of trimethylene glycol (DEP) appears to be an unusually effective agent for the protection of mice and cats from metrazol and strychnine convulsions. According to Berger, Ludwig, and Russo[122], the toxicity of DEP is very low by all routes of administration. DEP is well absorbed, even after oral administration. It is rapidly inactivated in the body and has only a short duration of action. After large doses, DEP causes loss of the righting reflex and induces paralysis. After intraperitoneal administration of DEP in doses of 200 mg./kg. to mice (one-half of the mean paralyzing dose), metrazol in doses of 250 mg./kg. can be injected intravenously without producing persistent convulsions. Cats anesthetized with Dial and given intravenous doses of 50 mg./kg of DEP did not convulse after large doses of strychnine or metrazol[123]. Conversely, when convulsions were induced in such cats with these drugs, it was possible to control the seizures with DEP. Rapid intravenous injection of DEP was followed by slowing of the heart rate, a drop in mean arterial pressure, and a slowing or cessation of respiration.

2-Ethyl-1,3-hexanediol. Granett and Haynes[124] noted that 2-ethyl-

1,3-hexanediol can be applied to human skin without irritation or sensitization. Calvery, Draize, and Woodard[121] reported its acute oral toxicity to be intermediate in a group of twelve insect repellents, but that it was almost the least toxic when the twelve were tested for skin absorption.

The same investigators later gave the oral LD_{50} as 2.5 g./kg. for rats, 4.2 for mice, 1.9 for guinea pigs, and 1.4 for chickens. The LD_{50} on rabbits by skin absorption was above 10 ml./kg. but daily inunction on rabbits of 2 ml./kg. killed half of the animals within 90 days. No dermatitis was demonstrated in man. An excess of the compound caused hydropic degeneration in the kidney and moderate tubular atrophy in the testis, but animals which survived had no lesions. They concluded the compound is severely toxic when it enters the body but that skin absorption is poor[125].

During a period of 90 days, doses of 0.48 g./kg. per day produced no injury and 0.70 g./kg. per day retarded growth slightly without giving liver or kidney pathology.

2-Ethyl-2-butyl-1,3-propanediol. The rat oral LD_{50} of 2-ethyl-2-butyl-1,3-propanediol is 3.0 g./kg.

Literature Cited

1. Wiley, F. H., Hueper, W. C., and von Oettingen, W. F., *J. Ind. Hyg. Toxicol.*, **18,** 123 (1936).
2. Hansen, K., *Samml. Vergiftungsfällen*, **1,** 175 (1930).
3. Brekke, A., *Norsk Mag. Laegevidenskap.*, **91,** 381 (1930).
4. Pons, C. A., and Custer, R. P., *Am. J. Med. Sci.*, **211,** 544 (1946).
5. Browning, E., "Toxicity of Industrial Organic Solvents," London, H. M. Stationery Office, 1937.
6. Wiley, F. H., Hueper, W. C., Bergen, D. S., and Blood, F. R., *J. Ind. Hyg. Toxicol.*, **20,** 269 (1938).
7. Mulinos, M. G., Pomerantz, L., and Lojkin, M. E., *Am. J. Pharm.*, **115,** 51 (1943).
8. Fitzhugh, O. G., and Nelson, A. A., *J. Am. Pharm. Assoc., Sci. Ed.*, **36,** 217 (1947).
9. Miura, S., *Biochem. Z.*, **36,** 25 (1911).
10. Laug, E. P., Calvery, H. O., Morris, H. J., and Woodard, G., *J. Ind. Hyg. Toxicol.*, **21,** 173 (1939).
11. Morris, H. J., Nelson, A. A., and Calvery, H. O., *J. Pharmacol. Exptl. Therap.*, **74,** 266 (1942).
12. Calvery, H. O., and Klumpp, T. G., *Southern Med. J.*, **32,** 1105 (1939).
13. Akazaki, K., and Wakamatu, E., *Trans. Soc. Path. Japon.*, **29,** 405 (1939).
14. Cannon, P. R., *J. Am. Med. Assoc.*, **109,** 1537 (1937).
15. Newman, B. A., *J. Am. Med. Assoc.*, **111,** 25 (1938).
16. Haag, H. B., and Ambrose, A. M., *J. Pharmacol. Exptl. Therap.*, **59,** 93 (1937).
17. Fitzhugh, O. G., and Nelson, A. A., *J. Ind. Hyg. Toxicol.*, **28,** 40 (1946).
18. Robertson, O. H., Loosli, C. G., Puck, T. T., Wise, H., Lemon, H. M., and Lester, W., Jr., *J. Pharmacol. Exptl. Therap.*, **91,** 52 (1947).
19. Jennings, B. H., Bigg, E., and Olson, F. C. W., *Heating, Piping, Air Conditioning*, **16,** 538 (1944).
20. Latven, A. R., and Molitor, H., *J. Pharmacol. Exptl. Therap.*, **65,** 89 (1939).
21. Lauter, W. M., and Vrla, V. L., *J. Am. Pharm. Assoc., Sci. Ed.*, **29,** 5 (1940).

22. Gross, E., in Lehmann, K. B., and Flury, F., "Toxicology and Hygiene of Industrial Solvents," Baltimore, The Williams and Wilkins Co., 1943.
23. Smyth, H. F., Jr., Carpenter, C. P., and Shaffer, C. B., *J. Am. Pharm. Assoc., Sci. Ed.*, **34**, 172 (1945).
24. Smyth, H. F., Jr., Carpenter, C. P., and Shaffer, C. B., *J. Am .Pharm. Assoc., Sci. Ed.*, **36**, 157 (1947).
25. Shaffer, C. B., Critchfield, F. H., and Nair, J. H., *J. Am. Pharm. Assoc., Sci. Ed.*, **39**, 340 (1950).
26. Middendorf, L., *Münch. med. Wochnschr.*, **86**, 95 (1939).
27. Friedman, M. H. F., *J. Lab. Clin. Med.*, **29**, 530 (1944).
28. Smyth, H. F., Jr., Carpenter, C. P., Shaffer, C. B., Seaton, J., and Fischer, L., *J. Ind. Hyg. Toxicol.*, **24**, 281 (1942).
29. Shaffer, C. B., and Critchfield, F. H., *J. Am. Pharm. Assoc., Sci. Ed.*, **36**, 152 (1947).
30. Smyth, H. F., Jr., Carpenter, C. P., and Weil, C. S., *J. Am. Pharm. Assoc., Sci. Ed.*, **39**, 349 (1950).
31. Strauss, M. J., *Arch. Dermatol. Syphilol.*, **61**, 420 (1950).
32. Anderson, E., Kinsell, L. W., Daniels, T. C., and Henderson, E., *J. Clin. Endocrinol.*, **9**, 1324 (1949).
33. Bliss, C. I., *Ann. Applied Biol.*, **22**, 134–67 (1935).
34. Smyth, H. F., Jr., Seaton, J., and Fischer, L., *J. Ind. Hyg. Toxicol.*, **23**, 259 (1941).
35. Young, E. G., and Woolner, L. B., *J. Ind. Hyg. Toxicol.*, **28**, 267 (1946).
36. Donley, D. E., *J. Ind. Hyg. Toxicol.*, **18**, 571 (1936).
37. Parsons, C. E., and Parsons, M. E. M., *J. Ind. Hyg. Toxicol.*, **20**, 124 (1938).
38. Greenburg, L., Mayers, M. R., Goldwater, L. J., Burke, W. J., and Moskowitz, S., *J. Ind. Hyg. Toxicol.*, **20**, 134 (1938).
39. Greenburg, L., Mayers, M. R., Goldwater, L. J., and Burke, W. J., *J. Ind. Hyg. Toxicol.*, **20**, 148 (1938).
40. Waite, C. P., Patty, F. A., and Yant, W. P., *U. S. Pub. Health Service, Pub. Health Repts.*, **45**, 1459 (1930).
41. Werner, H. W., Mitchell, J. L., Miller, J. W., and von Oettingen, W. F., *J. Ind. Hyg. Toxicol.*, **25**, 157 (1943).
42. Werner, H. W., Nawrocki, C. Z., Mitchell, J. L., Miller, J. W., and von Oettingen, W. F., *J. Ind. Hyg. Toxicol.*, **25**, 374 (1943).
43. Werner, H. W., Mitchell, J. L., Miller, J. W., and von Oettingen, W. F., *J. Ind. Hyg. Toxicol.*, **25**, 409 (1943).
44. Cook, W. A., *Ind. Med.*, **14**, 936 (1945).
45. Cranch, A. G., Smyth, H. F., Jr., and Carpenter, C. P., *Arch. Dermatol. and Syphilol.*, **45**, 553 (1942).
46. Meininger, W. M., *Arch. Dermatol. and Syphilol.*, **58**, 19 (1948).
47. Calvery, H. O., Private communication to H. F. Smyth, Jr.
48. Hanzlik, P. J., Lawrence, W. S., and Laqueur, G. L., *J. Ind. Hyg. Toxicol.*, **29**, 233 (1947).
49. Hanzlik, P. J., Luduena, F. P., Lawrence, W. S., and Fellows, J. K., *Federation Proc.*, **6**, 336 (1947).
50. Hanzlik, P. J., Lawrence, W. S., Fellows, J. K., Luduena, F. P., and Laqueur, G. L., *J. Ind. Hyg. Toxicol.*, **29**, 325 (1947).
51. Fellows, J. K., Luduena, F. P., and Hanzlik, P. J., *J. Pharmacol. Exptl. Therap.*, **89**, 210 (1947).
52. U. S. Food and Drug Administration, Trade Correspondence 402 (May 14, 1943).
53. Kesten, H. D., Mulinos, N. G., and Pomerantz, L., *Arch. Path.*, **27**, 447 (1939).

54. Smyth, H. F., Jr., and Carpenter, C. P., *J. Ind. Hyg. Toxicol.*, **30**, 63 (1948).
55. Rosser, E., in Lehmann, K. B., and Flury, F., "Toxicology and Hygiene of Industrial Solvents," Baltimore, The Williams and Wilkins Co., 1943.
56. Lepkovsky, S., Ouer, R. A., and Evans, H. M., *J. Biol. Chem.*, **108**, 431 (1935).
57. Shaffer, C. B., and Critchfield, F. H., *Federation Proc.*, **7** (March, 1948).
58. Marshall, C. R., *J. Physiol. London*, **22**, 1 (1897–98).
59. Gross, E., Bock, M., and Helbrung, F., *Arch. exptl. Path. Pharmakol.*, **200**, 271 (1942).
60. Hoehn, D., *J. Am. Med. Assoc.*, **128**, 513 (1945).
61. Flury, F., and Wirth, W., *Arch. Gewerbepath. Gewerbehyg.*, **5**, 52 (1934).
62. Smyth, H. F., Jr., and Carpenter, C. P., *J. Ind. Hyg. Toxicol.*, **27**, 93 (1945).
63. Koelsch, F., *Zentr. ges. Hyg. u. Grenzg.*, **14**, 312 (1927).
64. Middleton, E. L., *J. Ind. Hyg. Toxicol.*, **12**, 265 (1930).
65. Molitoris (1931) and Kaminski and Seelkopf (1933), quoted by Lehmann, K. B., and Flury, F., "Toxicology and Hygiene of Industrial Solvents," Baltimore, The Williams and Wilkins Co., 1943.
66. Browning, E., Industrial Health Research Board, Rept. 80, H. M. Stationery Office, 1937.
67. Cavallazzi, D., *Samml. Vergiftungsfällen*, **12**, 79 (1942).
68. Dierker, H., and Brown, P. G., *J. Ind. Hyg. Toxicol.*, **26**, 277 (1944).
69. Goldblatt, M. W., and Chiesman, W. E., *Brit. J. Ind. Med.*, **1**, 207 (1944).
70. Goldblatt, M. W., *Brit. J. Ind. Med.*, **1**, 213 (1944).
71. Bush, A. F., Abrams, H. D., and Brown, H. V., *J. Ind. Hyg. Toxicol.*, **31**, 352 (1949).
72. McLaughlin, R. S., *Am. J. Opthalmology*, **29**, 1355 (1946).
73. Hess, L. G., and Tilton, V. V., *Ind. Eng. Chem.*, **42**, 1251 (1950).
74. Cotton, R. T., and Roark, R. C., *Ind. Eng. Chem.*, **20**, 805 (1928).
75. Waite, C. P., Patty, F. A., and Yant, W. P., *U. S. Pub. Health Service, Pub. Health Rpts.*, **45**, 1832 (1930).
76. Walker, W. J. G., and Greeson, C. E., *J. Hyg.*, **32**, 409 (1932).
77. Flury, F., *Arch. exptl. Path. Pharmakol.*, **157**, 107 (1931).
78. Enke, H., Inaugural Dissertation, Cologne, 1936, quoted in "Occupation and Health," International Labour Office, 1939.
79. Metz, E., *Arztl. Sachverst. Ztg.*, **44**, 155 (1938).
80. Sexton, R. J., and Henson, E. V., *J. Ind. Hyg. Toxicol.*, **31**, 297 (1949).
81. Barber, H., *Guy's Hosp. Repts.*, **84**, 267 (1934).
82. Yant, W. P., Schrenk, H. H., Patty, F. A., Waite, C. P., *U. S. Pub. Health Service, Pub. Health Repts.*, **45**, 2023 (1930).
83. Schrenk, H. H., and Yant, W. P., *J. Ind. Hyg. Toxicol.*, **18**, 448 (1936).
84. Fairley, A., Linton, E. C., and Ford-Moore, A. H., *J. Hyg.*, **34**, 486 (1934).
85. Fairley, A., Linton, E. C., and Ford-Moore, A. H., *J. Hyg.*, **36**, 341 (1936).
86. De Navasquez, S., *J. Hyg.*, **35**, 540 (1935).
87. Wirth, W., and Klimmer, O., *Arch. Gewerbepath. Gewerbehyg.*, **7**, 192 (1936).
88. Hynd, A., *J. Physiol. London*, **70**, 9 (1930).
89. Krop, S., Gold, H., and Paterno, C. A., *J. Am. Pharm. Assoc., Sci. Ed.*, **34**, 86 (1945).
90. Barnes, R. H., and Lerner, A., *Proc. Soc. Exptl. Biol. Med.*, **52**, 216 (1943).
91. Martin, G. J., and Stenzel, W., *Arch. Biochem.*, **3**, 325 (1944).
92. Scinola, P. E., and Kosunen, T., *Suomen Kemistilehti*, **11B**, 22 (1938).
93. Milhorat, A. T., and Toscani, V., *J. Biol. Chem.*, **114**, 461 (1936).
94. Herkel, W., and Koch, K., *Deut. Arch. klin. Medi.*, **178**, 511 (1936).

95. "New and Non-Official Remedies," Chicago, American Medical Assoc., 1942.
96. Lehman, A. J., and Newman, H. W., *J. Pharmacol. Exptl. Therap.*, **60,** 312 (1937).
97. Hanzlik, P. J., Newman, H. W., Van Winkle, W., Jr., Lehman, A. J., and Kennedy, N. K., *J. Pharmacol. Exptl. Therap.*, **67,** 101 (1939).
98. Van Winkle, W., Jr., *J. Pharmacol. Exptl. Therap.*, **72,** 344 (1941).
99. Newman, H. W., and Lehman, A. J., *Proc. Soc. Exptl. Biol. Med.*, **35,** 601 (1936–37).
100. Whitlock, G. P., Guerrant, N. B., and Dutcher, R. A., *Proc. Soc. Exptl. Biol. Med.*, **57,** 124 (1944).
101. Salter, W. T., Robb, P. D., and Scharles, F. H., *J. Nutrition*, **9,** 11 (1935).
102. Hanzlik, P. J., Lehman, A. J., Van Winkle, W., Jr., and Kennedy, N. K., *J. Pharmacol. Exptl. Therap.*, **67,** 114 (1939).
103. Hunt, R., *Ind. Eng. Chem.*, **24,** 361 (1932).
104. Seidenfeld, M. A., and Hanzlik, P. J., *J. Pharmacol. Exptl. Therap.*, **44,** 109 (1932).
105. Braun, H. A., and Cartland, G. F., *J. Am. Pharm. Assoc.*, **25,** 746 (1936).
106. Weatherby, J. H., and Haag, H. B., *J. Am. Pharm. Assoc.*, **27,** 466 (1938).
107. Holck, H. G. O., *J. Am. Med. Assoc.*, **109,** 1517 (1937).
108. *J. Am. Dental Assoc.*, **31,** 355 (1944).
109. U. S. Food and Drug Administration, Trade Correspondence 374 (Dec. 10, 1941).
110. Albright, F., Butler, A. M., and Bloomberg, E., *Am. J. Diseases Children*, **54,** 529 (1937).
111. Van Winkle, W., Jr., *J. Pharmacol. Exptl. Therap.*, **72,** 227 (1941).
112. Newman, H. W., Van Winkle, W., Jr., Kennedy, N. K., and Morton, M. C., *J. Pharmocol. Exptl. Therap.*, **68,** 194 (1940).
113. Van Winkle, W., Jr., and Kennedy, N. K., *J. Pharmacol. Exptl. Therap.*, **69,** 140 (1940).
114. Shideman, F. E., and Moe, G. K., *Federation Proc.*, **8,** 332 (1949).
115. Procita, L., and Shideman, F. E., *Federation Proc.*, **9,** 309 (1950).
116. Granett, P., Haynes, H. L., Connola, D. P., Bowery, T. G., and Barber, G. W., *J. Econ. Entomol.*, **42,** 281 (1949).
117. Lehmann, K. B., and Flury, F., "Toxicology and Hygiene of Industrial Solvents," Baltimore, The Williams and Wilkins Co., 1943.
118. Hinrichs, A., Kopf, R., and Loeser, A., *Pharmazie*, **3,** 110 (1948).
119. Von Oettingen, W. F., *U. S. Pub. Health Service, Pub. Health Bull. No. 281*, 1943.
120. Zwikker, J. J. L., *Pharm. Weekblad.*, **78,** 1261 (1941).
121. Calvery, H. O., Draize, J. H., and Woodard, G., *Federation Proc.*, **3,** 67, (1944).
122. Berger, F. M., Ludwig, B. J., and Russo, C., *Federation Proc.*, **9,** 258 (1950).
123. Slater, I. H., Leary, D. E., and O'Leary, J. F., *Federation Proc.*, **9,** 229 (1950).
124. Granett, P., and Haynes, H. L., *J. Econ. Entomol.*, **38,** 671 (1945).
125. Draize, J. H., Alvarez, E., Whitesell, M. F., Woodard, G., Hagan, E. C., and Nelson, A. A., *J. Pharmacol. Exptl. Therap.*, **93,** 26 (1948).

CHAPTER 16

ANALYSIS AND TEST METHODS

E. F. HILLENBRAND, JR.

The discussion of the analytical chemistry of the glycols is divided into three parts: (1) qualitative identification, (2) quantitative determination, and (3) evaluation of commercial-grade materials. Although a substantially complete survey of the available methods is included, only those which are believed to be the most reliable and generally useful are discussed in detail.

QUALITATIVE IDENTIFICATION

The qualitative methods for identifying glycols include colorimetric tests and the preparation of solid derivatives. Most of the colorimetric tests are based on the oxidation of the glycols to aldehydes or other compounds that form characteristic colors with various reagents. A number of aromatic esters and ethers are suitable solid derivatives for the identification of the glycols.

COLORIMETRIC TESTS

Oxidation with Bromine or Permanganate

According to Gauthier[1], ethylene glycol and propylene glycol are oxidized by dilute bromine water to glycolic aldehyde and acetol (acetyl carbinol, CH_3COCH_2OH), respectively. The same products are obtained with potassium permanganate, which is preferable in the case of ethylene glycol because there is less possibility of the glycolic aldehyde being oxidized further. The oxidations are conducted as follows:

(a) **Bromine.** Heat 0.1 ml. of the glycol with 10 ml. of an 0.6 per cent aqueous bromine solution in a steam bath for 20 minutes.

(b) **Permanganate.** Pour 2 or 3 drops of the glycol in a test tube, add 3 ml. of distilled water, and acidify with 0.1 ml. of concentrated sulfuric acid. Heat to boiling and add 5 drops of a 2 per cent solution of potassium permanganate. Shake the tube and, if necessary, add a few drops of a saturated solution of oxalic acid to clear up any turbidity which has not disappeared after one minute.

The reaction mixture from (a) or (b) above: (1) reduces Fehling's solution, ammoniacal silver nitrate, and Nessler's reagent; (2) gives in sulfuric acid medium the different colors with phenols shown in Table 16.1 (to 0.4 ml. of the reaction mixture add 0.1 ml. of a 5 per cent alcoholic solution of the reagent and 2 ml. of concentrated sulfuric acid); (3) reacts with phenylhydrazine acetate, volume for volume, to form a characteristic precipitate; in the case of ethylene glycol, upon heating the solution for several minutes on a steam bath, a crystalline deposit of long, sharp, yellow

TABLE 16.1

Phenol	Color, for	
	Ethylene Glycol	Propylene Glycol
Codeine	Blue-green	Violet
Thymol	Bordeaux red	Blood red
Resorcinol	Currant red	Cherry red (band of absorption in yellow)
β-Naphthol	Green with fluorescence	—
Guaiacol	—	Wine red which increases on warming

needles mixed with clear yellow plates of irregular shape with notched edges is formed upon cooling; in the case of propylene glycol there are formed almost immediately without heating yellow crystals that appear under the microscope to be irregular spheres; (4) forms with propylene glycol only (due to the presence of the CH_3CO- group) a heavy precipitate of iodoform when made alkaline and treated with a solution of iodine in potassium iodide.

Oxidation with Nitric Acid

Middleton[2] describes a qualitative test for ethylene glycol based on the oxidation of this material to oxalic acid and identification of the latter by its characteristic reaction with potassium permanganate. The test is sensitive to 0.1 g. of glycol and serves to detect 0.3 g. of glycol in the presence of 0.7 g. of glycerol in 10 ml. of aqueous solution. The following procedure is recommended:

To 10 ml. of the solution to be tested, add 2 ml. of concentrated nitric acid and evaporate to about 1 ml. Add 5 ml. of 20 per cent ammonium chloride and allow to cool. Add sodium hydroxide until a slight odor of ammonia is evolved. Add 1 ml. of 10 per cent barium chloride, filter, and wash the precipitate with a little water. Rinse the solid into a small beaker with 5 ml. of water, add 7.5 ml. of $2N$ H_2SO_4, and heat to boiling. Filter off the precipitate of barium sulfate, cool the filtrate, and add $0.6N$ $KMnO_4$ dropwise until a color is imparted to the cold solution. Then heat to boiling and titrate the hot solution with permanganate. Reduction of the permanganate by the hot acid solution indicates the presence of oxalic acid.

Oxidation with Periodic Acid

Glycerol and those glycols containing adjacent hydroxyl groups are oxidized by periodates to aldehydes which may be detected colorimetrically. From the nature of the oxidation products it is possible to distinguish between ethylene glycol, propylene glycol, and glycerol:

Ethylene glycol → formaldehyde
Propylene glycol → formaldehyde and acetaldehyde
Glycerol → formaldehyde and formic acid

The following procedure for the oxidation of the hydroxy compounds and subsequent determination of the aldehydes is adapted from the quantitative method of Desnuelle and Naudet[3].

Mix in a small flask or glass-stoppered test tube 2.5 ml. of 6.6 per cent sodium periodate and 5 ml. of a 4 per cent aqueous solution of the sample. Allow the solution to stand for 20 minutes, cool to 0°C., and precipitate the excess sodium periodate by the addition of 0.5 ml. of saturated potassium nitrate. Allow the precipitate to settle by placing the flask in an ice bath for an additional 10 minutes. Formic acid, formaldehyde, and acetaldehyde are determined on three separate portions of the supernatant liquid.

Determine the formic acid by acidimetric titration using methyl red indicator.

To detect formaldehyde, add 2 ml. of 1 per cent aqueous phenylhydrazine hydrochloride and 1 ml. of 2 per cent aqueous potassium ferricyanide, $K_3Fe(CN)_6$, both freshly prepared. Cool in an ice bath and add 5 ml. of chilled concentrated hydrochloric acid. A red color indicates the presence of formaldehyde.

To detect acetaldehyde, add 1 ml. of saturated piperazine hydrate and 0.5 ml. of 4 per cent sodium nitroprusside. A blue color indicates the presence of acetaldehyde.

Allen, Charbonnier, and Coleman[4] describe the following rapid test based on the periodic acid reaction for distinguishing between glycerol and ethylene glycol solutions:

Take about 2 ml. of the solution to be tested, add a drop of methyl red indicator solution, and cautiously neutralize with dilute sodium hydroxide or dilute acid, leaving the solution just on the alkaline side of methyl red. Take about 2 ml. of a solution of periodic acid, add a drop of methyl red, and adjust to the neutral point of the indicator, leaving the solution just on the alkaline side. An adjusted solution of sodium paraperiodate or potassium metaperiodate may be used. Mix the sample with the periodate solution and observe. If glycerol is present, the solution will turn pink immediately.

Reaction with Certain Phenols

According to Hovey and Hodgins[5], dilute aqueous solutions of the glycols and glycerol react with certain polyhydroxy phenols in the presence of alkali or sulfuric acid with the formation of colored substances. Their results are questionable inasmuch as phenols themselves are readily oxidized in air to colored products, especially in alkaline solution. However, one reaction which these authors describe may be used satisfactorily to distinguish the glycols from glycerol. The latter forms a blood-red color when heated with catechol in the presence of concentrated sulfuric acid (presumably through the intermediate formation of acrolein), whereas no color is formed by ethylene glycol, diethylene glycol, and ethanol, and only a faint pink color by triethylene glycol and propylene glycol. The test is made as follows:

Mix in the order given, 3 ml. of the solution to be tested, 3 ml. of freshly prepared 10 per cent aqueous catechol solution, and 6 ml. of concentrated sulfuric acid. If glycerol is present the color will appear upon heating the solution at 140 to 145°C. for 30 seconds.

PREPARATION OF SOLID DERIVATIVES

Certain esters and ethers are suitable solid derivatives for the identification of the glycols. Those compounds which have been found most generally useful include: (1) diesters of benzoic, *p*-nitrobenzoic, and 3,5-dinitrobenzoic acids; (2) diesters of N-substituted carbamic acids (urethanes); and (3) bis(triphenylmethyl) ethers. Melting points of derivatives reported in the literature are given in Table 16.2. For additional derivatives and references to the original papers, see Huntress and Mulliken[6].

TABLE 16.2. MELTING POINTS (°C.) OF SOME SOLID DERIVATIVES OF THE GLYCOLS

Glycol	Dibenzoate	Di(*p*-nitrobenzoate)	Di(3,5-dinitrobenzoate)	N-Phenylcarbamate	N-(α-Naphthyl)carbamate	Bis(triphenylmethyl) ether
Ethylene glycol	73	140; 141	169	157; 156	176	187–188; 185–186
Diethylene glycol	liquid	—	149	—	—	157.5–158
Triethylene glycol	—	—	—	—	—	142–142.5
Propylene glycol	—	—	—	153; 143–144	—	176.5–176.7
dl-2,3-Butanediol	53–54	—	—	199.5; 201	—	—
meso-2,3-Butanediol	75–76	—	—	—	—	—
1,3-Butanediol	—	—	—	122–123	—	—

Esters of Benzoic Acid and Nitrobenzoic Acids

These esters are prepared by the reaction of the corresponding acid chloride with the glycol in the presence of pyridine. The following procedure is adapted from that described by McElvain[7]:

Mix 0.5 ml. of the glycol with two equivalents of the acid chloride and 5 ml. of pyridine in a 50-ml. round-bottom flask and heat under a reflux condenser for one hour. Cool the reaction mixture to room temperature and add 20 ml. of a 5 per cent aqueous solution of sodium bicarbonate. Place the flask in an ice bath until the precipitate solidifies, then filter. Recrystallize the diester from a mixture of alcohol and water: dissolve it in the least possible quantity of hot alcohol, add warm water dropwise until the solution just becomes turbid, and allow the solution to cool and crystallize.

Alkyl N-Arylcarbamates (Phenyl- and α-Naphthylurethanes)

The dicarbamates are obtained by reaction of the glycol with two equivalents of phenyl or α-naphthyl isocyanate. McElvain[7] gives the following method of preparation:

Mix in a test tube a 10 per cent excess of the theoretical quantity of phenyl isocyanate or α-naphthyl isocyanate and 0.5 g. (less may be used if necessary) of the
glycol. If no sign of reaction appears, heat the mixture in a steam bath for 10 minutes,
taking care to protect the reaction from moisture. Then extract the reaction mixture
with 5 ml. of hot ligroin (petroleum ether, b.p. 100–120°C.) which dissolves the urethane but leaves undissolved any diarylurea. Filter any insoluble material from the
hot ligroin solution and allow the urethane to crystallize in the filtrate as it cools.
Recrystallize from alcohol.

Bis(triphenylmethyl) Ethers

Seikel and Huntress[8] recommended the bis(triphenylmethyl) ethers as
derivatives for the identification of the glycols. The solid ethers crystallize
readily and are easy to purify; furthermore, no purification or dehydration
of the reactants is necessary in most cases. The following method of preparation is given for ethylene glycol, diethylene glycol, and triethylene glycol:

Heat on a steam bath 0.10 ml. of ethylene glycol or 0.25 ml. of diethylene glycol or
triethylene glycol with exactly two equivalents of triphenylmethyl (trityl) chloride
and 1 to 2 ml. of pyridine in a 150-ml. test tube (protected by a calcium chloride
tube) either for 15 minutes in the case of the ethylene glycol and triethylene glycol
or for one hour in the case of the diethylene glycol. Isolate the product in the usual
way and recrystallize the crude directly from acetone (15 to 30 ml./g.), evaporating
the solution to one-half volume before cooling.

A similar preparation of the diether of propylene glycol is described by
Nancy Green and M. W. Green[9].

QUANTITATIVE DETERMINATION

Quantitative analytical methods for the glycols are based on characteristic reactions of the —OH group, principally acylation and oxidation.
Except for certain oxidation methods which are specific for those compounds containing hydroxyl groups on adjacent carbon atoms, these reactions are common to all glycols and polyglycols as well as their monoethers and monesters. However, by the proper application of one or more
of these methods it is possible to analyze directly a variety of mixtures
containing glycols and glycol derivatives. In some cases it may be necessary
to separate the components of certain complex mixtures by distillation or
other means before chemical methods can be applied.

In selecting the best method for a particular analysis, consideration
must be given to the sensitivity, accuracy, and speed required as well as
the possible interference of the other components. In the case of two-com-
ponent mixtures, methods based on such physical properties as specific

gravity or refractive index may be more accurate and faster than chemical methods.

This discussion includes a brief history of each method, the principle involved, limitations, and useful applications. Detailed procedures are given for those methods believed to be the most generally useful.

ACYLATION METHODS

Acetic Anhydride

The use of acetic anhydride-pyridine reagent for the determination of hydroxyl compounds was first proposed by Verley and Bölsing in 1901[10]. Peterson and West[11] used the same reagent, but prevented hydrolysis of the ester by addition of ice water to the reaction mixture before titrating. This modification was used by Marks and Morrell[12] for the determination of high molecular weight hydroxyl compounds.

A comprehensive study of the acetic anhydride-pyridine method was made in the Carbide Laboratories. This study included reagent concentration, reaction conditions, and relation of sample size to reagent concentration. A total of 53 hydroxyl compounds were investigated, including the glycols in Table 16.3.

TABLE 16.3

Glycol	Sample Size, grams	Reaction Time, hours	Factor
Ethylene glycol	0.4 to 0.6	0.5	3.103
Diethylene glycol	0.7 to 0.9	0.5	5.306
Triethylene glycol	0.9 to 1.1	1.0	7.509
Propylene glycol	0.55 to 0.65	2.0	3.805
2,5-Hexanediol	0.7 to 0.9	4.0	5.909
2-Ethyl-1,3-hexanediol	1.1 to 1.2	3.0	7.311

The following procedure, which was developed as a result of this investigation, is recommended. The average and standard deviation of 12 determinations made by this procedure on substantially pure ethylene glycol was 99.8 ± 0.2 per cent. Similar accuracy and precision were obtained for the other glycols.

Principle. Acetic anhydride combines with pyridine to form acetyl pyridinium acetate according to the equation:

$$CH_3CO \diagdown O + C_5H_5N \rightarrow C_5H_5N \diagup COCH_3$$
$$CH_3CO \diagup \qquad \qquad \diagdown OCOCH_3$$

Two mols of acetyl pyridinium acetate react quantitatively with one mol of glycol forming two mols of titratable acid:

$$
\begin{array}{c}
CH_2OH \\
| \\
| \\
CH_2OH
\end{array}
\quad + \quad 2C_5H_5N
\begin{array}{c}
COCH_3 \\
\diagup \\
\diagdown \\
OCOCH_3
\end{array}
\quad \rightarrow \quad
\begin{array}{c}
CH_2OCOCH_3 \\
| \\
| \\
CH_2OCOCH_3
\end{array}
\quad + \quad 2C_5H_5N
\begin{array}{c}
H \\
\diagup \\
\diagdown \\
OCOCH_3
\end{array}
$$

After the sample and reagent have reacted, the excess reagent is decomposed with water. One mol of acetyl pyridinium acetate reacts with water forming two mols of titratable acid according to the equation:

$$
HOH \quad + \quad C_5H_5N
\begin{array}{c}
COCH_3 \\
\diagup \\
\diagdown \\
OCOCH_3
\end{array}
\quad \rightarrow \quad C_5H_5N
\begin{array}{c}
H \\
\diagup \\
\diagdown \\
OCOCH_3
\end{array}
\quad + \quad CH_3COOH
$$

The total liberated acid is determined by titration with standard sodium hydroxide. A blank is run in which the reagent is allowed to react with water under the same conditions, and from the difference in the amount of alkali consumed by the sample and the blank, the amount of glycol can be calculated.

Limitations. Primary and secondary alcohols, phenols, and primary and secondary amines also react quantitatively with the reagent and therefore interfere unless they can be determined independently and a suitable correction applied. Since the determination is based on an acidimetric titration, a suitable correction must be applied if an aqueous solution of the sample is not neutral to phenolphthalein indicator.

Low molecular weight aldehydes such as acetaldehyde cannot be tolerated in concentrations above 2 per cent. Tertiary alcohols, which do not react quantitatively with the reagent, and easily saponifiable esters such as methyl acetate or the alkyl formates also interfere.

Water reacts with the reagent, but if the amount present is known so that the sample size can be reduced accordingly, small percentages may be tolerated. The limiting factor is the reduction in precision as a result of the decreased sample size.

Reagents Required. (1) Acetic anhydride-pyridine reagent: Add 60 g. of C.P. acetic anhydride to 440 g. of freshly distilled pyridine. Shake the reagent vigorously to obtain complete reaction. Preserve the solution in a dark-colored, glass-stoppered bottle. *Do not use the reagent if it becomes discolored.* The additon of 2 ml. of distilled water before storage will improve the stability of the reagent. (2) Standard 0.5 N sodium hydroxide. (3) Phenolphthalein indicator, 1 per cent *pyridine* solution.

Procedure. Prepare a sufficient number of clean, dry, heat-resistant pressure bottles to make all blank and sample determinations in duplicate. Carefully pipet 20 ml. of the acetic anhydride-pyridine reagent into each of the bottles, using the same pipet for each transfer.

Reserve two of the bottles for blanks. Into each of the other bottles introduce an amount of sample calculated to contain not more than 18 milliequivalents of hydroxyl. Refer to Table 16.3 for the proper size sample when analyzing substantially pure materials. Weigh the sample to the nearest 0.1 mg. using a Grethen or similar weighing pipet.

Stopper the bottles and wrap each securely in a canvas bag. Place the samples and blanks as close together as possible in a steam bath at 98 ± 2°C. for the time indicated in the table. Maintain the water in the bath at a level just above the liquid in the bottles.

Remove the bottles from the bath and *allow them to cool in air to room temperature. Do not remove the wrappers from the bottles while they are hot or attempt to hasten the cooling by immersing them in cold water, as a serious accident can result from the breakage of the bottles.*

When the bottles have cooled, loosen the wrappers, uncap to release any pressure, and then remove the wrappers.

To each of the bottles add clean crushed ice until about one-half full, then wash down the inside walls with 20 to 30 ml. of distilled water. Carefully wash any liquid on the stopper into the bottle.

Add 1 ml. of a 1 per cent *pyridine* solution of phenolphthalein indicator and titrate immediately with standard 0.5N sodium hydroxide to the first pink end-point permanent for at least 15 seconds. *Agitate the contents of the bottle vigorously during the titration.*

Calculation.

$$\frac{(B - A) \times N \times F}{g. \text{ sample}} = \text{glycol}, \% \text{ by weight}$$

where A = ml. of N normal NaOH used for the sample
   B = average ml. of N normal NaOH used for the bank
   F = factor = 100 × milliequivalent weight. See Table 16.3.

Microprocedures for the determination of hydroxyl compounds by reaction with acetic anhydride-pyridine have been reported by Stodola[13] and Petersen, Hedberg, and Christensen[14]. The latter investigators developed a simple microchemical technique based on the reaction of the sample and reagent in a sealed glass tube. The procedure was applied with excellent results to a large number of hydroxyl compounds including ethylene, propylene, and diethylene glycols.

An adaptation of the acetic anhydride-pyridine method to the determination of dilute aqueous solutions of ethylene glycol and glycerol is described by Shaefer[15]. A 50-ml. sample is distilled through a 3-bulb Snyder column until the volume of liquid in the flask is reduced to about 10 ml. A 50-ml. portion of dry pyridine is then added to the flask and the distillation continued until the temperature reaches 110°C. The column is washed down with 10 ml. of the pyridine and the acetylation is conducted on the residue or a suitable aliquot.

Acetyl Chloride

The use of acetyl chloride-pyridine as the acylating agent for the quantitative determination of hydroxyl compounds was first described by Smith and Bryant[16]. The principal advantage claimed for this reagent over acetic anhydride-pyridine is its greater reactivity under similar conditions of concentration and temperature, although later investigators have shown that the reaction of acetyl chloride with glycols is slower than with the monohydroxyl alcohols[17].

The procedure is similar in principle to that followed in using acetic anhydride-pyridine. The sample is reacted with a slurry of solid acetyl pyridinium chloride formed by the addition of excess pyridine to a solution of acetyl chloride in toluene or 1,4-dioxane. After the reaction is complete the excess reagent is decomposed with water and the resultant acidity determined by titration with standard alkali. A blank is run on the same quantity of reagent.

In general, the same limitations apply to both the acetyl chloride and acetic anhydride procedures. However, the interference of aldehydes is less pronounced where acetyl chloride is employed, and as much as 10 per cent of these substances may be present without detrimental results. Although the reaction of acetyl chloride with tertiary alcohols is more complete, it is not quantitative.

By comparison with the modification of the acetic anhydride-pyridine method described by Marks and Morrell[12], the acetyl chloride procedure was found to be equally as accurate, although the average precision was somewhat lower (± 0.5 per cent compared with ± 0.2 per cent for the older method).

Christensen, Pennington, and Dimick[18] have proposed a modified procedure using pure acetyl chloride instead of acetyl pyridinium chloride as the acylating agent. Although the experimental technique appears to offer difficulties, the authors obtained good precision on a large number of compounds. Quantitative results are reported for ethylene glycol, diethylene glycol, and propylene glycol when reacted for 20 minutes at 40°C. However, Montes[17] claims that the glycols require at least 30 minutes for complete reaction.

Phthalic Anhydride

The use of phthalic anhydride-pyridine for the determination of alcohols has been investigated by Elving and Warshowsky[19]. The principal advantages of this method are its specificity for alcoholic hydroxyl groups and its applicability to aqueous solutions. The authors found that such substances as ketones, saturated and unsaturated aldehydes, acids, esters, and phenols do not interfere. Samples containing as high as 85 per cent water have been analyzed successfully. In general, the method is accurate to one per cent (relative) with an average precision of three parts per thousand.

Good results were reported using the standard procedure on ethylene glycol and propylene glycol, although longer reaction periods were required for the butylene glycols. Glycols which contain a tertiary hydroxyl group, such as 2-methyl-2,4-pentanediol, did not react quantitatively.

The determination is similar to that described for acetic anhydride, but the addition of ice is not necessary because the phthalic ester is not easily hydrolyzed. The solution is titrated with standard sodium hydroxide using a 1.0 per cent solution of phenolphthalein in pyridine as indicator. A blank is run on the same quantity of reagent.

OXIDATION METHODS

Periodic Acid

In 1928 Malaprade[20] reported the quantitative oxidation of 1,2-glycols by periodic acid and described an analytical method based on this reaction. Since then, many new applications and modifications of Malaprade's procedure have been published.

Some of the methods measure the excess periodate after oxidation, whereas others determine the amount of oxidation products formed. For samples containing but one oxidizable material, determination of the excess periodate is the simplest procedure and probably the most accurate. One of the most satisfactory methods is that adapted by Siggia[21] from the method of Pohle, Mehlenbacher, and Cook[22]. The experimental procedure used in the Carbide laboratories is given below:

Principle. Ethylene glycol, propylene glycol, and 2,3-butylene glycol are oxidized rapidly and quantitatively by periodic acid according to the equations:

$$CH_2OHCH_2OH + HIO_4 \rightarrow 2HCHO + HIO_3 + H_2O$$

$$CH_3CHOHCH_2OH + HIO_4 \rightarrow HCHO + CH_3CHO + HIO_3 + H_2O$$

$$CH_3CHOHCHOHCH_3 + HIO_4 \rightarrow 2CH_3CHO + HIO_3 + H_2O$$

The excess reagent and the iodic acid formed are reduced by the addition of potassium iodide:

$$HIO_4 + 7KI + 7CH_3COOH \rightarrow 7CH_3COOK + 4I_2 + 4H_2O$$

$$HIO_3 + 5KI + 5CH_3COOH \rightarrow 5CH_3COOK + 3I_2 + 3H_2O$$

The amount of reagent consumed, which is determined by net titration of the liberated iodine with sodium thiosulfate, is a measure of the ethylene glycol originally present.

Limitations. Compounds containing adjacent carbon atoms to each of which is attached one of the following groups of atoms, $=O$, $—OH$, $—NH_2$, and $—NHR$, are oxidized by periodic acid and consequently interfere. Such compounds include glycerol, acetoin, biacetyl, glyoxal, monoethanolamine, and diethanolamine.

Care must be taken to follow the directions closely, as formaldehyde is subject to slow, though definite, oxidation at room temperature. Simple aldehydes, ketones, alcohols, ethers, glycol ethers, and the polyglycols are not oxidized. The method is applicable to aqueous solutions.

Reagents Required. (1) Periodic acid, 0.029 M. Dissolve 5.5 g. of C.P. periodic acid in 200 ml. of distilled water and dilute to 1 liter with glacial acetic acid. Store this reagent in a well-stoppered brown bottle. (2) Potassium iodide, 20 per cent aqueous solution. (3) Standard 0.1 N sodium thiosulfate. (4) Starch, 1 per cent solution, freshly prepared.

Procedure. Into a 500-ml. volumetric flask containing about 200 ml. of distilled water introduce an amount of sample calculated to contain 0.030 to 0.050 mol of glycol. Refer to Table 16.4 for the proper size sample when analyzing substantially pure materials. Weigh the sample to the nearest 0.1 mg. using a suitable weighing pipet. Swirl the contents of the flask to effect solution and dilute to the mark with additional distilled water.

Pipet 50 ml. of the 0.029 M periodic acid into each of a sufficient number of 500-ml. glass-stoppered Erlenmeyer flasks to make all blank and sample determinations in duplicate. Reserve two of the flasks as blanks.

Into each of the other flasks pipet a 10-ml. aliquot of the diluted sample. Allow the flasks to stand for 30 minutes at room temperature.

Add 10 ml. of the 20 per cent potassium iodide solution to each of the samples and blanks.

To each flask add exactly 50 ml. of standard 0.1 N sodium thiosulfate, using the same pipet and the same drainage time for each addition. *This amount of reagent is not included in the final calculation.*

Titrate with the standard 0.1 N sodium thiosulfate to a pale yellow color. Add 1 ml. of the starch indicator and titrate to the disappearance of the blue color. *If the sample titration is less than 60 per cent of the blank titration, too much sample is indicated and the entire determination must be repeated using a smaller amount.*

Calculation.

$$\frac{(B - A) \times N \times F}{\text{g. sample in aliquot}} = \text{glycol, \% by weight}$$

where A = ml. of N normal thiosulfate used for the sample
B = ml of N normal thiosulfate used for the blank
F = factor = 100 × milliequivalent weight. See Table 16.4.

Malaprade[20] pointed out that the oxidation of 1,2-glycols was much more rapid in acid than in basic or neutral solution; this was confirmed by Price and Kroll[23] who made a thorough study of the kinetics of the reaction. Shupe[24] and others have recommended the use of neutral potassium periodate without the addition of sulfuric acid for the oxidation. Under these conditions a reaction period of one hour or longer is required.

Fleury and Lange[25] and Reinke and Luce[26] determined the periodic acid remaining after the oxidation by reaction with an excess of sodium aresenite which in turn was titrated with standard iodine. Allen, Charbonnier, and Coleman[4] described a direct titration method for the determination of the unreacted periodic acid.

TABLE 16.4

Glycol	Sample Size, grams	Factor
Ethylene glycol	2.0 to 3.0	3.103
Propylene glycol	2.5 to 3.5	3.805
2,3-Butanediol	3.0 to 4.0	4.506

A number of procedures are based on the determination of formaldehyde, acetaldehyde and, in the case of glycerol, formic acid formed by the oxidation with periodic acid. The fact that it is possible to determine all three of these oxidation products in the presence of each other provides a means of analyzing mixtures of the two glycols with each other or with glycerol. Based on the work of Nicolet and Shinn[27], Clausen[28], and Shupe[24], a method was published by Reincke and Luce[26] for the determination of mixtures of ethylene glycol and propylene glycol in which the aldehydes from the oxidation were separated by blowing them through a saturated solution of sodium bicarbonate containing a definite quantity of glycine. This removed the formaldehyde, and the acetaldehyde was determined by reaction with sodium bisulfite. Hoepe and Treadwell[29] and Courtois[32] determined the aldehydes cyanometrically, the former employing the cyano-silver method of Romijn[30, 31] to determine formaldehyde in the presence of acetaldehyde. Desnuelle and Naudet[3] employed colorimetric methods for the determination of the formaldehyde and acetaldehyde, whereas Warshowsky and Elving[33] accomplished the same result polarographically by applying the method of Whitnack and Moshier[34].

The determination of acetaldehyde from oxidation of 2,3-butanediol has been described by Brockmann and Werkman[35], Freeman and Morrison[36], and Johnson[37].

Lead Tetraacetate

In 1931 Criegee[38] showed that 1,2-glycols could be oxidized quantitatively by lead tetraacetate according to the equation:

$$
\begin{array}{c}
R_1 \\
\diagdown \\
C\!\!-\!\!C\!\!\diagup^{\,R_3} \quad + \quad Pb(OCOCH_3)_4 \quad \rightarrow \\
\diagup \,|\ \ |\ \diagdown_{R_4} \\
R_2\ OH\ OH
\end{array}
\qquad
\begin{array}{c}
R_1 \\
\diagdown \\
C\!\!=\!\!O \quad + \\
\diagup \\
R_2
\end{array}
$$

$$
\begin{array}{c}
R_3 \\
\diagdown \\
C\!\!=\!\!O \quad + \quad 2CH_3COOH \quad + \quad Pb(OCOCH_3)_2 \\
\diagup \\
R_4
\end{array}
$$

To apply the reaction analytically, the excess lead tetraacetate is reacted with potassium iodide and the liberated iodine titrated with standard thiosulfate. There are relatively few references in the literature to the use of lead tetraacetate for this purpose, inasmuch as periodic acid reacts similarly and has several advantages. However, Seikel[39] used this method with apparently satisfactory results for the determination of ethylene glycol in commercial alkyl ethers of diethylene glycol.

The oxidation is usually conducted in an anhydrous medium such as glacial acetic acid, since it has generally been assumed that the presence of water would hydrolyze the reagent. Unfortunately, the rate of oxidation in such media is quite slow; in the case of the determinations made by Seikel on ethylene glycol, 25 to 40 hours were required for substantially complete reaction. Baer, Grosheintz, and Fischer[40] have shown that the reaction can be carried out in aqueous solutions inasmuch as the rate of oxidation in water is much more rapid than the rate of hydrolysis of the lead tetra-acetate. For all the glycols studied, the oxidation was complete in 10 minutes or less. Although these investigators did not emphasize the analytical aspects of the reaction, it is possible that their work could be used as a basis for the development of a method of analysis for glycols which would compare favorably with the periodic acid method.

Potassium Dichromate

The determination of monohydroxy alcohols and other aliphatic derivatives by oxidation with potassium dichromate-sulfuric acid solutions has been known for many years. It is not known when this method was first applied to the glycols; it was used by Carbide as early as 1925 for the analysis of ethylene glycol in process control samples. Since then a number of improvements have been effected in the experimental procedure and conditions have been established for the determination of a number of glycols and glycol derivatives. The following procedure is presently being used:

Principle. In the presence of sulfuric acid, ethylene glycol is oxidized quantitatively to carbon dioxide and water by the action of potassium dichromate:

$$3CH_2OHCH_2OH + 5K_2Cr_2O_7 + 20H_2SO_4 \rightarrow 5K_2SO_4 + 5Cr_2(SO_4)_3 + 6CO_2 + 29H_2O$$

Similar equations may be written for diethylene glycol and triethylene glycol.

A measured excess of potassium dichromate is used for the reaction in the presence of an amount of sulfuric acid equal to the total volume of sample and dichromate. The amount of dichromate consumed, which is determined by titrating the excess reagent with standard ferrous ammonium sulfate, is a measure of the ethylene glycol present in the sample.

Limitations. This method is especially useful for the determination of glycols in dilute aqueous solutions such as process waste water. In the case of substantially pure compounds, such a small sample must be taken for dilution that the buret readings in the final titration are quite critical.

Substances which are oxidized under the conditions of the reaction interfere with the analysis. In addition to most organic materials these include certain inorganic salts, particularly chlorides.

Reagents Required. (1) Standard $0.5N$ potassium dichromate. (2) Sulfuric acid, C.P., concentrated. (3) Ferrous ammonium sulfate, 0.1 to $0.2N$. Standardize daily against standard potassium dichromate using o-phenanthroline indicator. (4) o-Phenanthroline indicator. Weigh 0.6950 g. of ferrous sulfate, $FeSO_4 \cdot 7H_2O$, into a 100-ml. volumetric flask containing 50 ml. of distilled water. Add 1.4580 g. of o-phenanthroline crystals, swirl the flask to effect solution, and dilute to the mark with additional distilled water.

Sample Size. It is essential to maintain a consistent volume of aliquot and reagent so that the amount of acid specified may account for one-half the volume of the reaction mixture. Table 16.5 shows the approximate size sample for a number of pure glycols using 35 ml. of 0.5*N* potassium dichromate, a 10-ml. aliquot from a 250-ml. dilution, and 45 ml. of concentrated sulfuric acid. The specified amount of sample would consume approximately 25 ml. of the dichromate reagent. In analyzing dilute aqueous solutions, sufficient additional acid must be added to compensate for the diluting effect of the sample.

TABLE 16.5

Glycol	Sample Size, grams	Factor
Ethylene glycol	2.0 to 2.2	0.621
Diethylene glycol	1.7 to 1.9	0.531
Triethylene glycol	1.6 to 1.8	0.501

Procedure. Transfer 100 ml. of distilled water to a 250-ml. volumetric flask. Introduce an amount of sample containing the weight of glycol shown in Table 16.5. For substantially pure material, weigh the sample to the nearest 0.1 mg. by means of a suitable weighing pipet. Swirl the contents of the flask to effect solution and dilute to the mark with additional distilled water.

From a buret add exactly 35 ml. of standard 0.5*N* potassium dichromate to a 250-ml. Soxhlet flask. Carefully add 45 ml. of concentrated sulfuric acid from a suitable buret or container. Swirl the contents of the flask slightly to dissipate the heat evolved.

Introduce a 10-ml. aliquot of the aqueous dilution by means of a transfer pipet.

Place the flask on an electric hot-plate and heat just to boiling, then carefully remove the flask and allow to cool. Wash down the inside walls of the flask with 50 to 60 ml. of distilled water and again allow to cool.

Place the flask on a titrating bench provided with a sheet of translucent glass illuminated from below in such a manner that the light is transmitted through the solution when viewed from above. At this point the solution should appear orange to brown in color. If it is green, too much dichromate has been consumed and the determination must be repeated using a smaller sample or aliquot. Titrate with the freshly standardized 0.2*N* ferrous ammonium sulfate until the solution begins to turn brilliant green in color. Add 2 to 4 drops of the *o*-phenanthroline indicator and continue the titration to a red-violet end-point. The indicator changes from blue to red, but the end-point is red-violet because of the green color of the reduced chromium salts.

Calculation.

$$\frac{(AN - BN') \times F}{\text{g. sample in aliquot}} = \text{glycol, \% by weight}$$

where A = ml. of N normal $K_2Cr_2O_7$ used
$\quad B$ = ml. of N' normal $FeSO_4(NH_4)_2SO_4$ required
$\quad F$ = factor = 100 $\times$ milliequivalents of glycol. See Table 16.5.

In the original Carbide method, an excess of ferrous ammonium sulfate was added to the unreacted dichromate and the excess titrated with standard potassium permanganate. The direct titration with ferrous ammonium sulfate using o-phenanthroline indicator has the double advantage of providing a sharper end-point and eliminating one standard solution.

Allen, Charbonnier, and Coleman[4] used a dichromate oxidation procedure in conjunction with periodic acid oxidation for the analysis of glycerol, ethylene glycol, and diethylene glycol mixtures. These investigators reacted the excess dichromate with potassium iodide and titrated the liberated iodine with standard sodium thiosulfate.

Wise, Puck, and Stral[41] developed a procedure for the determination of propylene glycol or triethylene glycol vapors in air. The vapors are absorbed in water and oxidized with acid dichromate. The amount of reagent consumed is determined colorimetrically by measuring the green color of the chromic ions formed.

Werner and Mitchell[42] and Elkins, Storlazzi, and Hammond[43] applied the dichromate oxidation method to the determination of the monoalkyl ethers of ethylene glycol.

Potassium Permanganate

Cuthill and Atkins[44] described a procedure for the determination of ethylene glycol by oxidation with potassium permanganate. The reaction is conducted under such conditions that the glycol is completely oxidized to carbon dioxide and water. The unreacted permanganate is determined by adding an excess of potassium iodide and titrating the liberated iodine with standard sodium thiosulfate. This method apparently possesses no advantages over the dichromate oxidation method and the reaction time is much longer (4 to 5 hours at room temperature).

MISCELLANEOUS

Reaction with Hydriodic Acid

In 1885 Zeisel[45] described a procedure for the determination of alkyl ethers by reaction with constant-boiling hydriodic acid to form the corresponding alkyl iodides. Since then, many modifications and improvements have been made in the original Zeisel method, but until recently, any attempts to apply the method to the determination of the glycols and their derivatives have proved unsuccessful. In each case it was found that the glycols yielded low and inconsistent quantities of alkyl iodides.

However, in 1946 Morgan[46] investigated the products of the reaction of numerous glycols and glycol derivatives with constant-boiling hydriodic acid and found that without exception ethylene was a product of the reaction as well as ethyl iodide, and that these two products accounted quantitatively for the starting material. On the basis of these observations Morgan developed a semi-micro method of analysis which he applied successfully to solvents, pasticizers, polyethylene glycol ethers, and hydroxy-ethyl celluloses, as well as to compounds containing halogen or sulfur substituents in place of oxygen in the ethylene glycol residue.

Mono- and polyethylene glycols and their ether and ester derivatives react with constant-boiling hydriodic acid to form ethyl iodide and ethylene, probably through the intermediate formation of ethylene diiodide:

$$ROCH_2CH_2OH + 3HI \rightarrow RI + ICH_2CH_2I + 2H_2O$$

$$ICH_2CH_2I + HI \rightarrow CH_3CH_2I + I_2$$

$$ICH_2CH_2I \rightarrow CH_2{=\!=}CH_2 + I_2$$

$$CH_2{=\!=}CH_2 + HI \rightarrow CH_3CH_2I$$

Propylene glycol and its derivatives follow the same course of reaction, forming propylene and isopropyl iodide. The ratio of ethyl iodide to ethylene varies with reaction conditions, but the sum of the two is equivalent to the original glycol.

The ethyl iodide formed is volatilized into alcoholic silver nitrate and the excess reagent determined by the Volhard method[47]. Ethylene is absorbed in a bromine solution and the excess bromine determined iodimetrically.

Substances that would interfere with the analysis include: alcohols, ethers, esters, or sulfides which react with hydriodic acid to form volatile iodides; and structures which might produce 1,2-diiodides and subsequently gaseous olefins but from which relatively nonvolatile monoiodides would result. Acetone is an interfering substance because it reacts readily with bromine. If used for drying purposes, it must be carefully purged from the apparatus before the analysis is performed.

Methoxy and methyl ester groups, if present, may be determined independently by the recent modification of the Willstätter method by Cooke and Hibbert[48]. Ester groups also may be determined by saponification.

For a complete description of the apparatus, reagents, procedure, and calculations, Morgan's original article should be consulted.

Reaction with Ammonium Hexanitrato Cerate Reagent

A quantitative colorimetric method based on the reaction of hydroxyl compounds and ammonium hexanitrato cerate to form a colored complex has been found especially applicable to the analysis of dilute aqueous glycol solutions. Under the conditions specified by Duke and Smith[49], who originally proposed the reaction as a qualitative test for hydroxyl compounds, the bright red color produced faded rapidly on standing. By modifying the reagent concentration and acidity, a procedure was developed in the Carbide Laboratories whereby the color was stabilized sufficiently to permit its quantitative measurement.

Principle and Limitations. Dilute solutions of hydroxyl compounds react with ammonium hexanitrato cerate to form a colored complex:

$$(NH_4)_2Ce(NO_3)_6 + ROH \rightarrow (NH_4)_2Ce(NO_3)_5OR + HNO_3$$

The intensity of the color developed, which is a function of the hydroxyl concentration, is measured photometrically and the amount of hydroxyl compound read directly from a calibration curve.

The following substances are known to interfere: mono- and polyhydroxy compounds, inorganic and organic acids, bases and salts, phenols, aldehydes, epoxy compounds, and *beta*-dicarbonyl compounds.

Procedure. Prepare the reagent by dissolving 6.25 g. of ammonium hexanitrato cerate, $(NH_4)_2Ce(NO_3)_6$, in 100 ml. of $0.25N$ nitric acid.

In the case of ethylene or propylene glycols, dilute the sample with distilled water to a concentration of approximately 0.2 per cent which, under the specified conditions, corresponds to the maximum desirable absorbance of 0.6. For diethylene and triethylene glycols the concentration may be increased to 0.35 and 0.5 per cent, respectively.

Add exactly 2 ml. of the diluted sample to 3 ml. of the reagent and measure the absorbance at once at 450 millimicrons, using a 1-cm. cell. Run a blank on 3 ml. of the reagent and 2 ml. of distilled water.

Prepare a calibration curve by measuring the absorbance of known concentrations of the glycol treated in exactly the same manner as described above. Care should be taken not to extrapolate the curve too far beyond the experimental points.

The method has been specifically applied to the determination of diethylene glycol in tobacco. The glycol is leached from the tobacco with ethyl acetate from which it is in turn extracted with water. The colorimetric determination is made on the aqueous extract using as a blank untreated tobacco which is subjected to exactly the same treatment as the sample. By selection of the proper extractants the method may be applied to the determination of glycols in other biological and botanical materials.

Precipitation with Silicotungstic or Phosphomolybdic Acid

Two methods[50] have been developed for the quantitative determination of the solid polyethylene glycols ("Carbowax" compounds) in biological materials. These methods, one gravimetric, the other colorimetric, are based on a reaction of the polyglycols with the heteropoly acids, silicotungstic and phosphomolybdic.

In the gravimetric method, the polyglycol is precipitated in hydrochloric acid solution with silicotungstic acid and barium chloride. The precipitate is filtered, washed, dried, and ignited at 700°C. in a muffle furnace. The residue, consisting of the mixed oxides of barium, silicon, and tungsten, is weighed. The amount of polyglycol originally present in the sample is calculated from the weight of residue by means of an empirical factor determined by treating known quantities of the particular polyglycol in the same manner. This procedure is suitable for quantities of polyglycol of the order of 5 to 100 mg. where an ordinary macroanalytical balance is used.

In the colorimetric modification, the polyglycol is precipitated from the sample in a small centrifuge tube by the addition of barium chloride and phosphomolybdic acid. The precipitate is isolated and washed by repeated centrifugation, after which it is digested in concentrated sulfuric acid. The digest is diluted, neutralized, and made up to a definite volume, in an aliquot of which molybdenum is determined. The useful range of this method is of the order of 0.05 to 1.0 mg. of polyglycol at a minimum concentration of 0.01 mg. per ml. Phosphomolybdic acid is substituted for silicotungstic acid in this case because molybdenum can be determined somewhat more satisfactorily than tungsten.

Determination as the Ditrityl Ether

In addition to the lead tetraacetate procedure (page 339), Seikel[39] described a gravimetric method for the determination of ethylene glycol in commercial alkyl ethers of diethylene glycol. The sample is heated with an excess of trityl chloride (triphenylmethyl chloride) in the presence of pyridine and the reaction product leached with ice water and then with 95 per cent ethanol. The weight of the alcohol-insoluble residue, which is substantially pure ditrityl ether (m.p. 170 to 180°C.) is determined in the usual manner. Seikel claimed this method to be rapid and to give excellent proximate results.

SPECIFICATIONS AND METHODS OF TESTING COMMERCIAL GLYCOLS

Specifications for commercial-grade glycols as well as the methods used for their evaluation vary slightly according to the manufacturer. Table 16.6 contains typical specification limits.

The specific gravity and standard distillation are good indications of the amount of homologous compounds in commercially available glycols. Because the chemical methods for the determination of the glycols are time-consuming and the homologous compounds usually interfere, physical methods are preferable as a means of evaluating the purity of these materials. In special cases a minimum purity based on hydroxyl content is included in the specification.

The control of acidity is important from the standpoint of corrosion. The acidity is customarily calculated as per cent acetic acid, although in most cases it probably is due to other acidic oxidation products. The tendency of the glycols to develop acidity upon standing at ordinary temperatures and in the absence of metals is very slight. However, for certain uses, such as in anti-freeze solutions or as coolants in aircraft engines, the glycols must be inhibited to prevent the formation of excessive acidity.

TABLE 16.6. TYPICAL SPECIFICATIONS FOR COMMERCIAL GLYCOLS

	Ethylene Glycol	Diethylene Glycol	Triethylene Glycol	Propylene Glycol	Dipropylene Glycol	2-Methyl-2,4-pentanediol	2-Ethyl-1,3-hexanediol
Specific gravity at 20/20°C.							
min.	1.1151	1.1170	1.122	1.0370	1.020	0.921	0.939
max.	1.1156	1.1200	1.127	1.0400	1.030	0.924	0.943
Distillation at 760 mm. initial boiling point, °C., min.	193	235	275	185	220	193	240
dry point, °C., max.	210	255	300	194	240	200	250
Acidity, % by wt. as acetic acid, max.	0.01	0.02	0.02	0.005	0.01	0.01	0.01
Water, % by wt., max.	0.30	0.30	0.30	0.5	0.50	a	—
Water solubility at 25°C.	Complete	—	—	—	—	—	—
Chlorides, % by wt. as Cl, max.	—	—	—	0.1	—	—	—
Ash, g./100 ml., max.	0.005	0.10	0.10	0.01	—	—	—
Color, Pt-Co (APHA) units, max.	15	15	50	15	15	15	15
Odor	Mild	—	Mild	—	Mild	Mild	—
Suspended matter	b	b	b	b	b	b	b

[a] Miscible with 19 volumes of 60° API gasoline at 20°C. [b] Substantially free.

The presence of an inhibitor may necessitate changes in the specification requirements or limits. Inhibited ethylene glycol specifications usually contain requirements for pH and inhibitor content.

The qualitative gasoline test for water content in most cases has been superseded by the quantitative sulfur dioxide-iodine method[51]. The latter is rapid and accurate to ±0.1 per cent or better. Some specifications also contain a water miscibility test to insure the absence of water-insoluble impurities.

The ash content is a measure of any inorganic residue present in these materials. Occasionally, nonvolatile matter is determined instead, but this is inconvenient because of the low vapor pressure of the glycols and consequently their slow rate of evaporation, even at 100°C. For certain purposes it is necessary to control the presence of specific inorganic impurities such as iron, heavy metals, chlorides, or sulfates. A test for arsenic also is included in the National Formulary specification for propylene glycol to be used in pharmaceutical preparations[52].

The color of most of the commercial grades of the monoglycols is equal to or less than 15 platinum-cobalt (APHA) units[53]. The polyglycols are usually somewhat darker in color, ranging from light-straw to amber.

Some specifications contain an odor requirement to eliminate any burnt or other objectionable odor which might be undesirable for certain applications. The requirement for suspended matter is a precaution against excessive contamination from dirt, lint, and metallic particles during manufacture and storage.

SPECIFICATION TEST METHODS

Specific Gravity

Determine four-place specific gravities by means of a 60-ml. Pyrex glass pycnometer calibrated to give the apparent specific gravity at 20/20°C. Maintain the constant temperature bath at 20 ± 0.05°C.

Determine three-place specific gravities by means of a hydrometer calibrated to give the apparent specific gravity at 20/20°C. and capable of being easily read to the nearest 0.0005 unit. Maintain the constant temperature bath at 20 ± 0.05°C.

Distillation

Observing the modifications described below, conduct the distillation in accordance with ASTM Standard Method D 86, Distillation of Gasoline, Naphtha, Kerosine, and Similar Petroleum Products[54].

Apparatus. (a) Standard 200-ml. Pyrex benzol distilling flask conforming to the following approximate dimensions: bulb, 76 mm. OD; neck, 105 mm. in length by 23 mm. OD; vapor tube, 50 mm. from top of neck. (b) Thermometer, partial immersion for general use, graduated in °C., having a range suitable for the material tested, and conforming to ASTM standard specification E1 (2C-39 or 3C-39). (c) Asbestos board, 6 by 6 by 0.25 inches, with opening 1.5 inches (38 mm.) in diameter.

Procedure. Clamp the burner so that its top is 55 to 60 mm. from the bottom of the 200-ml. distilling flask. Adjust the flame so that it burns with a hissing but not roaring sound.

Apply heat uniformly at such a rate that the first drop forms in not less than 10 nor more than 15 minutes, then distill the sample at a rate of 4 to 5 ml. per minute. After 95 ml. of distillate have been collected, regulate the heat so that the dry point is attained in not less than 3 and not more than 5 minutes.

Record the temperature corresponding to the initial boiling point; the 2, 5, 10, 20, etc., milliliter intervals; and the dry point, when the last drop of liquid leaves the bottom of the flask.

Conduct the distillation at 760 mm. or add the temperature correction indicated in Table 16.7 for every mm. under 760.

TABLE 16.7. DISTILLATION CORRECTIONS

	Correction °C. per mm.
Ethylene glycol	0.043
Diethylene glycol	0.049
Triethylene glycol	0.054
Propylene glycol	0.042
Dipropylene glycol	0.050
2-Methyl-2,4-pentanediol	0.043
2-Ethyl-1,3-hexanediol	0.049

Acidity

Measure a volume of sample equivalent to 60 g. in a graduate and transfer to a 250-ml. Erlenmeyer flask. Add a few drops of a 1.0 per cent alcoholic solution of phenolphthalein indicator and titrate with standard 0.1N alcoholic KOH to the first pink end-point permanent for at least 15 seconds.

$$\text{ml. KOH} \times 0.01 = \text{acidity, } \% \text{ by weight as acetic acid}$$

Water

Sulfur Dioxide-Iodine Method. *Preparation of Reagent.* Transfer 487 ml. of freshly distilled anhydrous pyridine to a 4-liter bottle having a 29/42 ground-glass neck. Add 154 g. of reagent-grade iodine, stopper securely, and place on a mechanical roller for 30 minutes or until the iodine is completely in solution. Dilute the contents of the bottle to 3500 ml. with reagent grade anhydrous methanol.

By means of a suitable glass tube extending to the bottom of the bottle add 155 g. of refrigerant-grade sulfur dioxide dried by passing through concentrated sulfuric acid. Allow the contents of the bottle to cool.

Fit the bottle with a 50-ml. automatic buret having a 29/42 ground-glass joint and similar to Model J-740 supplied by Scientific Glass and Apparatus Company, Bloomfield, New Jersey. Protect all vents open to the air with suitable Ascarite tubes. Much of the accuracy of the method is lost if an ordinary buret is used without special precautions.

Standardization of Reagent. Transfer 25 ml. of anhydrous methanol to each of two 125-ml. glass-stoppered Erlenmeyer flasks. From the buret add the sulfur dioxide-iodine reagent to each flask until a permanent light reddish-brown color is obtained. Match the colors of the solutions by the dropwise addition of reagent. Reserve one of the flasks as a blank.

Into the second flask introduce 2 or 3 drops (0.05 to 0.06 g.) of distilled water weighed to the nearest 0.1 mg. by means of a Grethen or similar weighing pipet. Immediately titrate with the sulfur dioxide-iodine reagent until the color matches that of the blank in transmitted light.

Reserve the titrated solution as a blank and use the untitrated blank for a check determination, again matching the colors of the two solutions. Duplicate standardizations should agree within 0.002 g. water per 100 ml. of reagent.

$$\frac{\text{g. water} \times 100}{\text{ml. titration}} = F = \text{g. of water equivalent to 100 ml. of reagent}$$

Procedure. Transfer 25 ml. of anhydrous methanol to each of two dry 125-ml. glass-stoppered Erlenmeyer flasks. Titrate the contents of each flask with sulfur dioxide-iodine reagent to the same light reddish-brown color. Reserve one of the flasks as a blank.

Into the second flask introduce 10 ml. of the sample by means of a pipet.

Titrate immediately with the reagent until the color matches that of the blank.

$$\frac{A \times F}{10 \times \text{sp. gr.}} = \text{water, } \% \text{ by weight}$$

where A = ml. of sulfur dioxide-iodine reagent required for the sample and F = g. of water equivalent to 100 ml. of reagent.

Precautions in Using the Reagent. Use only apparatus which has been carefully dried. When titrating, add the reagent to the solution in the flask without shaking until the brown color of the iodine persists. During the titration the solution turns yellow after additon of the first few milliliters of the reagent. Do not confuse this color with the true end-point, for although the yellow color deepens towards the end of the titration, the transition from yellow to reddish-brown is quite sharp and easily reproducible.

Swirl the contents of the flask near the end of the titration and continue titrating until the color change to a light reddish-brown is permanent. Keep the flask stoppered as much as possible, as there is sufficient moisture in the air to fade the end-point.

Gasoline Miscibility Test. Pipet 5 ml. of the sample into a 100-ml. glass-stoppered graduate. Add 19 volumes (95 ml.) of 60° API gasoline in 5-ml. portions, shaking well after each addition. Maintain the temperature of the solution at 20°C. Examine the solution after each addition for evidence of cloudiness or turbidity.

Water Solubility

Transfer 25 ml. of the sample to a 100-ml. glass-stoppered graduate. Add 25 ml. of distilled water in 5-ml. portions, shaking the flask well after each addition. Maintain the temperature of the solution at 25°C.

Add 25 ml. of the sample to 25 ml. of distilled water in the same manner. The sample is completely miscible if there is no cloudiness or turbidity at any time.

Ash

Weigh 50 g. of the sample in a 125-ml. platinum dish which has been ignited to constant weight and tared to the nearest 0.1 mg.

Heat the dish until the vapors continue to burn after the flame is withdrawn. Protect the combustion from drafts, and allow the vapors to burn spontaneously. Ignite the dish to a dull red heat, allow to cool in a desiccator, and weigh to the nearest 0.1 mg. The increase in weight is residue.

$$\text{g. residue} \times 2 = \text{ash, \% by weight.}$$

Chlorides

Pipet 50 ml. of the sample into a clean 300-ml. porcelain evaporating dish. Add 100 ml. of distilled water and one ml. of a 10 per cent solution of potassium chromate indicator. Agitate the contents of the dish with a piece of hard rubber rod and titrate with standard 0.1N silver nitrate to the first permanent reddish-brown color.

$$\frac{\text{ml. AgNO}_3 \times \text{normality} \times 3.55}{50 \times \text{sp. gr.}} = \text{chlorides, \% by weight as Cl}$$

Color

Prepare suitable color standards by proper dilution of a standard solution equivalent to 500 platinum-cobalt units (500 mg. of metallic platinum per liter). This solution should be prepared by the method described in "Standard Methods for the Examination of Water and Sewage"[53].

Transfer 100 ml. of the sample to one of two matched tall-form Nessler tubes. Fill the second tube to the mark with the platinum-cobalt standard representing the maximum limit permitted by the specification. Compare the colors of the sample and the standard by looking vertically down through the tubes against a white background. If the exact color of the sample is desired, replace the standard in the second tube with other standards until an exact match is obtained.

Odor

Pour a few milliliters of the sample on a clean filter paper and observe the odor at once.

Suspended Matter

Invert a bottle of the sample and examine immediately by transmitted light.

Literature Cited

1. Gauthier, B., *Ann. pharm. franç.*, **2,** 29–33 (1944).
2. Middleton, A. W., *Analyst*, **59,** 522–4 (1934).
3. Desnuelle, P., and Naudet, N., *Bull. soc. chim. France*, (5) **12,** 871–4 (1945).
4. Allen, N., Charbonnier, H. Y., and Coleman, R. M., *Ind. Eng. Chem., Anal. Ed.*, **12,** 384–7 (1940).
5. Hovey, A. G., and Hodgins, T. S., *Ind. Eng. Chem., Anal. Ed.*, **9,** 509–11 (1937).
6. Huntress, E. H., and Mulliken, S. P., "Identification of Pure Organic Compounds," New York, John Wiley & Sons, Inc., 1941.
7. McElvain, S. M., "The Characterization of Organic Compounds," New York, The Macmillan Co., 1946.
8. Seikel, M. K., and Huntress, E. H., *J. Am. Chem. Soc.*, **63,** 593–5 (1941).
9. Green, N., and Green, M. W., *J. Am. Chem. Soc.*, **66,** 1610–1 (1944); *Bull. Natl. Formulary Comm.*, **12,** 55 (1944).
10. Verley, A., and Bölsing, Fr., *Ber.*, **34,** 3354–8 (1901).
11. Peterson, V. L., and West, E. S., *J. Biol. Chem.*, **74,** 379–83 (1927).
12. Marks, S., and Morrell, R. S., *Analyst*, **56,** 428–9 (1931).
13. Stodola, F. H., *Mikrochemie*, **21,** 180–3 (1937).
14. Petersen, J. W., Hedberg, K. W., and Christensen, B. E., *Ind. Eng. Chem., Anal. Ed.*, **15,** 225–6 (1943).
15. Shaefer, W. E., *Ind. Eng. Chem., Anal. Ed.*, **9,** 449–50 (1937).
16. Smith, D. M., and Bryant, W. M. D., *J. Am. Chem. Soc.*, **57,** 61–5 (1935).
17. Montes, A. L., *Anales asoc. quím. argentina*, **31,** 109–13 (1943).
18. Christensen, B. E., Pennington, L., and Dimick, P. K., *Ind. Eng. Chem., Anal. Ed.*, **13,** 821–3 (1941).
19. Elving, P. J., and Warshowsky, B., *Ind. Eng. Chem., Anal. Ed.*, **19,** 1006–10 (1947).
20. Malaprade, L., *Compt. rend.*, **186,** 382–4 (1928); *Bull. soc. chim. France*, (4) **43,** 683–96 (1928).
21. Siggia, S., "Quantitative Organic Analysis via Functional Groups," p. 8, New York, John Wiley and Sons, Inc., 1949.
22. Pohle, W. D., Mehlenbacher, V. C., and Cook, J. H., *Oil & Soap*, **22,** 115–9 (1945).
23. Price, C. C., and Kroll, H., *J. Am. Chem. Soc.*, **60,** 2726–9 (1938).
24. Shupe, I. S., *J. Assoc. Offic. Agr. Chemists*, **26,** 249–56 (1943).
25. Fleury, P. F., and Lange, J., *J. pharm. chim.*, (8) **17,** 107–13 (1933).
26. Reinke, R. C., and Luce, E. N., *Ind. Eng. Chem., Anal. Ed.*, **18,** 244–5 (1946).
27. Nicolet, B. H., and Shinn, L. A., *J. Am. Chem. Soc.*, **63,** 1456–8 (1941).
28. Clausen, S. W., *J. Biol. Chem.*, **52,** 263–80 (1922).
29. Hoepe, G., and Treadwell, W. D., *Helv. Chim. Acta.*, **25,** 353–61 (1942).
30. Romijn, G., *Z. anal. Chem.*, **36,** 18–24 (1897).

31. Walker, J. F., "Formaldehyde," A. C. S. Monograph No. 98, p. 262, New York, Reinhold Publishing Corp., 1944.
32. Courtois, J., *Ann. chim. anal.*, (4) **25**, 2–4 (1943).
33. Warshowsky, B., and Elving, P. J., *Ind. Eng. Chem., Anal. Ed.*, **18**, 253–4 (1946).
34. Whitnack, G. C., and Moshier, R. W., *Ind. Eng. Chem., Anal. Ed.*, **16**, 496–8 (1944).
35. Brockmann, M. C., and Werkman, C. H., *Ind. Eng. Chem., Anal. Ed.*, **5**, 206–7 (1933).
36. Freeman, G. G., and Morrison, R. I., *Analyst*, **71**, 511–20 (1946).
37. Johnson, M. J., *Ind. Eng. Chem., Anal. Ed.*, **16**, 626–7 (1944).
38. Criegee, R., *Ber.*, **64**, 260–6 (1931).
39. Seikel, M. K., *Ind. Eng. Chem., Anal. Ed.*, **13**, 388–9 (1941).
40. Baer, E., Grosheintz, J. M., and Fischer, H. O. L., *J. Am. Chem. Soc.*, **61**, 2607–9 (1939).
41. Wise, H., Puck, T. T., and Stral, H. M., *J. Biol. Chem.*, **150**, 61–7 (1943).
42. Werner, H. W., and Mitchell, J. L., *Ind. Eng. Chem., Anal. Ed.*, **15**, 375–6 (1943).
43. Elkins, H. B., Storlazzi, E. D., and Hammond, J. W., *J. Ind. Hyg. Toxicol.*, **24**, 229–32 (1942).
44. Cuthill, R., and Atkins, C., *Analyst*, **63**, 259–61 (1938).
45. Zeisel, S., *Monatsh.*, **6**, 989 (1885); **7**, 406 (1886).
46. Morgan, P. W., *Ind. Eng. Chem., Anal. Ed.*, **18**, 500–4 (1946).
47. Volhard, J., *Ann.*, **190**, 23 (1878); *J. prakt. Chem.*, (2) **9**, 217 (1874).
48. Cooke, L. M., and Hibbert, H., *Ind. Eng. Chem., Anal. Ed.*, **15**, 24–5 (1943).
49. Duke, F. R., and Smith, G. F., *Ind. Eng. Chem., Anal. Ed.*, **12**, 201–3 (1940).
50. Shaffer, C. B., and Critchfield, F. H., *Anal. Chem.*, **19**, 32 (1947).
51. Fischer, K., *Angew. Chem.*, **48**, 394 (1935).
52. "The National Formulary," 8th Ed., Washington, D. C., American Pharmaceutical Association, 1946.
53. "Standard Methods for the Examination of Water and Sewage," 8th Ed., New York, American Public Health Association, 1936.
54. "A.S.T.M. Standards," Part II, Philadelphia, American Society for Testing Materials, 1946.

AUTHOR INDEX

SUBJECT INDEX

359